Developmental and Intermediate Algebra

Second Edition

Dr. Shubhangi Stalder
University of Wisconsin Waukesha

Dr. Paul Martin
University of Wisconsin Marathon

Change the course.

ISBN 13: 978-1-50669-648-5

Second Printing

Dr. Shubhangi Stalder
University of Wisconsin Waukesha
shubhangi.stalder@uwc.edu

Dr. Paul Martin
University of Wisconsin Marathon
paul.martin@uwc.edu

Change the course.
530 Great Road
Acton, MA 01720
800-562-2147
www.xanedu.com

Dedication

This book is dedicated to

All students who want to learn

And

All teachers who want to teach.

About the authors

Dr. Shubhangi Stalder is a full professor of mathematics at the University of Wisconsin Waukesha. She has received her doctoral degree in mathematics from the University of Wisconsin Milwaukee in 1993. She has decades of teaching experience and her focus has

always been to reach out to those who are struggling in mathematics. Her main belief is that everyone can learn basic mathematics if they tried. The key is to understand the "Why" and the "How, and to be able to see the patterns across different mathematical processes. She believes that in the long run rote memorization does not work to learning mathematics. She uses yoga and meditation techniques with her students who experience math and test anxiety and continues to include mindfulness practice in her teaching of mathematics. She has received the UW System Board of Regents Teaching in Excellence Award (the state of Wisconsin's highest teaching award), the UW Colleges Chancellor's Excellence in Teaching Award, and the UW Colleges Kaplan Teacher Award.

Dr. Paul Martin is a full professor of mathematics at the University of Wisconsin Marathon. He

received his doctoral degree in mathematics from the University of Wisconsin Madison in 1994. He has decades of teaching experience and his focus has always been to help his students see how mathematics connects to the real world. He does this through building 3-dimensional models, modeling physical processes such as heat loss through the attic of a house, to connecting mathematics to his students' other classes from chemistry to music. As a teacher, Martin stresses the importance of reasoning over memorization. He has received several teaching awards over his career including the prestigious UW Colleges Chancellor's Excellence in Teaching Award.

Acknowledgements

This book is the second edition. The material in this book is inspired by Sybilla Beckmann's work in her *Mathematics for Elementary Teachers* textbook, brain plasticity research, and Jo Boaler's growth mindset research.

The authors would like to thank their families who gave their professional opinions, their constant support and put up with long hours on this project (without their support it would have been difficult to put this book together in a such a short time).

We thank our teachers of mindfulness practice whose teachings helped us put in words our ideas on mindfulness practice in the learning of mathematics (special thanks to Dr. Paul Norton). A special thank you to Kris Luedke for his help.

The IT support we received was invaluable throughout all parts of the project, especially David Weber, Jenn Weber, Denise Spleas, and all the other IT staff at UW-Waukesha. Without their help the book and lectures would not exist.

We would also like to thank Barb Reinhart who helped us with suggestions for the cover of this book.

Lastly, we want to thank Kent Kromarek who was our sounding board for the nontraditional ideas presented in this book, for reviewing and editing the book. We would also like to thank Mark Fuller for his valuable contribution in editing the book and suggestions to improve the exercise sets. In addition, we want to thank all the countless brave souls (students and teachers) who were willing to give us their time in trying this material, and giving us their feedback to make this project better. We hope their work and ours has made it possible to get a product that we hope will be useful to other students and teachers.

Table of Contents

MODULE 0: MINDFULNESS OF LEARNING MATHEMATICS

MODULE 1: INTRODUCTION TO MATHEMATICAL OBJECTS

MODULE 2: ARITHMETIC OF ALGEBRAIC OBJECTS

MODULE 3: SOLVING EQUATIONS AND INEQUALITIES

MODULE 4: APPLICATIONS AND GRAPHING

Module 0: Mindfulness of Learning Mathematics

Introduction
Lecture

- 💻 Introduction To Authors (3 min)

  http://www.youtube.com/watch?v=oShZs_1U0Xk

- 💻 Introduction to Content (3min)

  http://www.youtube.com/watch?v=SiXM29eUw2k

If you are reading this chapter, then it probably means that you are taking an introductory math course and have come upon this book or that you are interested in learning or reviewing mathematics. We will assume you have a K-12 education and have been exposed to some basic mathematical concepts.

For many students, mathematics does not bring happy memories or feelings. Some even dread learning mathematics. One important question is why do so many students dislike a subject that is called the "Queen of all Sciences" by Carl Friedrich Gauss (a famous scientist and mathematician). Many say how important mathematics is, and how it is used to understand the world around us through many different fields. Some say mathematics is a universal language and that humans are hardwired to do basic mathematics. Yet many struggle and come to associate this subject with negative feelings. Most never attain an appreciation for how mathematics is used in their day-to-day lives.

We are asking every student who has picked up this book and has made a decision to learn basic algebra to let go of their past experiences, and perhaps temporarily to let go of their ego and pride. We want you to finish reading this chapter even if you feel that some of the things in it are useless, anxiety-provoking, or even stupid. Perhaps you already do the things recommended in this chapter. Our recommendation is that you at least read the chapter, and see if any of it could be useful to you.

Throughout this book while doing mathematics, we will introduce ways of doing problems that at times may look very different from how you may have learned it in the past, and at times may even seem more difficult or silly. You may at times also feel how you do not want to waste your time learning a way of solving a problem that you already know how to solve. Our experience is that many students find that going through the motions of what we suggest will pay dividends later in the course. Many students have told us so. We hope you will try.

There are many things that affect people's views about their ability and their like or dislike of any subject. For some, an aversion to mathematics begins in elementary school when they are first exposed to fractions. Early failures in a math class or in-class punishments or embarrassments can stay with some students for years. In some cultures, parents and peers maintain norms that math is hard or stupid. In some cultures, girls more than boys learn to question their ability. It is difficult to identify a single cause for a dislike, anxiety, or negative self-view that developed over many years. However, with careful attention it is possible to overcome these feelings and modify these thoughts. We all have our strengths and weaknesses. However, as human beings we can also develop new skills and abilities through diligence, practice, and becoming conscious of our thought processes.

Before you read any further, please pause and write a short essay about your math history so far (the courses or teachers you particularly remember, what others told you about math or your own math ability, and any good or bad experiences that stick out in your memory). You might be surprised at what you find. If you do feel anxiety while taking math tests or doing mathematics, pay careful attention to your biography for stories that you consider bad experiences. In your history there may be some anxiety-provoking events that may surface. Once you finish looking at any negative math-related events from your past, put them away. Put away any self-views such as "I am just bad at math." We don't believe that. Start with a fresh attitude and a new approach. (If you have no negative events to recall, that is good news.)

Lecture

🖥 Brain https://www.youtube.com/watch?v=4eDXAAVylJs (15:37 min)

Children do not have much control over what is taught to them and how they are treated by others. But as adults, you can take charge of your own learning and how you approach things. Don't let someone tell you what your ability is. You need to find this out for yourself. Don't let what you think others think of you affect what you think of yourself. You are not a robot with fixed or predictable programming; people cannot say for sure how you will perform before you try; you have the ability to change. People's brains have the capacity to grow. They are built to learn new things. People can even benefit by learning what kinds of things help learning. With new technology and the internet, there are plenty of lectures and documents at your fingertips making it easier for you access and gain knowledge (though some websites are more trustworthy than others).

The world moves fast. You can click on a link and there is information within seconds. You can dial a number and reach someone on the phone and see them within seconds even if they are on the other side of the planet. Yet in this fast and changing world, the content or learning of mathematics has mostly remained the same across hundreds and thousands of years. The way the subject is presented has perhaps changed, but how you process it cognitively has probably not changed much. New research on brain plasticity shows that you are capable of learning mathematics, that you are hardwired for mathematics and can do basic mathematics whether you like the subject or not. We are not saying everyone wants to learn or enjoys the subject or can learn it equally quickly. But we are saying you are capable of learning (and passing an introductory course) with the right approach, effort, and help.

From our experience of teaching this material for 20+ years, we are convinced that all students can do well at basic mathematics by changing their attitudes (if necessary), filling in the gaps of mathematical knowledge that might be missing from K-12, and taking enough time to practice. We will present material to you in both traditional and nontraditional ways. Most of the content can be viewed on YouTube video lectures to help you understand the material at your own pace. To learn mathematics, many factors have to come together before you can process, synthesize, and retain the material. Learning mathematics is like learning a new language. So getting familiar with the vocabulary is extremely important; learning the syntax and grammar of the subject is next; and then practice will give you the power to later recall, elaborate on, and think critically about the material.

As we have mentioned, many factors can affect your learning and attitudes. We hope the later sections in this module give you ideas to maximize your learning. We hope to give you a systematic way to address any anxiety or negative feelings you may have regarding mathematics. We hope this module brings you hope if you need it to start learning mathematics in Module 1.

We call this Module 0 for a reason. The number zero, or "shunya" as it is called in Sanskrit, is used to represent nothing. That is how knowledge of any subject starts, as nothing. However, with the right guidance and hard work, people can start to learn; their knowledge space changes; and people may start to gain insight into new objects or subjects. Acquiring knowledge is a long process with multiple layers to it, and it will require your patience and persistence. It is important to understand the boundary between what you know very well and things that you are not so sure of. For that you need to pay attention to yourself and how you think and process (a core component of "mindfulness"). Many students want quick fixes and to travel a path of least resistance. For example, some just want to pass a course to fulfill a degree requirement. That approach will result in minimal learning and in difficulties in subsequent courses. In mathematics especially, a solid foundation is needed to move forward. The boundary between knowledge and uncertainty needs to be advanced in each course, as you gain mathematical knowledge and experience, in order to more easily succeed in the next course. If you concentrate on learning, then the grades will automatically follow. Give this learning process a try and keep an open mind.

Things may not be as hard as you imagine. There are a lot of factors that affect learning. Some of these factors are in your control and others are not. We recommend several recent books on how people learn and how the brain works to help you understand the current thinking on learning. Those books are "The Brain that Changes Itself," "You Are Here," and "Blink." They are very accessible and provide insight into your own prejudices as well as basic information on brain plasticity and mindfulness practices. No matter what your age, you can change your brain and make it work more in the way you might want. In this context, doing mathematics is exercise for the brain.

Below we discuss some of the general factors that can affect your learning. The factors are not necessarily in order of importance because they affect different people differently. We all have different lives and backgrounds. As you go through each section, try to write down something from that section that makes sense to you and that you can use to enhance your learning process.

Content Related

Please answer the questions below on your own before reading any further. Do not peek and look at the answers for these questions in the text ahead. Thinking about these questions will help you to see the differences that might exist between your thinking and our (the authors') views. It might give you an insight into your own learning habits and thinking processes that will benefit you in learning not only this subject but perhaps even other subjects.

Lecture

🖥 Introduction to the class and study skills (11 min)

http://www.youtube.com/watch?v=th4cl8ugE-I

Assuming you spent some time writing what you think the answers are to the critical thinking questions, above; let us discuss the reasonable answers to it below.

a. What is "Mathematics"?

➢ The dictionary meaning: "The study of numbers and their form, arrangement, and associated relationships using rigorously defined literal, numerical, and operational symbols."

➢ Mathematics is observing the world around you, characterizing things/objects in different groups/components based on certain attributes, problem solving, and generalizing structures and patterns.

b. What is a "Problem"?

- ➢ The dictionary meaning: "A question raised for inquiry, consideration, or solution." Or "A proposition in mathematics or physics stating something to be done." Or, my favorite, "An intricate unsettled question, a source of perplexity, distress, or vexation, or "difficulty in understanding or accepting."

- ➢ So as you can see, if in a mathematics course you are mostly solving problems, then it is natural to expect some or even a lot of discomfort depending on your previous preparation. If you could solve all problems in this book, then your mastery level would put you in the next course ready to deal with more sophisticated and abstract problems. In other words, it is okay to be confused in this course.

c. What is a "Mistake"?

- ➢ The dictionary meaning: "To blunder in the choice of; to misunderstand the meaning or intention of; to identify wrongly: confuse with another."

- ➢ Making mistakes while doing mathematics is often related to misunderstanding the meaning of the symbols or rules, or misapplying these to the problem at hand.

- ➢ Students often think they have to be able to do problems flawlessly from the very beginning. They see their teachers doing problems on the board almost always flawlessly and without much energy, and expect the same from themselves. This assumption leads to many frustrations. When you see professional athletes perform incredible feats in their sport, you probably don't expect yourself to be able to do that. Hours of dedicated practice and study of the fundamentals of the sport are required to reach such levels of mastery. You need to remember that your teacher is just like the professional athlete with years and many hours per day of practice. You cannot expect the same performance from yourself right away. You will have to work at it yourself, and every problem you solve helps build skills for further development. We will discuss more on this a little later.

The Sequential Nature of Mathematics

Mathematics builds upon itself, starting with learning to count as a child. Given this sequential nature, once we fail along some branch, the hopes of succeeding in the next level are diminished greatly. When a person is moved to the next level with inadequate understanding of earlier material, the problems and exercise sets tend to be too hard, and there is substantially less hope for that person to succeed. People in this situation are going to have feelings of desperation and can easily lose their motivation to work. Many other areas of study are optional or require only an introductory level understanding. However, basic mathematics courses are a core requirement for many degrees and prerequisite for many fields. If somehow you manage through a path of least resistance and scrape by with a grade of C early in the math sequence, then your chances of success in the next course are greatly diminished because you are missing approximately 30% of the earlier material. For this reason, you should aim for mastery level understanding of the material in this course (it is easier than it sounds). Our grades here are based upon the knowledge level that you attain and not where you stand relative to the rest of the class.

In addition to the sequential nature of the math content, there is a sequential nature of sorts to math studying. Mathematics learning often requires a lot of steady practice without many breaks. Many students cram before tests and think they spent so much time working on their homework, and yet they still perform worse than they hoped. However, cramming before tests does not usually work, because mathematics is like athletic training. You have to build your skills slowly and surely. If you stop working for weeks in physical training, then your muscles start to lose their strength and you have to rebuild them. The same thing happens with mathematics. So if you take a year off and come back, then you cannot expect the same level of mastery without reviewing previous concepts. Even a few weeks of break for some students could make a difference. So steady practice, and mastery are very important as you embark upon this journey.

Acceptance of Mistakes and the "I don't know" Phenomenon

In many eastern cultures, they say if you want to learn or teach any subject, you need to leave your ego at the door. This principle applies to <u>the teacher and the student</u> and is usually difficult for both to enact. But we want you to try. Students so often associate their ability or potential to do mathematics with the grades they receive on their math exams. This assumed connection is unfortunate, because an exam is really just a snapshot in one moment of time. In addition, although doing well on an exam usually does indicate ability, having ability or potential does not always translate into good exam scores. Many different things can constrain how well you do on a particular exam. Unfortunately, however, failing an exam or getting low grades can make people lower their self-worth. To help you to leave your ego at the door, keep in mind that many different attributes and characteristics play a role in defining a person. In the big picture of life, doing poorly on exams does not reflect on the whole person. Ultimately, of course, you can decide how you feel about yourself after you receive an exam score, but we hope you will keep these issues in mind.

More specifically, when students make mistakes on solving problems, some may feel ridiculed, judged, or even stupid. This conditions students to be afraid of making mistakes. But keep in mind that making mistakes teaches you a lot about the subject, and understanding why you made the mistake will allow you to fill in the holes or gaps in your mathematical knowledge. Ask any mathematician and they will tell you they have made many mistakes that eventually led them to a solution of an unsolved problem, especially when they were first learning to solve problems. You should not expect to solve a problem flawlessly right away. This is an absurd expectation. You should try to exhibit patience and diligence while solving problems. You should expect to become conscious of your thought processes while solving problems and to have the presence of mind to analyze your logic to see if you are applying the right ideas or principles to each step. Not making rush judgments about your ability and truly becoming conscious of your learning process will take you a long way. Your attitude about learning has a lot to do with how well you learn, even more so than the actual brain power you may have. Learning mathematics requires a lot of patience, tenacity, and ability to think under pressure.

If you solve a problem step by step, then your brain generated those steps. So even if on the surface it might look like you do not know why you wrote something down, just spending some time to reflect on and to articulate your reasoning for the steps will eventually clarify what thought processes you engaged to get your answer. In other words, you usually do know or can independently figure out why you wrote what you wrote, whether it is wrong or right. Yet there is an urge to quickly say "I don't know" when asked why you wrote something that is wrong. You may not realize that you actually do know why. But it may also be what psychologists call a defense mechanism, to protect the ego. Perhaps you feel that if you say "I don't know," then you might be able to somehow shift the blame to others, or might be able to remove your responsibility in making that mistake. Perhaps you are just trying to stop the attention currently focused on yourself and your mistake. You want to let the teacher take it from there.

Trying to articulate your logic in solving problems, however, requires a good vocabulary. Thus, paying attention to how you speak and write mathematics will go a long way in problem solving and in avoiding the habitual response of "I don't know." By stopping this instant reaction, you will cultivate a habit for your brain, and eventually you will become conscious of your reasoning and become better able to articulate and catch your own mistakes. Focus on building a bridge from where you are to where you want to be. How you recover from your mistakes will actually shape and develop your analytical skills which are needed in many aspects of life outside of a mathematics course. In fact, it is possible many times you may not be using mathematics directly in your life but the quantitative and analytical skills of problem solving you learn in this subject better allow you to solve other problems in life as well.

For most students, it is unrealistic to think that they can go through a math class without making any mistakes. What we want you to learn is how to accept making a mistake and try to understand "why" you did what you did. We want you to think about "why" you wrote what you wrote, what was your logic or intuition, and then figure out "why" what you wrote was wrong. Building your logic skills in this fashion will increase your confidence and make you mathematically stronger.

Don't just expect an answer from your teacher or someone else on what your mistake was. That will not take you very far. If you figure it out yourself, you will retain the material longer.

Take the effort to develop your reasoning skills. We want you to experience the freedom in mathematical thinking beyond rote memorization. Just memorizing the steps for a particular problem will not allow you to use your skills in a later course where you may not see the exact same problem. In many subsequent courses, you may see problems where you have to recognize the material at hand as something you learned earlier. This recognition will allow you to apply your knowledge to this new situation. Understanding the process will allow you to solve new problems that use similar logic. So remember to focus on the process and not just the correct answer.

Learning to Become Conscious of Your Mathematical Thought Processes

For many students, as mentioned earlier, it seems like self-worth is determined by a few timed exams taken at particular moments in time. But assessing learning is much more complicated than that and has many layers. If someone cannot perform well on a timed test, that does not necessarily mean that he or she has not learned the content or processes. Also remember not to base your worth on the course grades you receive. For many, life is complicated and you are pulled in many different directions at the same time. If you have made up your mind that you want to get through college algebra, then you have to start at the beginning. Starting at the beginning will allow you to fill in any holes you may have in your understanding of mathematical content from K-12. As mentioned earlier, mathematics is sequential learning like any language. You need to learn its alphabet, vocabulary, and grammar if you expect to gain basic fluency in this language.

Much of the mathematics you have learned so far probably came from rote memorization. Mathematics does contain rules and axioms to memorize or learn. At a higher level, mathematics is about applying those rules and axioms, and using them to build mathematical structures with different patterns. But even beyond that level, mathematical reasoning can be applied directly or indirectly in many different fields and aspects of life. Our aim in this course is to teach you problem solving skills that will prepare you for college algebra, but also eventually to solve life problems. Sometimes you may apply mathematical tools without even realizing it. As problem solving techniques become deeply assimilated, you may start using them subconsciously which explains why many adults falsely say they don't really use mathematics in real life. Learning this subject is like climbing a ladder. You cannot get to the top without having gone through the steps below. If you have forgotten some basic mathematics, then learning intermediate algebra concepts becomes harder. So we will ground much of what we do in primary school ideas and quickly work our way up. Along the way we will point out how even much higher level mathematics uses the same basic principles you learned in elementary school.

Many come to mathematics courses with a lot of apprehension and previous emotional baggage that can cause different kinds of anxieties. You can change that experience into a positive one with some techniques that are proven to work not just in the mathematics classroom but in the classroom of life. There are many studies done on mind-body connections and the practice of mindfulness as applied to various aspects of life. We apply some of these techniques to mathematics learning in the hope of making your experience more positive and productive.

We believe that your focus in learning mathematics should be on understanding the mathematical processes, the "How" and "Why" of the material, and becoming conscious of your thinking processes. If you do this faithfully, the grades will automatically follow. In addition, other courses that require Intermediate Algebra as a prerequisite should become easier as you are likely to retain the material more deeply. To make sure you understand or have learned the process and the whys behind the material, you will have to learn to read, write, and speak using correct mathematical vocabulary.

Thinking and Problem Solving Strategies

There are many ways to solve a math problem. So the first thing we would like you to remember is to use your own creativity in solving the problem. As long as you can justify every step mathematically, you can use it. George Polya in 1945 described a basic framework on how to approach solving a problem in mathematics.

The process or framework is outlined below in four stages or steps and we elaborate each as to how what they mean to us.

Polya's Four Stages of Solving a Problem.

1. **Understanding the problem**

   Many times students don't read the wording or directions for the problems thoroughly. If you do not understand what the problem is asking you to do, then your solution is highly unlikely to answer what is being asked. There are strategies in understanding the directions. As you read the text or hear the lectures, make a vocabulary sheet so you know what the different mathematical terms mean to you. Then rework these terms and come up with your own examples of what they mean or how they work. You might display a concept graphically or in diagrams or in table form. When reading a problem, try to organize the information in a way that makes sense to you. See if you can break the problem into smaller doable tasks, or work on a simplified version of the same problem to get insight into it. If it is a word problem, then you may want to work on isolating questions like "how much", "how far," or "find," which will help you to clarify what is being asked of you.

2. **Devising a plan**

   Once you understand the problem statement, make a list of topics/concepts/formulas you think are relevant. Use a scratch sheet of paper or a "For My Eyes Only" column as shown in the note taking section later in this module. This list will act as your tool box. Just like plumbers or electricians have their tools, you can start using them one by one to see which tool will do the job. If none of them work, don't give up. Try other tools from what you have learned so far, and one of them is likely to work. A lot of times you may find that the first thing that comes to your mind will be the correct tool. This is your intuition which results from working through many problems at all the rungs of the ladder below your current position. Sometimes our unconscious mind works on problems and we are not always aware how we decide to use a particular tool to solve the problem. The attainment of a conscious and subconscious set of tools is achieved by working through many problems over an extended period of time.

3. **Carrying out the plan**

   Once you have the tools you want to use and a plan, then it is time for action, which is doing the problem. Mathematics is all about doing and is an active process. At this stage, you are trying to incorporate the information given in the problem statement into an equation or system of equations or diagram or perhaps to develop a formula or prediction as the final result. This act of applying appropriate tools is something that you need to do for yourself. Passively watching someone else do the problem is unlikely to help you gain this skill.

4. **Looking Back**

   Review or see if you have actually answered what was asked of you and also whether you can extend the ideas. We call this checking or playing. We will have sections in the book labeled "Playing." We think of playing in the land of mathematics as seeing if the techniques you have learned can be applied to other objects or extended with slight modifications to solve other problems. Checking that your answer is reasonable should catch major mistakes. For example, when asked to determine an area, the answer should be a positive number. As we have said, making mistakes is just fine – you just have to regroup and try again. Mistakes will require you to go back to steps 2 and 3 above and adjust your approach. Keep working until you have solved the problem, or if not, at least identify where you are stuck. If stuck, then seek assistance from someone who can see what you have tried and explain how to proceed. Once you have solved the problem and are confident, it might feel rewarding, exciting, and even exhilarating. (At this point, you might be thinking, "Okay let's not get all carried away here.")

Video Log 0.1a

1. Write a brief biography of your mathematics experience so far. Please include anything you think is relevant in forming your attitude toward mathematics, your expectations of success in a math course right now. Please be sure to also include answers to the following questions below in your biography.
    a. How long has it been since your last math course?
    b. Describe your own view of your abilities in mathematics so far.
    c. Describe your positive or negative experiences with specific topics, for e.g., fractions, geometry, and what is called the word problems.
2. What does learning a subject mean to you?
3. Please write briefly in your own words what you think the following words mean to you-
    a. Mathematics
    b. Problem
    c. Mistakes
4. Solving problems in mathematics involves making choices on what mathematical technique or principle to apply at every step. This requires conscious processing of every step you take in solving a problem (especially a multistep problem). Getting a math problem wrong usually results from misapplying a mathematical technique or principle, perhaps due to misremembering or just writing something without processing your choice of logic applied to a particular step. In this context, explain how "mistakes" can be processed to impart learning so that the mistake is less likely in the future.
5. How long do you think a student SHOULD wait to say "I don't know" after reading a problem?
6. How long do you think you wait before you say "I don't know" after reading a problem?
7. Describe briefly Polya's four stages of solving a problem.

Lecture

- 🖥 Introduction to the class and study skills (8 min)
  http://www.youtube.com/watch?v=I5OktRxH79c

- 🖥 Mindfulness of thoughts https://www.youtube.com/watch?v=5xrKjyLRnAw (3 min)

- 🖥 Body Scan https://www.youtube.com/watch?v=vdm06q3AmwY (17:29 min)

- 🖥 Exam Part 1 https://www.youtube.com/watch?v=NllnoZeJ2X4 (5:13min)

- 🖥 Exam Part 2 https://www.youtube.com/watch?v=14g0h3AA9_o (4:54min)

1. Breathing
2. Attitudes
3. Discursive Mind
4. Past failures affecting your perception of your ability now

The next few techniques are to help with any anxieties or negative feelings that may arise during your mathematics experience. These techniques are taken from the mindfulness practices as taught by Dr. Paul Norton (president of the Milwaukee Mindfulness Practice Center; http://milwaukeemindfulness.wordpress.com) using works from Buddhist psychology and from Thich Nhat Hahn, including his book, "The Miracle of Mindfulness" (1987). The techniques might sound simple, and therefore many of you might be skeptical that they are effective. Even if you feel skeptical about them, as I did initially, try using them. You might be surprised by their power.

There are many different stressors that can shut down your higher level thinking processes that are required for doing mathematics. Stress tends to put your body and mind into a fight, flight, or freeze response. It is difficult to break this response. Practice in a less stressful environment can be helpful. When you are anxious doing problems for homework, or in the classroom, or on an exam, just take a short pause, put your pencil down, and observe your thoughts. Watch what comes and goes through your mind. If your mind starts saying that you are stupid or that you are never going to get it, then just accept them as thoughts. You do not have to take every thought that comes into your brain as being true. Let the thoughts come and go as they please, but focus on your breath. Just breathe in and say, "Breathing in, I am aware I am breathing in," and, "Breathing out, I am aware I am breathing out." Feel the breath passing through your nostrils, and observe your body. You can also add the following directions to your breathing: While breathing in, smile, and while breathing out, feel the calmness and peace that is generated by this focus. After 3-10 breaths, return to your problem and you will have a better focus. This will likely lessen your discomfort and allow you to do mathematics, hopefully more free of fear and anxiety and without worrying about what someone else is thinking of you. Many students have reported feeling calmer and less anxious.

The breathing we are asking you to do is very important to reduce any stress. Care should be taken that you are breathing diaphragmatically. For those who may not know what the diaphragm is, the diaphragm is an internal muscle attached to the bottom of your ribs that allows your lungs to expand and contract. For more information, see http://en.wikipedia.org/wiki/Thoracic_diaphragm. So when you breathe in, or inhale, your stomach should expand out, and when you breathe out, or exhale, your stomach should contract. This is diaphragmatic breathing. It is important to always breathe in this manner, but especially when you are stressed or anxious. If you have trouble with this kind of breathing, then you may want to practice lying down. Put a heavy book like a phone book on your stomach while lying down. Then try breathing in and lifting the book up, and breathing out and letting the book recede downward. There are other techniques you can look up and online videos to help you with this. But correct breathing will help you fully oxygenate to optimize your brain function. Over time, this kind of breathing will become natural. Remember that the more oxygen you get into your blood stream, the happier your brain will be.

For many students, being able to articulate their questions and learning mathematics consciously will be difficult at first. The obstacle is something called "habit energy" in the mindfulness practices. However, for most students, by the end of the second chapter, they start to recognize their habit energy and can stop their negativity. They can see how their own beliefs about their mathematical skills have changed.

We ask you keep an open mind throughout this journey and be honest with yourself when you are assessing what you have learned. Do not let your own mind tell you stories of how bad you are at math (called your "discursive mind" in the mindfulness practices). This negative self-attitude does not really serve any practical purpose. Positive or neutral attitudes can take you a long way. It is not very important that you learn the material as fast as you can. It is more important that you learn it well. People are all wired differently, have different backgrounds, and have different training. This makes learning individualistic. If you learn a topic faster than your friend, then helping your friend will make it stick with you even longer. This connection you make with fellow learners will also help you with how you view learning. You may view learning not just as a solitary activity but as a community experience.

As mentioned earlier, many students believe that when they learn a mathematical concept and do not understand it right away, somehow that makes them inferior or dumb. They see their teachers doing problems flawlessly at the board and expect the same results from themselves. But we want to emphasize that learning to do mathematics takes time. If you were as good as your teacher right away, then you would not have to be learning it right now. Also remember that doing mathematics is all about the "doing." If you somehow think that observing someone else do it is enough for you to get it, then you are very likely mistaken. Learning mathematics is like going to the gym. You have to flex the muscles and do the hard work necessary for your own brain to develop these skills. We know that if you work hard and get help when you need it, it will take you a long way. Just keep that in mind the next time your discursive mind and habit energy take over. You can change or overcome these mental obstacles.

So don't let your past experiences or worries about the future dictate your performance. Be in the moment and with your cognition to solve the problems at hand. You might find with all the baggage temporarily set aside, that you have more room to think in your head. Remember that things are not as hard as they may look. Looks can be deceiving and so don't let your prejudice about how something looks constrain your ability. Try to keep an open mind. Make a list of topics or tools you think might be useful for you to solve the problem at hand and use them one by one to see which tool is useful.

Getting Help
Lecture

🖥 Introduction to the class and study skills

http://www.youtube.com/watch?v=6WXLIf0FVIc

When you are learning to do mathematics, getting help when needed is important. Remember that it will be more productive to spend your own time before rushing to get help. But after a reasonable amount of time is spent and you still cannot figure it out, it is important to ask your teacher or a fellow classmate, or go online for some help. Before you actually sit down with a helper, you should try to identify where your difficulty lies. You should ask for assistance to work at the spot or level where you are stuck. There are plenty of people willing to help you. Sometimes pride keeps students from asking for help. You might feel inferior if you have to ask for help. It is important to remember that you are not born with all the knowledge you need. You need others' help to gain more knowledge so you can improve your life. So don't hesitate to get help. Getting help will reduce your frustrations and can make your learning experience a more efficient and productive one. We know how hard it can be to ask for help. Learning is one activity where you need a guide or a helping hand to show you the path. Ultimately though, it is you who are doing the walking.

1. Organizational Skills
2. Time Management

Organizational Skills

Most students begin the course with some organizational skills, but it does not hurt to start reviewing some organizational basics that will help you prepare to start your course work. We recommend that you start with a 2- or 3-inch, 3-ring binder with 5 tabs. Set up the tabs as follows:

1. Handouts
2. Lecture Notes
3. Video Logs

The remaining two tabs may be needed if you are using this book with a course in which case your remaining two tabs would be

1. Classroom problems

2. ALEKS (if you are using the ALEKS program as a supplement to this learning, go to www.aleks.com if you want to see what this program is about)

As an example of organizing your work, put the questions you answered in Video Log 0.1 (listed earlier in this module) in your binder under the Video Log Tab.

When you take notes from the video lectures that accompany this book or from in-class lectures, always label your paper with that day's date and the topic. So right now you could write today's date and "Introduction." Divide the page into two columns as shown below. On the left-hand side, you can write the answers to your video log questions. On the right-hand side, you can create a "for my eyes only" column. Anything you put in this right-hand column is not graded by the teacher and can contain your scratch work, the list of your tools, or your thoughts and observations. This column is like a mini-diary that might help you overcome thinking blocks or anxieties if you encounter them.

A sample of a student's work follows if you wanted to see how it might look in the notebook page.

Date: *Monday June 11, 2012*

Introduction

Questions

    i.   What does learning a subject mean to you?
       To understand and reproduce it at a later date.

   ii.   What do you think Mathematics is?
       To solve problems using letters and numbers.

  iii.   What do you think a "Problem" is?
       A problem is something that needs solving. Like being stuck?

FOR MY EYES ONLY

1. I have no idea what this question is asking— My throat is dry. I have not even begun to do mathematics yet and I am feeling stressed already.

2. Just that word "Mathematics" brings me negative emotions....

Note to self: BREATHE

When working on homework problems or practice problems, you may want to discuss the answers to these questions with a classmate or your teacher. Sometimes discussing it with others or even just talking out loud to yourself may help you realize that your answer needs clarification, or that you had some misconceptions about the problem. Throughout the book we show you, through practice problems, how to write the solutions. Writing in this way will aid you in clearer thinking, and over time it will become natural.

The organization of the material shown in the textbook is based on our trials with students and their feedback. We welcome your feedback as well. So this book is dynamic and will change as our experience with new students warrants it.

Time Management

It is important to manage your time wisely. We all have important lives and commitments. However, if you have decided you want to learn this material in a 15-week semester (for our 4-credit course), then we recommend you spend 6-8 hours per week outside of class time listening to lectures and doing the homework. That recommendation might sound crazy, and it will vary from person to person depending on your previous preparation and what you remember. But we are not kidding. That's 6-8 hours per week outside of class time. What is important is to really spend an hour or two every day doing some mathematics. If you cram all 8 hours into one day, then you will be much less likely to retain it all. Cramming may work for some students for other subjects but very rarely for mathematics. Cramming to learn mathematics is like asking your muscles to gain strength by doing nothing for a week, working out one day for 8 hours, and nothing again for the next week. There needs to be gradual progress with repeated stimulation of brain pathways that makes them more robust and helps you to retain the knowledge and skills. Regular practice allows a habit to form, and the material will come to you naturally eventually.

Personal Care That Could Affect Learning

1. Poor Sleep
2. Poor Nutrition
3. Lack of Exercise

In order to do mathematics, you need to have access to the higher level thinking processes in your brain. If you do not get enough sleep, it is hard for the brain to do simple tasks. Studies show that even an hour deficit of sleep makes simple arithmetic problems a chore. So make sure you get 7 to 8 hours of sleep. Sleeping is also shown to be what allows our brain to process what has happened during the day and store it in your long term memory. So if you want to maximize long-term retention, then you need to get enough sleep. In order for your brain to be optimally functional for exams, try to get enough sleep at least the two nights before the exam. This is another reason to avoid procrastination and cramming.

Many studies show how a diet that is rich in fruits, vegetables, nuts, and legumes helps you increase your brain power. If you have a busy life, then you can carry an apple with you, or some almonds, walnuts, or any nuts to sustain you until you have time for a fuller meal. Almonds and walnuts are very good for the brain. So pay attention to your nutrition to give yourself energy and overall good health, which will lead to higher brain function.

We talked about breathing before as that is important for your brain as well. Studies show that exercise is also key in keeping your brain healthy. New brain research shows that exercise actually generates new neurons in your brain. So just 25-30 minutes of walking 3 times a week will help you immensely. Poor nutrition and exercise have also been shown to reduce a human's brain size.

Family or Personal Problems

1. Illnesses
2. Worried About Family
3. Worried About Making Ends Meet
4. Worried About Grades and Future Plans

We all have lives outside the classroom that can interfere with the learning process. Prioritizing activities in your life and practicing time management will help you organize and set aside the time needed to do the work to learn this material. It is important to find the right balance among personal health, family, finances, and school. This is something you will have to figure out, but as teachers, we are aware of this struggle. Sometimes people try to do too much in their lives. It might be that you will need to take fewer credits or find someone to help with some of the other responsibilities in your life. Just remember that you are not alone and there is often help available to you, whether it is a university counselor, your teacher, a social service, or a friend or family member. Your school and community have resources if you need them.

Video Log 0.1b

1. What do you think about asking for help?
2. Describe at least one technique you might use in dealing with stress or anxiety during studying or taking exams in mathematics or any other subject.
3. One can respond to "being stuck" by immediately asking for help, or to first contemplate for a few minutes where your uncertainty begins.   Express briefly a benefit to delaying seeking help and struggling and coming with strategies to get unstuck.
4. Also state what length of contemplation you feel would be optimal, e.g., minutes, hours, or a day or two.
5. What is mindfulness?
6. How might you adopt these principles to help you in your learning or when being assessed?
7. What is brain plasticity?
8. What do you think your potential for learning new concepts or even relearning old concepts might be based on what you now know about the brain?

Module 1: Introduction to Mathematical Objects

Introduction

In this chapter, we use an innovative approach to bridge the ideas of arithmetic learned in middle school to the more abstract and general ideas of algebra that are used extensively in the natural and social sciences. We will introduce some vocabulary you are familiar with and other perhaps not so much. We will also review some of the foundational objects like numbers of different types, then introduce a variety of types of algebraic objects (polynomials, rational expressions, and radical expressions), introduce the concept of functions, and then some geometric objects. Many of these objects will involve arithmetic operations on variable expressions, e.g. $\sqrt{x + y^2}$ and $3x^2 - 5x - 2$, that we will assume you have been exposed to some time in your k-12 education. We will also spend some time discussing similarities and differences amongst all of these objects.

1.1 A Brief History of Numbers

A brief history illustrates how mathematics has developed and what it now entails. The earliest mathematics was devoted to counting objects. This may seem simple, but it took many millennia to develop the sophisticated decimal number system we take for granted today.

Watch the following video and attempt the project below which is also mentioned in the video to help you understand the complexities that arise in developing a number system.

Lecture

🖥 Decimal Number System

https://www.youtube.com/watch?v=B6GA-o6YoLw (12 min)

Project: Give yourself about 15-20 minutes (http://www.online-stopwatch.com/full-screen-stopwatch/). Take a whole handful (about 25-50) toothpicks (you could use nails, pins, paper clips,...). Come up with your own method to express or communicate how many toothpicks you have without using our base ten number system (i.e. you cannot use counting numbers like 1,2,3,4,5,6,7,8,9,10,...).

Then try to answer the following questions

     A. Describe the system you developed.
     B. Could you generalize your system to higher or lower amount of toothpicks?
     C. What difficulties did you encounter in doing this exercise?
     D. Would someone else be able to understand your system?

If you are having trouble starting this project, think about what the key factors are that allow you to count in our decimal system. Then use these factors to develop your own system. You may want to talk to another person to run your ideas by. This discussion will help you understand our decimal system and its benefits so we hope you give it a try. Remember to wait 3-5 minutes and then take a break, come back and spend more time thinking on this problem before giving up.

Number Systems and Mathematical Objects

Ways of Counting

Ways of Counting Objects

How does one come up with a mathematical number system? As you may have seen from the project, it is not trivial to develop a useful number system. You may have noticed if you compared your work with others that various systems have some common themes. We first need to identify a unit of an object. Based on this unit we then need symbols to represent the amounts greater than this object which requires some form of grouping method. This method then allows us to group these objects so we can handle a larger number of objects. We also need to make sure our system is universal and unambiguous so that others could use it to count. Almost all cultures had to answer questions of this type as soon as trade and commerce developed. The use of numbers and standard units of measure are necessary to facilitate communication and record keeping amongst each other, and be able to make sense of the quantitative world around us.

The oldest form of numeration was by use of tally marks in the Stone Age approximately 25,000 to 35,000 years ago. In this system numbers were arranged in groups of 5 with 1 stick representing one unit and then 4 vertical tick marks and one side ways tick mark representing a bundle of 5. As human societies got more complicated, the tally system became cumbersome which prompted the development of many different number systems.

Babylonian Numbers

Babylonians used base 60 system (3000-2000 B.C.). For example the decimal number 12074 in base 60 is 3:21:14 which in Babylonian symbols is:

$$= 3 \times 60^2 + 21 \times 60^1 + 14 \times 60^0$$

This may seem cumbersome, but it is precisely the way we measure time with the units being seconds and the bundles of 60 units a minute and bundles of 60 minutes as an hour. The above number would represent 3:21:14 or 3 hours 21 minutes and 14 seconds.

Aztec and Mayan Numbers

Aztec and Mayans used a base 20 system (~4th century C.E.). The Mayan system was sophisticated in that it had a zero symbol to represent having no amounts of some place values. The numbers below illustrate the Mayan base-twenty system.

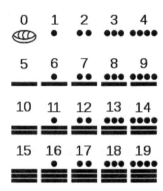

	20	40	445	508	953	30,414
8,000						•••
400			•	•	••	(line symbol)
20	•	••	••	—	••	(zero symbol)
units	(zero symbol)	(zero symbol)	—	•••	•••	••••

Adding and subtracting are actually quite easy in Mayan.

    a. Try to write the numbers 35 and 43 in Mayan.

    b. Use these Mayan numbers for 35 and 43 to try adding them by combining the one's, and then twenty's place values.

    c. Try using the Mayan representations for 953 and 508 in the table above to perform the subtraction 953 – 508.

All three of these civilizations did very complex astronomical computations. What is common to all of these numeration systems and many others that we use in everyday life is that a unit is fixed for an object, and then the objects being counted are bundled into groups of units, then again put into groups of groups etc. In our base-ten system, the rate of combining into groups is ten to one, i.e. ten single units is one ten, and ten ten's is one hundred, ten hundreds is one thousand etc.

The most common use of numbers is to measure a particular characteristic of an object like distance, area, volume, weight, money, time, or how many of a certain object and so on. In this respect the metric system is the most common system for measurement that fully aligns with the principles of the decimal number system. However, we do still have systems for specialized measurements in some countries which don't align with the ten to one ratio of the decimal number system, e.g. for distances we measure in inches and bundle 12 of these to get a foot, 3 of these to get a yard, and then 1760 of these to get a mile, or for time we use seconds, minutes, hours, days, weeks, and so on. The main benefit of the metric system is that all the rates of combining are in line with the decimal system, i.e. we bundle at a ratio of ten to one or perhaps a power of ten to one. With the ten to one bundling, one can go to smaller units by breaking or unbundling a unit into tenths of a unit. This is done repeatedly e.g. in metric measurement where one meter equals 10 decimeters and each decimeter is equal to 10 centimeters, each centimeter equals 10 millimeters. Compare this to say the English units of volume where 1 gallon unbundles to four quarts, each quart unbundles to two pints, each pint to 2 cups and each cup to 8 fluid ounces, etc.

Video Log 1.1a

1. Determine what numbers are represented below and which civilization used this numeration system.

   a.

   b.

   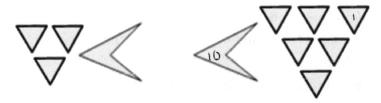

c.

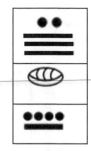

d. *MCMXCVIII*

Decimal Numbers

The numbers you have worked with in k-12 use the base ten. This is called the decimal number system. Our decimal number system is sometimes referred to as the Hindu Arabic system and was developed between 1st and 5th century by Indian mathematicians. The concept of zero as a number (which was referred to as "shunya") and not just a place holder did not come until much later, about 7th to 9th century.

The decimal number system uses place-value where the position of a digit determines which sized group it represents. The system uses a decimal marker that you might have heard as decimal point to separate digits representing one or more units from digits that represent fractions of units. For example the decimal number 324.56 can be written in the expanded form

as $324.56 = 3 \times 100 + 2 \times 10 + 4 \times 1 + 5 \times \frac{1}{10} + 6 \times \frac{1}{100}$ or

as $324.56 = 3 \times 10^2 + 2 \times 10^1 + 4 \times 10^0 + 5 \times 10^{-1} + 6 \times 10^{-2}$

The numbers 3,2,4,5,6 are referred to as the coefficients or digits of the number. 3 is in the hundred's place, 2 is in the ten's place, 4 is in the units place, 5 is in the tenth's place and 6 is in the hundredth's place. (Remember: $10^2 = 10 \times 10$, where 10 is called the base and 2 is called the exponent; $10^{-2} = \frac{1}{10 \times 10}$, where 10 would be the base and -2 would be the exponent. We will do more with this notation a little later.)

You can move from one place value to the next as follows (see chart below) – to go from a decimal place value to the left one digit you multiply by 10 and to go right one digit you divide by 10.

Decimal numbers with no negative exponents of 10 in its expanded form are called **whole numbers**.

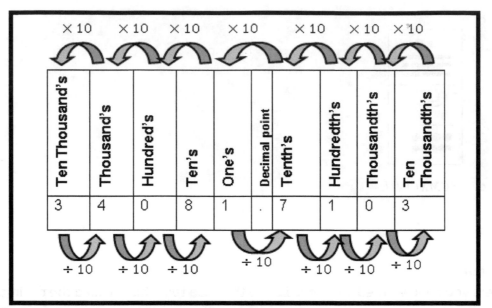

As we said before the grouping of our number system is base ten. So once we have one in the units place we count to nine and then the next number is 10 (written in words as ten) which can be interpreted as 0 in the units place, and 1 in the tens place (which is a bundle of ten). So in the number 324 (three hundred twenty-four) we have 4 in the units place, 2 in the tens place (2 bundles of tens), and 3 in the hundreds place (3 bundles of ten tens). With this structure, we can see that multiplying or dividing by 10, just makes the place value of each digit become larger or smaller respectively by the number of times we multiply or divide by 10. Thus 324×100 makes each digit correspond to 10^2 times more units and thus $324 \times 10^2 = 32400$. Likewise division by 1000, makes each place value smaller by a factor of 10 three times and $324 \div 1000 = 0.324$ where we moved the decimal point three places to the left. We use these numbers in our daily lives, for example, when you write a check or money order as shown below- (Image modified from

http://www.educationworld.com/tools_templates/template_kid_check.doc)

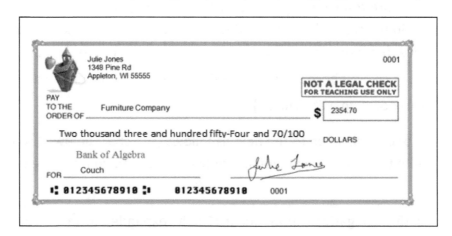

1. Determine how many blocks you have below.

   a.

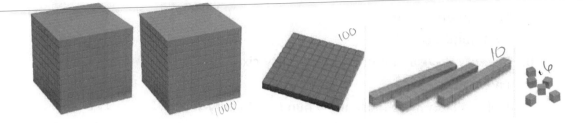

   b.

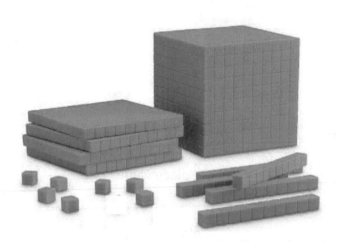

   c. How sure are you of your answers?
   d. Are there any other numbers that can be represented than the ones you came up with for parts a. and b.?
   e. Summarize the basics of the decimal number system that comes across after you finished parts a.-d.?

2. Write the numbers below in expanded form.
   a. 235
   b. 4847
   c. 5937303
   d. 0.0072
   e. 40.54
   f. 400000

3. Determine what decimal numbers are represented in the expanded form as shown below.

    a. $30000 + 400 + 5 + \frac{2}{100} + \frac{7}{10000}$

    b. $8 \times 10^3 + 4 \times 10^0 + 7 \times 10^{-1}$

4. Write the numbers below.

    a. Two hundred eight

    b. Seventy thousand four hundred thirty-six

    c. Five tenths

    d. Eight million five thousand six hundred twenty-four

5. The numbers below are multiplied or divided by powers of ten. Write them as decimal numbers showing clearly where the decimal point moves to.

    a. 375.87×100000

    b. 0.00458×10

    c. 7×100

    d. $117 \div 100$

    e. $375.87 \div 10000$

    f. $0.0458 \div 100$

6. Write the place value of the digits asked below.

    a. In the number 235

      ➢ the digit 2 is in the_____ place value.

      ➢ the digit 5 is in the _____ place value

    b. In the number 5937208

      ➢ the digit 9 is in the_____ place value.

      ➢ the digit 0 is in the _____ place value.

    c. In the number 40.056

      ➢ the digit 5 is in the_____ place value.

      ➢ the digit 6 is in the _____ place value.

7. Convert the base-ten decimal number 2016 using the number systems listed below.

    a. 2016 in Babylonian is:

    b. 2016 in Mayan is:

    c. 2016 in Roman Numerals is:

8. Create a number that has at least 4 non-zero digits with a 5 in the hundred's place.

9. Create a number that has at least 4 non-zero digits with a 3 in the thousandth's place.

10. We can think of our monetary system as a numeration system for counting how many pennies or dollars one has.
    a. Express the amount $13.45 in three different ways using any combinations of pennies, nickels, dimes, quarters, and one, five, or ten dollar bills.
    b. What benefit is there to having many ways to express a dollar value? (We could make it unique by only having pennies, dimes, dollars, ten dollar bills etc.)
11. How would you write a check for $450.67 to Best American where you bought your TV?

A decimal number with a finite number of digits is called a **terminating decimal number**. A decimal number that has infinitely many non-zero digits after the decimal point is called a **non-terminating decimal number**. Amongst the non-terminating decimal numbers, those which after the decimal point consist of a finite sequence of digits that repeat infinitely often are called **repeating decimals**. For example 3.4 is a terminating decimal, $3.\overline{41} = 3.41414141\ldots$ is a repeating decimal, and the number 3.41411411141111 …. where each group keeps on adding an additional 1 is a nonterminating nonrepeating decimal.

Playing in the land of mathematics:

In mathematics as soon as an object is introduced, you can replace different aspects of it with variables or any other object to see what kind of object it is and which properties from the previous object will be preserved in the new set of objects and what its usefulness would be. We will have this playful attitude throughout this book.

As an example, if we take our whole numbers written in the expanded form and replace the base 10 with a variable say x, then let's see what we get. So instead of

$3 \times 10^2 + 2 \times 10^1 + 4 \times 10^0$, we look at $3 \times x^2 + 2 \times x^1 + 4 \times x^0 = 3x^2 + 2x + 4$.

In general if we allow the coefficients 3, 2, and 4 to be any decimal numbers and allow all whole number exponents on the base x, we call these objects polynomials in one variable. If we take a generic decimal number (with positive and negative powers of 10) and replace the base 10 with a variable say x and allow the coefficients to be any decimal number we call this expression an algebraic expression in one variable. We will work on this object more thoroughly later.

1.2 Number Sets
Lecture

    🖥️ Natural through Complex Numbers
        http://www.youtube.com/watch?v=MH946PzUGlg (13 min)

Natural and Whole Numbers

Numbers, however they are represented, can be used in a variety of different ways. The earliest and most natural use is for counting objects and the set of numbers $N = \{1, 2, 3, ... \}$ is called the set of **natural numbers** or **counting numbers**. Another slightly different use of numbers is to put things in order, e.g. the first, second, third .... person in line at the ticket counter. When used in this fashion, the numbers are called **ordinal numbers** as they are used to order objects. (Another use of numbers is as **identifiers** or **labels** such as zip codes, driver's license numbers or serial numbers. These are not really quantitative and could just as well be accomplished using letters.)

It took a while for the importance of zero to be appreciated, but if we include zero with the counting numbers, then the set $W = \{0, 1, 2, 3, ... \}$ is called the set of **whole numbers**.

Note: The set of natural numbers is a subset of the set of whole numbers which we represent in the set notation as $N \subset W$. This means that all natural numbers are also whole numbers. It is also true that not all whole numbers are natural numbers. This relates to the concept of extension of the sets of numbers. Zero is a useful number for e.g. accounting when a zero balance is often the goal in balancing a ledger.

Integers

The advent of negative numbers is also very useful in accounting when a $250 debt can be assigned the value of $-\$250$. The set of numbers $Z = \{... - 2, -1, 0, 1, 2, ... \}$ that we get by appending the negative counting numbers to the set of whole numbers is called the set of **integers.** (In case you are wondering why the letter Z is used to represent integers, it comes from Zahlen which stands for numbers in German.)

Note: The set of whole numbers is a subset of the set of integers ($N \subset W \subset Z$). This means that all natural and whole numbers are also integers but not all integers are natural or whole numbers).

Rational Numbers

In order to deal with partial quantities, fractions and decimal numbers provide two ways to describe quantities that are in between integer amounts. A fraction is a quotient of whole numbers e.g., $\frac{2}{3}$ can be interpreted in terms of some "whole" quantity or unit, e.g. $\frac{2}{3}$ cup of sugar or $\frac{2}{3}$ of an hour where the whole is one cup of sugar or one hour. But $\frac{2}{3}$ can also be interpreted

---

as being made of two $\frac{1}{3}$ units, just like when we write $2cm = 1cm + 1cm = 2 \times (1cm)$ it means two $1cm$ units (in $\frac{2}{3}$ cups of sugar can be thought of as two $\frac{1}{3}$ cups of sugar). Sometimes fractions can be interpreted as a ratio 2: 3 or 2 parts to 3 parts. So if I were to say make a punch using the ratio of 2: 3 of grape juice to sprite, this means you can use 2 cups of grape juice and 3 cups of sprite, or 4 cups of grape juice and 6 cups of sprite and so on. Sometimes fractions are interpreted as percentages e.g., if you got $\frac{1}{2}$ of your questions correct on an exam it would mean that you scored 50% on your exam (or that you got 1 question correct out of every two questions on the exam). In all cases in the fraction $\frac{a}{b}$, the bottom number b (a natural number) is called the **denominator** and represents how many equal pieces the whole is cut into and the top number a is called the **numerator** and indicates how many of these pieces the fraction $\frac{a}{b}$ represents. Thus $\frac{2}{3} hr$ represents two time units that are each of duration such that three of them would be equal to one hour (that means two times units of 20 minutes or 40 minutes total). When one appends to the integers all possible positive and negative fractions we get the set of numbers called the **rational numbers**. In symbols, we might describe the set of rational numbers as $Q = \left\{ \frac{a}{b} \mid a \text{ and } b \text{ are integers with } b \neq 0 \right\}$, Q stands for Quotient. You can read that sentence as "Q is the set of all fractions $\frac{a}{b}$ such that a and b are any integers where b is not equal to zero".

Note: The set of natural numbers, whole numbers, and integers are all subsets of the set of rational numbers, and in set notation we have $N \subset W \subset Z \subset Q$. This means that all natural numbers, whole numbers, and integers are also rational numbers. Note that an integer a can be written as $\frac{a}{1}$ making all integers rational numbers.

We will study number lines in detail in section 1.5, but for now you can think of a number line as a long straight road and the place you are standing at corresponds to the number zero. From zero, each positive number corresponds to the point that many feet ahead of you and each negative number corresponds to moving that many units behind you on the road. If all decimal numbers were to be plotted on this number line, they form the set of real numbers. Any section of finite length on a number line, no matter how small, contains a rational number. (In fact it contains infinitely many rational numbers.) Number sets having this property are said to be dense on a number line. For example in the interval between $\frac{1}{2}$ and $\frac{3}{4}$ there are infinitely many rational numbers, but there are not any integers. Thus the integers are not dense on a number line. Even the subset of rational numbers where all denominators are powers of two is a dense subset. Can you think of why?

Irrational Numbers

What is amazing and was discovered to great surprise by the Pythagoreans more than two thousand years ago is that there are numbers that cannot be written as a ratio of two integers. Some familiar examples are the numbers π, and $\sqrt{2}$. These numbers are easily described geometrically as the circumference of a circle of diameter one unit and as the diagonal length of a right triangle when both legs are one unit long, but neither π nor $\sqrt{2}$ can be written as a ratio of two integers. A common approximate value for π is $3\frac{1}{7}$ or 3.14, but π is actually about 0.04% smaller than $\frac{22}{7}$ and 0.05% bigger than 3.14. If all the decimal numbers were to be plotted on a number line (which we will talk about in more detail in section 1.5), they form the set of real numbers. The set of all decimal numbers (positions on a number line) that are not rational numbers are referred to as the **irrational numbers**. In set notation it is denoted as $\bar{Q} = \{a\mid a \notin Q\}$, the bar on the set of rational numbers in set theory stands for complement or numbers not in the set of rational numbers.

Real Numbers

Note: *The set of all rational and irrational numbers together form the set of real numbers **R** or all decimal numbers. In set theory notation we can say that $R = Q \cup \bar{Q}$. All decimal numbers are either rational or irrational. In other words, the set of all decimal numbers is the set of **real numbers**. This also means that $\bar{Q} \subset R$ and $N \subset W \subset Z \subset Q \subset R$.*

It can be shown that all rational numbers have either terminating decimal representations, e.g. $\frac{5}{8} = 0.625$, or non-terminating repeating decimal representation, e.g. $\frac{23}{11} = 2.09090909\ldots$

We will discuss further in Module 2 how all terminating decimals and repeating decimals are rational numbers while all non-repeating decimal numbers are irrational. So for example 3.4, and $3.\overline{41} = 3.41414141\ldots$ are rational numbers, but $3.41411411141111\ldots$ is an irrational number.

If one were to somehow randomly choose each successive digit of an infinite decimal number amongst all decimal numbers it is very unlikely that the digits would have a repeating pattern. Thus it seems that a randomly chosen decimal number is much more likely to be an irrational number than a rational number. This suggests that in some sense the irrational numbers are much more common than the rational numbers on a number line! The irrational numbers are also **dense** on a number line, i.e. you can't find a finite piece of the number line that has no irrationals in it.

Complex Numbers

For a long time people believed that the set of real numbers accounted for all the numbers that there are. In 1545, Girolamo Cardano and others made progress on solving cubic equations such as $x^3 - 15x = 4$. Their technique gave a solution to this problem that involved $\sqrt{-121}$. The value of this square root cannot be any real number since any real number when squared will be positive. However their solution method simplified to a final result of $x = 4$ which is easily seen to make the above equation true. This leads to a deeper study of square roots of negative numbers. Today these kinds of numbers are absolutely essential in higher mathematics, engineering and physics. A simpler problem that shows the deficiency of the real numbers is to try to find a real number x such that $x^2 = -1$. Play with this for a while to convince yourself that no real number when multiplied by itself will produce the result negative one!

We define a new kind of number (which we label i) to be a solution of the equation $x^2 = -1$. So even though it is hard to imagine what i is, we know that its square is -1 or that $i \times i = -1$. With this definition of i we expand the set of real numbers to the set of **complex numbers** defined as $C = \{a + bi \mid a \text{ and } b \text{ are any real numbers and } i^2 = -1\}$. In the complex number $a + bi$, the number a is called the **real part** and b is called the **imaginary part** of the number $(a + bi)$.

Note: *The set of all real numbers is a subset of the set of complex numbers because every real number can be written as $a + 0i$, e.g., $2.4 = 2.4 + 0i$ in set notation it will look like $R \subset C$.*

You can represent all the sets of numbers we have discussed and how they are nested with the Venn Diagram shown below.

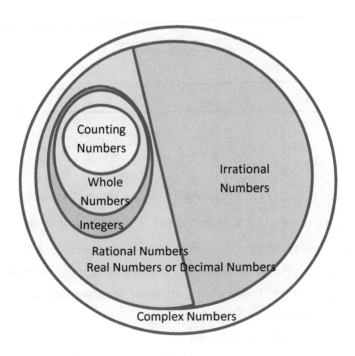

Project

After you have learned the names of all the numbers we have studied so far, pay attention to the real world that you live in and keep track of all the places and things where you see numbers. Numbers can appear in the many places like the fruits and vegetables you eat, barcodes on different products are also numbers in a disguised form, Highways, different parts in your cars, and nutrition labels on food products. So be observant and see where numbers appear in your life in the hours after you exit the classroom today and before you return the next class. Write the number you saw and the context or story behind the number (what information did the number give you) and the type of number ($N, W, Z, Q, \overline{Q}, R, C$) in the table below.

Numbers	Context (i.e., where the number appeared or the story behind it)
1.	
2.	
3.	
4.	
5.	

Practice Problems

1. Try to find a couple of numbers in each region of the Venn Diagram above. For example, outside of the integers region but within the set Q the numbers $\frac{7}{3}$ and $-\frac{345}{761}$ can be found.
2. Which of the following sets do you think have more numbers in them? Natural Numbers, Whole Numbers, Integers, Rational Numbers, Irrational Numbers or Real Numbers? Hint: How can you tell if one set has more elements than another set? Explain your reasoning.
3. List two rational and two irrational numbers
   a. Between the numbers 1.5 and 2.0
   b. Between the numbers -1 and -2.

Solutions

1. Starting at the smallest set the natural numbers we have 1, 2, 3 .... Then the set of whole numbers has all of the natural numbers in addition to the number zero. -2,-5 belong to the set of integers but not to the set of whole numbers or natural numbers. From there going outward beyond the integers but still within the set of rational numbers we get e.g. ½ and $\frac{25}{3}$. Outside of the set of rational numbers but inside the set of irrational numbers we find a lot of numbers like $\sqrt{3}$, π, and $2 + \sqrt{3}$. Finally numbers like $3 + i$, and $-\sqrt{2} - 3i$ belong to complex numbers but not to the set of real numbers or any of its subsets.

2. All the sets shown above have infinitely many numbers in them. However you know that the set of whole numbers has one number more than the set of natural numbers, the set of integers has infinitely many more numbers than the whole numbers since we added $-1, -2, -3, ...$ As we go to each larger set from the integers on up we continue to add infinitely many numbers at each stage. Thus the biggest set is the set of complex numbers even though all of the sets are infinite.

3.

   a. Two rational numbers between 1.5 and 2 are 1.6 and $1\frac{2}{3}$; two irrationals are
   $\pi - 1.5 \approx 1.64159$, and 1.5050050005 ....

   b. Two rational numbers between -1 and -2 are $-1\frac{2}{3}$ and $-1.2 = -\frac{12}{10} = -6/5$;
   two irrationals are $-\sqrt{2} \approx -1.414$ ..., and -1.023022302223 ... .

Note: *Mathematicians have investigated how we can compare sets with infinitely many numbers. When we look at the number of elements in the set of counting numbers, compared to whole numbers, compared to integers, compared to real numbers some of these sets that we extended out to are in a sense much larger than others. Mathematicians have characterized the natural or counting numbers, integers, and the rational numbers as countably infinite. (This means you could list these numbers in order and in that list every single fraction would show up at some point in the list.) Amazingly, it has been shown that the set of infinitely many real numbers cannot be put into such an ordered list and the real numbers are said to be* **uncountable.** *Thus, going from the set of integers to the set of rational numbers is a much smaller step than going from the rational numbers to the real numbers. The scope of this discussion is beyond this book but we thought some of you might like to know these facts.*

1. List at least two rational numbers and two irrational numbers between 3.3 and 3.4
2. List at least two rational numbers and two irrational numbers between -3.3 and -3.4
3. List, if possible, what number would be considered to be the smallest counting number.
4. List, if possible, what number would be considered to be the smallest whole number.
5. List, if possible, what number would be considered to be the smallest integer number.
6. List if, possible, what number would be considered to be the smallest rational number.
7. List if, possible, what number would be considered to be the smallest irrational number.
8. List, if possible, what number would be considered to be the smallest real number.
9. List, if possible, an integer between -34 and -33.
10. List, if possible, a rational and an irrational number between 2.313113111 .... and 2.323223222 ...
11. List at least one integer but not a whole number.
12. List at least one rational number that is not an integer.
13. List at least one real number that is not a rational number.
14. List at least one complex number that is not a real number.
15. Answer true or false and justify your answer
    a. 0 is a rational number
    b. $\frac{2}{0}$ is a rational number
    c. 0 is an irrational number
    d. 0 is a complex number
    e. -4 is an complex number
16.

For each column check all the labels that apply.		-35	$-2i$	$\frac{17}{43}$	5.41441 ...	$9 - 5.3i$	$\sqrt{9} = 3$	$\sqrt{11}$	-58.4	$5.0\overline{47}$
a. Whole Number										
b. Integer										
c. Rational	Irrational									
d. Real Number										
e. Complex Number										

1.3 Geometric Shapes

Lecture

🖥 Geometry

http://www.youtube.com/watch?v=X4v0CZzC9ec   (10 min)

When working with visual representations of numbers, we frequently use two dimensional geometric shapes. So before we discuss geometric representation of numbers we will focus on some basic 2 dimensional geometric objects.

Name	Representation of the Shape
Point	
	Notation: P
Line	
	Notation: $\overleftrightarrow{PQ}$
Line Segment: The part of the line that lies between two fixed points on the line.	
	Notation: $\overline{PQ}$
Ray: The part of line that lies on one side of a fixed point. The fixed point is called the start point.	
	Notation: $\overrightarrow{PQ}$, P is the start point.

Angle: Amount of rotation between two rays with a common start point.			
	Acute Angle: Measure of the angle is less than 90°.	**Obtuse Angle:** Measure of the angle is greater than 90°.	**Right Angle:** Measure of the angle is 90°.
	Notation for the Angle: $\angle LKM$	**Notation for the Angle:** $\angle BAC$	**Notation for the Angle:** $\angle EDF$

The measure of an angle is denoted by putting a little m in front of the angle notation:
So in other words the angle $\angle LKM$ is an acute angle if and only if any only if $m\angle LKM < 90°$.
So in other words the angle $\angle BAC$ is an obtuse angle if and only if any only if $m\angle BAC > 90.°$
So in other words the angle $\angle EDF$ is a right angle if and only if any only if $m\angle EDF = 90°$.

Note: Sometimes small letters are used to represent angles instead of the points on the ray.	 **Notation:** $\angle a$
Parallel Lines: Two lines in a plane that never intersect each other are called parallel lines.	 **Notation:** $l \mathbin{//} m$

Perpendicular Lines: Two lines that intersect each other at right angles are called perpendicular lines.	
	Notation: $l \perp m$
Transversal: A line that intersects two lines in the same plane is called a transversal.	
	Notation: The line n is a transversal to lines l, and , and m.
Vertical Angles: Any pair of two opposite angles formed at the intersection of two lines are called vertical angles (Sometimes also called opposite angles).	
	Notation: The pair of angles $\angle 1$, and $\angle 3$ are vertical angles, so are the pair of angles $\angle 2$, and $\angle 4$.

Alternate Interior Angles: A pair of angles on the opposite sides of a transversal, but on the inside of the two lines are called alternate interior angles.

Alternate Exterior Angles: A pair of angles on the opposite sides of a transversal, but on the outside of the two lines are called alternate exterior angles.

Corresponding Angles: A pair of angles on the same side of the transversal and the same side of the two lines are called corresponding angles.

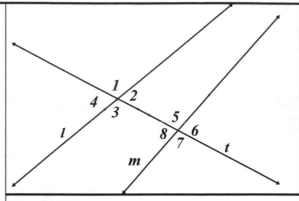

Notation:
The pairs∠2, and ∠8 are called alternate interior angles. So are ∠3, and ∠5.
The pairs∠1, and ∠7 are called alternate exterior angles. So are∠4, and ∠6.
The pairs ∠1 and ∠5 are called corresponding angles. So are∠3, and ∠7, ∠2, and ∠6, and also ∠4, and ∠8.

Complementary Angles: If the sum of the measures of two angles is 90°, they are called complementary angles.

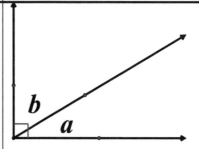

Notation: ∠a is called the complement of ∠b and vice versa.

Supplementary Angles: If the sum of the measures of two angles is 180°, they are called supplementary angles.

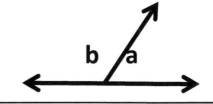

Notation: ∠a is called the supplement of ∠b and vice versa.

Polygon: A closed shape in a plane made of 3 or more finite noncrossing line segments joined at their endpoints. The number of sides determines the name of the shape. Some standard polygons are listed below.

Triangle: A polygon made of three sides. **Note:** In all triangles the side opposite the largest angle is the largest side.		
	Scalene Triangle: All three sides of different length. In other words, no two angles in the triangle have the same measure. **Obtuse Triangle:** One of the angles is obtuse.	**Isosceles Triangle:** Two of the sides are of the same length. In other words two of the angles have the same measure.
	Equilateral Triangle: All three sides are of the same length. In other words all three angles have the same measure. **Note:** An equilateral triangle is also an isosceles triangle.	**Right Triangle:** Measure of one of the angles is 90°.

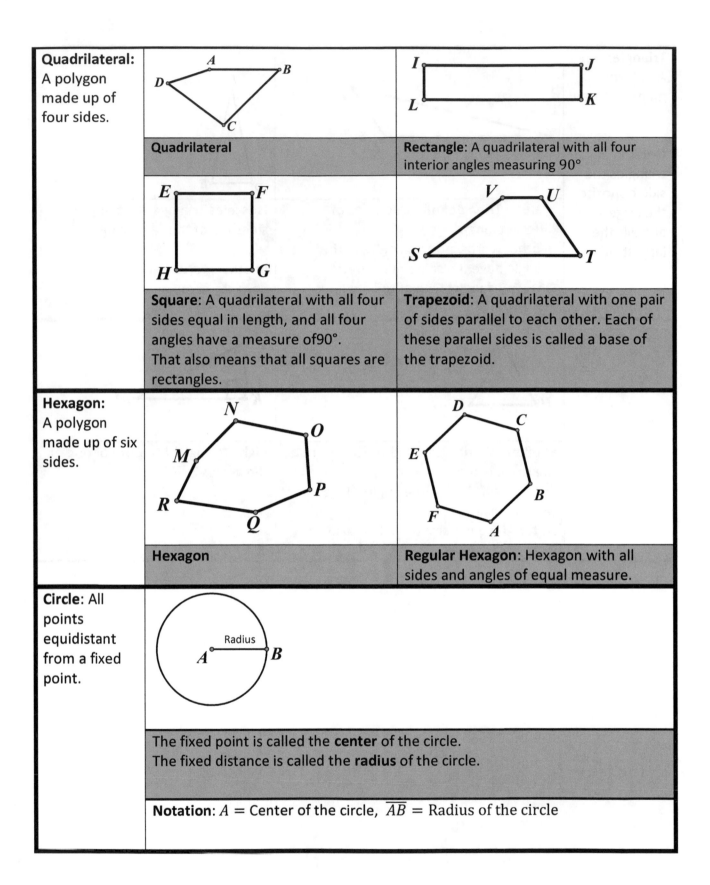

Quadrilateral: A polygon made up of four sides.	Quadrilateral	**Rectangle**: A quadrilateral with all four interior angles measuring 90°	
	Square: A quadrilateral with all four sides equal in length, and all four angles have a measure of 90°. That also means that all squares are rectangles.	**Trapezoid**: A quadrilateral with one pair of sides parallel to each other. Each of these parallel sides is called a base of the trapezoid.	
Hexagon: A polygon made up of six sides.	Hexagon	**Regular Hexagon**: Hexagon with all sides and angles of equal measure.	
Circle: All points equidistant from a fixed point.	The fixed point is called the **center** of the circle. The fixed distance is called the **radius** of the circle.		
	Notation: A = Center of the circle, $\overline{AB}$ = Radius of the circle		

1. Identify the objects below as a line, a ray, or a line segment. Use appropriate notation to describe the object.

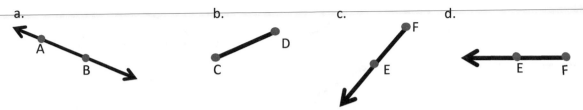

a.   b.   c.   d.

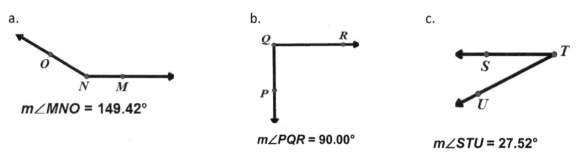

2. Identify the angles below as an acute angle, obtuse angle, or right angle.

a.

b.

c.

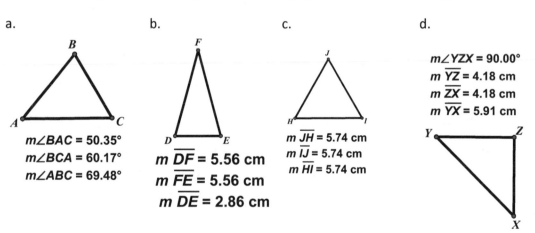

$m\angle MNO = 149.42°$

$m\angle PQR = 90.00°$

$m\angle STU = 27.52°$

3. Identify the triangles below as scalene, acute, obtuse, or right. If possible also identify them as an equilateral triangle, or an isosceles triangle.

a.   b.   c.   d.

$m\angle BAC = 50.35°$
$m\angle BCA = 60.17°$
$m\angle ABC = 69.48°$

$m\ \overline{DF} = 5.56$ cm
$m\ \overline{FE} = 5.56$ cm
$m\ \overline{DE} = 2.86$ cm

$m\ \overline{JH} = 5.74$ cm
$m\ \overline{IJ} = 5.74$ cm
$m\ \overline{HI} = 5.74$ cm

$m\angle YZX = 90.00°$
$m\ \overline{YZ} = 4.18$ cm
$m\ \overline{ZX} = 4.18$ cm
$m\ \overline{YX} = 5.91$ cm

4. Identify the quadrilaterals below as a rectangle, square, or a trapezoid.

a.

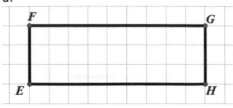

b.

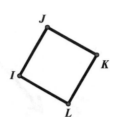

m∠JKL = 90.00°
m∠KLI = 90.00°
m∠LIJ = 90.00°
m∠IJK = 90.00°
m $\overline{IJ}$ = 3.00 cm
m $\overline{JK}$ = 3.00 cm
m $\overline{KL}$ = 3.00 cm
m $\overline{LI}$ = 3.00 cm

c.

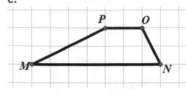

5. Determine if the lines below are parallel, perpendicular or neither.

a.

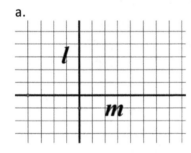

b.

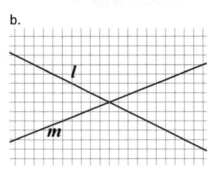

c.

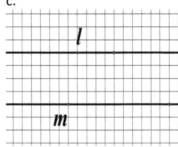

6.

   a. List all the pairs of alternate interior angles from the angles below.
   b. List all the pairs of alternate exterior angles from the angles below.
   c. List all the pairs of corresponding angles from the angles below.

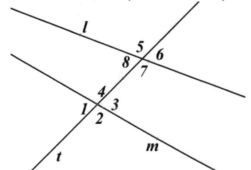

7. What is the measure of the complementary angle to 40°?

8. What is the measure of the supplementary angle to 80°?

1.4 Visualizations of Rational and Decimal Numbers

Lectures

🖥 One Visualization of Rational numbers

http://www.youtube.com/watch?v=79ZjO2MTiOc **(11 min)**

We can visualize real numbers in many different ways.

Geometric Representation of Positive Rational Numbers

We will work with positive rational numbers for this section. When we use a fraction or a rational number, the whole must be clear and should provide a visual interpretation of what the fractional number represents. See examples below for what the shaded parts of the whole represent

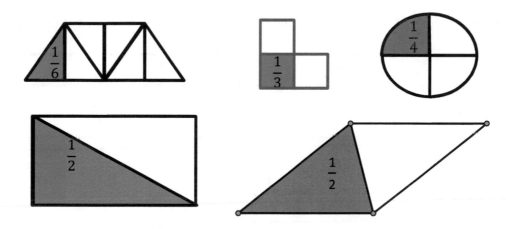

You can see how one part of a whole that is divided in b (b is a natural number) equal pieces can be thought of as the fraction $\frac{1}{b}$. The two pictures below represent the same wholes but different parts are shaded in them. The second picture can be thought of as having $\frac{2}{6}$ parts shaded or as $\frac{1}{3}$ parts shaded depending on what you see as the equal parts.

Consider three fourths of a candy bar which can be represented as three pieces of a candy bar that is cut into 4 equal pieces. What if you have two different size pizzas and the two pizzas together represent your whole. Then what is three fourths of that whole? See if you can make

sense of that below. A candy bar or pizza is often used to visualize this but any shapes that can be divided equally would do.

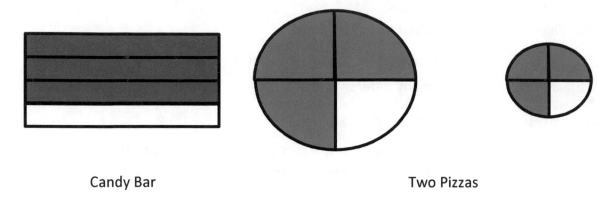

Candy Bar   Two Pizzas

Diagrams can also be used to express mixed numbers, e.g., $2\frac{3}{4} ft$ long board is 2 whole feet plus another $\frac{3}{4} ft$. The $\frac{3}{4} ft$ is three pieces each of $\frac{1}{4} ft$, i.e. 3 three inch pieces or 2 feet 9 inches.

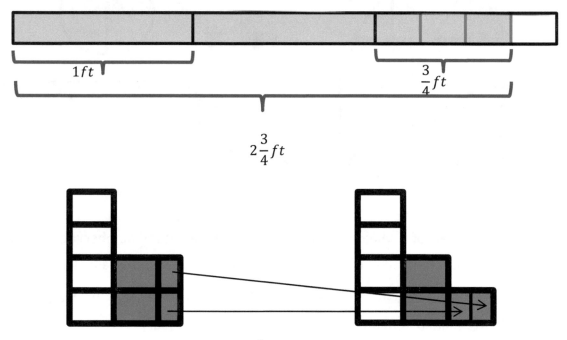

The shaded region is $\frac{3}{7}$ of the entire figure.

In the picture above you can see that sometimes you may not see the fraction until you move some of the pieces so that the whole is made up of equal pieces.

Sometimes when fractions of fractions are involved, one must be careful about the whole that each fraction refers to. For example if one has $\frac{3}{4} \ gal$ of milk in the refrigerator and the family drank 2/3 of that milk for breakfast, then how much milk is remaining? There are several ways to answer this question. One could accurately say that since $\frac{2}{3}$ of the milk was drunk, then $\frac{1}{3}$ of the milk remains. In this sense, the whole that the $\frac{1}{3}$ refers to is the $\frac{3}{4}\,gal$ that was present before breakfast. One could also take this $\frac{3}{4}\,gal$ whole and break it into three equal parts (each part would then be ¼ gal) and the amount remaining would then be one of these three parts or ¼ gal. This answer to how much remains has the whole being one gallon of milk.

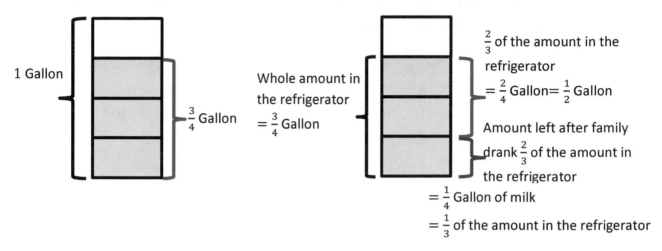

1 Gallon

$\frac{3}{4}$ Gallon

Whole amount in the refrigerator $= \frac{3}{4}$ Gallon

$\frac{2}{3}$ of the amount in the refrigerator

$= \frac{2}{4}$ Gallon $= \frac{1}{2}$ Gallon

Amount left after family drank $\frac{2}{3}$ of the amount in the refrigerator

$= \frac{1}{4}$ Gallon of milk

$= \frac{1}{3}$ of the amount in the refrigerator

You can see that the same amount can have different fractions attached to it depending on what is considered as a whole.

Practice Problems

1. Consider the seven picture frames below and see if you can answer the following questions.

a. How many picture frames would make $\frac{3}{7}$ of the total picture frames shown? What was the whole in this problem?

b. How many faces would make $\frac{1}{2}$ of all faces shown? What was the whole in this problem?

c. Of all the eyes shown, how many eyes would make $\frac{2}{7}$ of the total? What was the whole in this problem?

d. Of all the pairs of eyes shown, how many pairs of eyes would make $\frac{2}{7}$ of the total? What was the whole in this problem?

2. Now that you know the definition of a rational number written in the fraction form, explain the meaning of each of the following if you can. Draw appropriate pictures when necessary.

   a. $\frac{3}{4}$ c of yogurt makes one serving and a container of yogurt has 2 servings. What are all the different wholes here?

   b. The athlete had $\frac{3}{26}$ mi to the finish line. What is the whole here?

   c. You ate $\frac{1}{3}$ of a candy bar. What is the whole here?

   d. What if you ate $\frac{0}{3}$ of a candy bar, how big must the piece you ate be? What is the whole here?

   e. What if you ate $\frac{5}{0}$ of a pizza, how big must the piece you ate be? What is the whole here?

Attempt the following problem using visual representations of fractions. If it becomes too hard don't worry, we will work on this concept more in the second module. Remember it is important you at least try even if you make mistakes. Your brain will catch on to the mathematics involved when you start playing with these concepts. Visualizing will help you really understand.

Example: Determine how many gallons are in $\frac{3}{4}$ of a tank of gas when the whole tank is 9 gallons?

[Hint: Draw a rectangular array with 9 rectangles of equal size (each rectangle representing 1 gal) to represent the tank of gas. Then shade $\frac{3}{4}$ of each rectangle to show that $\frac{3}{4} tank = 6\frac{3}{4} gal.$ This example is related to multiplication of fractions and will be discussed further in Module 2.]

Playing

Remember how we played with the expanded decimal representation of whole numbers to come up with polynomials? In the same way we can now play with the definition of rational numbers which as you may recall was :

A **rational number** is a real number that can be represented as a fraction by an ordered pair of integers $\frac{a}{b}$, such that $b \neq 0$.

When we replace the two integers in the definition of rational numbers with other mathematical objects we create a new type of mathematical object that we call a rational expression. As before, we have to restrict the denominator to be non-zero! For example in the fraction $\frac{3}{5}$, we can replace the numerator and denominator with polynomials to get e.g. $\frac{3+x}{5+x^2}$ or $\frac{3a^2b^5}{5c^3\,d^4}$ or $\frac{3x^5-4x^2+5}{5x-7}$ all of which are different **rational expressions**. Again these rational expressions are valid so long as the denominator is nonzero.

Another example would be when you replace the numerator and the denominator with functions. (Don't worry if you have never heard of a function object, we will introduce it later in this module.) The result in this case is a new function which we'd call the quotient. If the two functions are polynomials we call the quotient a rational function.

Examples

Let $(t) = t^2 + 5t + 1, h(t) = 2^t$, then $\frac{r(t)}{h(t)} = \frac{t^2+5t+1}{2^t}$, this function $\frac{r(t)}{h(t)}$ would be called a quotient of functions. If $f(x) = x + 1$, $g(x) = x$, then $\frac{f(x)}{g(x)} = \frac{x+1}{x}$, with $x \neq 0$, this function $\frac{f(x)}{g(x)}$ is called a <u>rational function</u> because the numerator and denominator are polynomials.

Equivalent Fractions
Lecture

💻 Equivalent Fractions

<u>http://www.youtube.com/watch?v=xruSTzZcpns</u> (11 min)

Consider the fraction $\frac{3}{4}$ in terms of a round pizza that is sliced into 4 equal pieces where three of those pieces remain. Now visualize that each of the 3 remaining pieces are cut into 2 identical slices and also imagine the missing piece as being 2 thin slices missing. Now this $\frac{3}{4}pizza$ can be considered as 6 pieces out of an 8 piece whole pizza, i.e. $\frac{3}{4}pizza = \frac{3\times2}{4\times2}pizza = \frac{6}{8}pizza$.

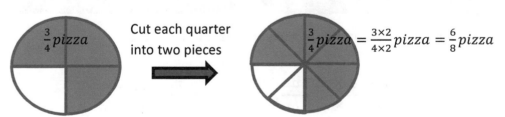

$\frac{3}{4}pizza$ Cut each quarter into two pieces $\frac{3}{4}pizza = \frac{3\times2}{4\times2}pizza = \frac{6}{8}pizza$

Consider the following equivalent fractions. In the left column we increase and in the right we decrease the number of pieces that the whole is divided into.

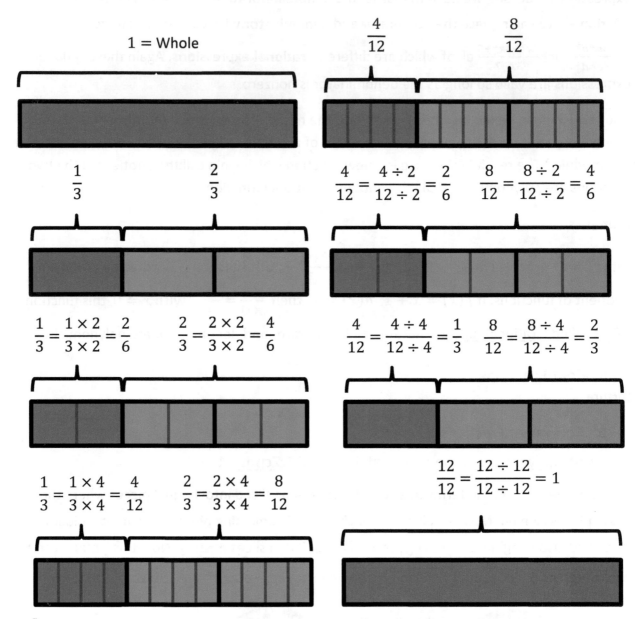

Let $\frac{a}{b}$ be any rational number, n and m be nonzero real numbers then

$$\frac{a}{b} = \frac{a \times n}{b \times n} = \frac{an}{bn}, \text{ and } \frac{a}{b} = \frac{a \div m}{b \div m} = \frac{\frac{a}{m}}{\frac{b}{m}}.$$

The fractions $\frac{a}{b} = \frac{an}{bn} = \frac{a \div m}{b \div m}$ are called **equivalent fractions** and this means that they are equal.

A rational number is said to be in the **lowest terms** if and only if its numerator and denominator do not share any common factors.

For example,

$$\frac{1}{3} = \frac{1 \times 2}{3 \times 2} = \frac{2}{6}, \qquad \frac{15}{10} = \frac{15 \div 5}{10 \div 5} = \frac{3}{2}, \qquad \frac{15}{10} = \frac{15 \times \frac{1}{5}}{10 \times \frac{1}{5}} = \frac{3}{2}$$

Fractions in lowest terms

The example below shows how to use division of numerator and denominator by a common nonzero real number to create an equivalent fraction describing the same part of the whole. This is used when using an English Unit tape measure which might be marked off in ¼ in increments.

E.g.,

$$\frac{18}{32} \ in = \frac{18 \div 2}{32 \div 2} \ in = \frac{9}{16} \ in, \text{ and } \frac{9}{16} \ in = \frac{\frac{9}{4}}{4} \ in = \frac{2.25}{4} \ in.$$

Playing

Again, we can apply the same logic of making equivalent fractions to other types of rational expressions as shown below.

$$\frac{3}{x} = \frac{3(x + 1)}{x(x + 1)} \text{ and } \frac{3}{x} = \frac{3(2)}{x(2)},$$

$$\frac{x(3x + 1)}{x(5x - 7)} = \frac{\big(x(3x + 1)\big) \div x}{\big(x(5x - 7)\big) \div x} \text{ and } \frac{x(3x + 1)}{x(5x - 7)} = \frac{3x + 1}{5x - 7},$$

$$\frac{x - 3}{x - 1} = \frac{(-1)(x - 3)}{(-1)(x - 1)} \text{ and } \frac{x - 3}{x - 1} = \frac{3 - x}{1 - x}$$

Note: *The main result for equivalent fractions is that the fractions remain equal whenever the numerator and the denominator are either multiplied by the same nonzero quantity or divided by the same nonzero quantity.*

We will make much use of this fundamental property of rational numbers or rational expressions when adding and subtracting these types of expressions in Module 2.

This aspect of rational numbers and expressions is used in writing them in an alternative form.

For example

$$\frac{3}{5} = \frac{3 \times 2}{5 \times 2} = \frac{6}{10} = 0.6, \text{ or } -\frac{17}{20} = -\frac{17 \times 5}{20 \times 5} = -\frac{85}{100} = -85\% = -0.85$$

This last example illustrates that percentages essentially represent a ratio per cent or per hundred. Thus 8% means 8 per hundred, $8\% = \frac{8}{100} = 0.08$. In this way any number given as a percentage can be written as a fraction or as a decimal. $☐\% = \frac{☐}{100}$ which is the number ☐ with the decimal point moved two units left due to division by 10 twice.

In these two examples you can see that the rational numbers could be represented as decimals using our equivalent fractions concepts. This suggests that all rational numbers that are written in the reduced form that have denominators with factors consisting of only 2's and 5's are terminating decimals. All other rational numbers are nonterminating decimals with repeating patterns.

You can also think of the rational numbers as division problems as follows. We can write the number $\frac{3}{4} = \frac{3 \div 4}{4 \div 4} = \frac{3 \div 4}{1}$ and use long division of the numerator (which we will look at it in detail in module 2) which gives us that $\frac{3}{4} = \frac{3 \div 4}{4 \div 4} = \frac{0.75}{1} = 0.75$. We can use division in this way to convert any rational number to a decimal. Thus $\frac{5}{6} = \frac{5 \div 6}{1} = 0.83333\ldots$ and $\frac{6}{7} = 6 \div 7 = 0.\overline{857142}$. The number of digits in the repeating cycle is at most one less than the value of the denominator. So if the denominator is 7 you know you cannot have more than 6 digits in the repeating cycle. The long division $(6 \div 7)$ shown below illustrates how you can only have 1, 2, 3, 4, 5, or 6 remaining after subtraction before the digits start to repeat.

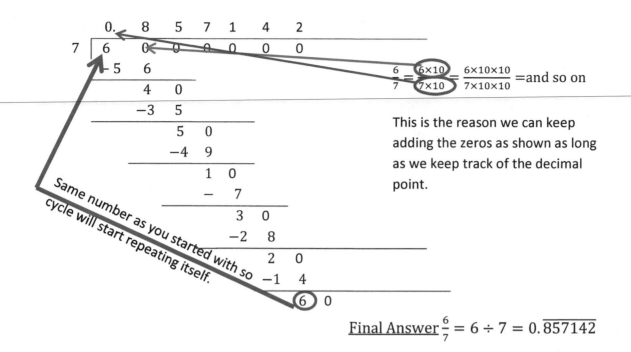

This is the reason we can keep adding the zeros as shown as long as we keep track of the decimal point.

Same number as you started with so cycle will start repeating itself.

Final Answer $\frac{6}{7} = 6 \div 7 = 0.\overline{857142}$

Ratios and Rates as Fractions

Lecture

🖥 Ratios and Percents

http://www.youtube.com/watch?v=Z5JYj_FQx7M (15 min)

Ratios express a comparison of how many of one type of object are associated with some number of another type of object. Some examples are: The cookie recipe calls for 3 cups of sugar for every 2 sticks of butter, ratio is 3:2; There were three defective sparkplugs for every 100 plugs made, ratio is 3:100; The baseball player's batting average was $0.235 = \frac{235}{1000}$ i.e 235 hits for every 1000 times at bat; The win loss ratio for the team was seven to four or 7:4; The cyclist traveled 32km per hour, $\frac{32\ km}{hr}$. For each of these ratios the actual numbers of each of the objects are not known, but only their ratio, e.g. the cookie recipe may actually have called for 9 cups of sugar and 6 sticks of butter. The ratio 9:6 is the same as 3:2 in that the number of sugar units is always 1.5 times the number of butter units. For this reason, we often write ratios as fractions, e.g. $\frac{3\ c\ sugar}{2\ sticks\ butter} = \frac{9\ c\ sugar}{6\ sticks\ butter}$ where the ratio remains the same when the top and bottom are multiplied (or divided) by the same number (Just like with fractions!). We can also think of ratios as somehow expressing an equivalency between the numerator and denominator quantities. Thus the ratio four dollars per 2.5 pounds of grapes $\frac{\$4}{2.5\ lbs\ grapes}$ can be used to express the cost of grapes. Note that if we multiply the top and bottom by 4, we obtain the cost of grapes as $\dfrac{\$4 \times 4}{2.5\ lbs\ grapes \times 4} = \dfrac{\$16}{10\ lbs\ grapes}$. Then if we divide the top and the bottom by 10, we can obtain a ratio that gives us the price per pound $\dfrac{\$16}{10\ lbs\ grapes} = \dfrac{\$1.60}{1\ lb\ grapes}$.

Ratios are used extensively in the process of converting units. For example the ratio of cm to inches is $2.54cm$: $1in$ or $\dfrac{2.54\ cm}{1\ in}$. If we had a 43 inch piece of wood, we could simply multiply the top and bottom by 43 to arrive at $\dfrac{2.54\ cm \times 43}{1\ in \times 43} = \dfrac{109.22\ cm}{43\ in}$ which says that 43" is equivalent to 109.22cm. We could also use ratios to convert in the other direction by first dividing the original ratio top and bottom by 2.54 to get $\dfrac{1\ cm}{0.3937\ in}$. Now if a flower is 4.6cm wide we can convert to inches simply by multiplying the top and bottom by 4.6 to get $\dfrac{4.6\ cm}{1.811\ in}$.

Visualizing Percent's

We saw earlier that percentages can be viewed as fractions with the whole cut into 100 pieces. If you pay attention, you will see that we use percentages often in our daily lives. What does it mean to say I got an 80% on my final exam? Well, it means that if the exam was out of 100 points, I received a score 80 on it; if the exam was worth 20 points, then since $\dfrac{80}{100} = \dfrac{80 \div 5}{100 \div 5} = \dfrac{16}{20}$, I received a score of 16 out of 20 on it. So most of us have some experience with the meaning of percentage. The word percent means per 100, "cent" refers to 100 as in century. **Percentage** can be expressions of ratios, e.g., 62% of the students on campus are female. Literally this means 62 female students per 100 students overall, i.e., $\dfrac{62}{100} = \dfrac{0.62}{1} = 0.62$. Thus a percentage always indicates how many hundredths place value units you have. Thus 7.25% equals 0.0725. In the other direction, 0.054 is 5.4hundredths or 5.4% and 1.35 is 135%.

We can visualize percentages using a strip diagrams, or 10 by 10 rectangles, or a grid to represent the whole that is divided into 100 pieces. Doing this makes it easy to see the common fractions associated with percentages such as 20%, 5%, 50%, 75%.

Below are some examples.

Examples

1. $5\% = \dfrac{5}{100} = \dfrac{1}{20}$

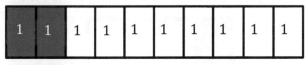

So for example the 5% sales tax on a TV that was sold for $1240, can be calculated using the above picture as follows: Imagine $1240 broken into 10 equal pieces as shown above, giving us that each piece was worth $\dfrac{\$1240}{10} = \$124$ and 5% of the price would be half of that which would be half of that, or $\dfrac{\$124}{2} = \$62$.

We will do more examples of this type in later modules.

2. $20\% = \dfrac{20}{100} = \dfrac{2}{10} = \dfrac{1}{5}$

3. $75\% = \dfrac{75}{100} = \dfrac{3}{4}$

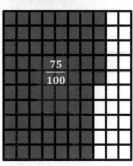  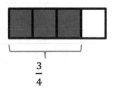

4. $33\dfrac{1}{3}\% = \dfrac{33\frac{1}{3}}{100} = \dfrac{100}{300} = \dfrac{1}{3}$

---

5. $26\% = 26/100$

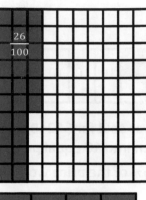

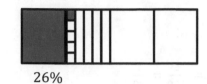

26%

6. $133.\overline{3}\%$

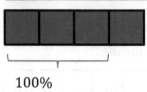

100%

7. What percentage of the picture below is shaded if the entire picture is 100%?

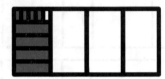

Since the 100% is the whole picture we have 24% is shaded, since each largest vertical rectangle represents a $\frac{1}{4}$th or 25%, each horizontal strip represents $\frac{1}{5}(25\%) = 5\%$, and each of the little vertical strips inside the small horizontal strip represents $\frac{1}{5}(5\%) = 1\%$.

1. What percentage of the picture below is shaded if the entire picture represents 100%?

a.

b.

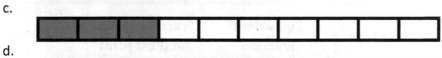

c.

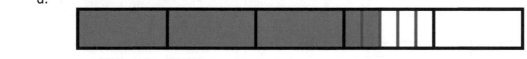

d.

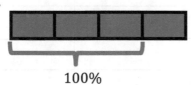

2. What percentage does the shaded part in each picture below represent? The whole is marked clearly in each picture so be careful in how you answer.

a.

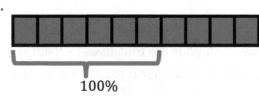

100%

b.

100%

c.

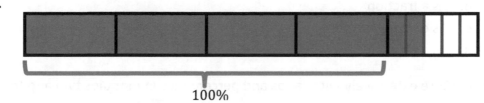

100%

3. Draw a strip diagram to represent the percentages below. If there are multiple ways to represent a percentage, then show all equivalent diagrams representing the percentage.
   a. 35%   c. 15%   e. 15%

   b. 40%   d. 125%   f. $66.\overline{6}\%$

4. Convert the percentages below to decimal numbers.
   a. 78%   b. 0.5%   c. 745%

5. Convert each decimal number below to a percentage.
   a. 89.4   b. 0.027   c. 0.0092

6. Fill in the missing entries the chart below. If an entry is greyed out, you do not have to fill anything in this entry. So just fill in the empty entries so that the items in that row make sense.

Decimal Number	Percentage	Equivalent Fraction	Fraction in the simplest form	Graphical representation
0.25				
		$\dfrac{\overline{}}{20}$		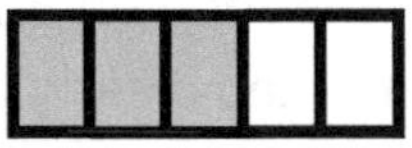
		$\dfrac{12}{18}$		
	0.75%			
		$\dfrac{\overline{}}{21}$	$\dfrac{2}{3}$	

7. List at least one scenario or an instance from your life that uses percentages (it could be the same instance in all 4 cases or one different scenario for each part below).
   a. Strip diagram
   b. As a fraction
   c. As decimal number
   d. As a ratio

We will work more extensively with ratios and percentages in modules two and four.

Lecture

💻 Ordering Numbers

http://www.youtube.com/watch?v=Wjcel8TB4mg (8min)

One important property of real numbers is that given any two real numbers, a and b, either $a < b$, $a > b$, or $a = b$. This is referred to as the **trichotomy property** of real numbers. This property will allow us to order any given finite set of real numbers in an ascending or descending order. When comparing two fractions it helps to use the concept of equivalent fractions so they are represented with a common denominator. When comparing a finite group of decimal numbers, we start by making all decimals have a digit in each of the place values that are present in the group of numbers. If a number is missing a digit in a certain place value, we fill in zero as our digit for that place value. Then to arrange the numbers in descending order for example the number that has the greatest digit in the highest place value (left most digit) is the largest number. If the digits in the largest place value are equal we continue the same process by looking at the digits in the next place value until all the numbers have been placed in order. E.g., if we wanted to arrange the numbers 2.3, 34.23, and 2.54, in descending order, we will rewrite these numbers as 02.30, 34.23, and 02.54.

02.30 ⬆ 0	34.23 ⬆ 3	02.54 ⬆ 0
Largest		
34.23	02.30 ⬆ 2	02.54 ⬆ 2
Largest		
34.23	02.30 ⬆ 3	02.54 ⬆ 5
Largest	2nd Largest	Smallest
34.23	02.54	02.30

The numbers in our list in descending order are: 34.53, 2.54, 2.3.

For negative decimal numbers the one with the largest highest place value is the smallest of the numbers. If you are comparing positive and negative decimal numbers order all the negative numbers in ascending order first, then order all the nonnegative decimal numbers in ascending order. The complete list in ascending order then starts with the negative list and continues through the non-negative list.

Practice Examples

Order the following numbers in ascending order.

1. $\frac{3}{4}$, and $\frac{2}{5}$;
2. $\frac{3}{7}$ and $\frac{4}{9}$;
3. $-1\frac{2}{3}$ and $-1\frac{2}{5}$;
4. 14.2, and 4.62;
5. -3.45, and -3.445 ;
6. -0.34, -43.45, 20, and 20.34;

Solutions

1. When working with fractions always make equivalent fractions so they have the same denominator, which will allow us to compare easily. So $\frac{3}{4} = \frac{3\times5}{4\times5} = \frac{15}{20}, \frac{2}{5} = \frac{2\times4}{5\times4} = \frac{8}{20}$, so our numbers in ascending order are $\frac{8}{20}, \frac{15}{20}$ or $\frac{2}{5}, \frac{3}{4}$.

2. Converting to denominator of $7 \cdot 9 = 63$, we have $\frac{3}{7} = \frac{27}{63}$ and $\frac{4}{9} = \frac{28}{63}$ and hence $\frac{3}{7} < \frac{4}{9}$

3. Converting to a common denominator of $3 \cdot 5 = 15$ we have $-1\frac{2}{3} = -\frac{5}{3} = -\frac{25}{15}$ and $-1\frac{2}{5} = -\frac{7}{5} = -\frac{21}{15}$ and hence $-1\frac{2}{3} < -1\frac{2}{5}$.

4. We rewrite the two numbers so that they have the same number of digits 14.20, and 04.62. Since the digit 1 is in the tens place for the first number and zero is in the highest place value in the tens place for the second number our conclusion is $4.62 < 14.20$. So the numbers in ascending order are 4.62, 14.2.

5. We write the two numbers so that they have the same number of digits -3.450, and -3.445 . In the numbers 3.450 and 3.445, the units place, and tenths place values are equal. We see that the hundredths place value is five for 3.450, which is greater than the hundredths place value of four in 3.445. Therefore, $3.450 > 3.445$. Since the original numbers are negative we get that the numbers in ascending order are -3.450, -3.445.

6. We write all the numbers so that they have the same number of digits -00.34, $-43.45,\ 20.00,\ 20.34$. Now amongst the negative numbers since zero is in the tens place for -00.34 and 4 is in the tens place for -43.45 we have $-43.45 < -0.34$. Amongst the positive numbers since tens and units place digits are equal, and zero is in the tenths place for 20.00 and three is in the tenths place for 20.34, we have $20 < 20.34$. Therefore the given numbers in ascending order are $-43.45,\ -0.34,\ 20,\ 20.34$

Video Log 1.4b

1. Write numbers below in descending order (largest to smallest).

   a. $9{,}987,\ 10{,}012,\ \ 8{,}999$

   b. $\frac{4}{13}\ and\ \frac{1}{3}$

   c. $-2\frac{3}{4},\ -2\frac{9}{13},\ -3\frac{1}{10}$

   d. $3,\ 3.458,\ 3.45.$

   e. $-15.75, -315.95$

   f. $-1.07,\ -73.81,\ 2.34,\ 2.078.$

   g. $\frac{2}{5},\ \frac{3}{8},\ \frac{1}{3}$

2. Determine which of the two fractions is larger without making common denominator.

   a. $\frac{4}{13},\ \ \frac{1}{3} = \frac{4}{12}$

   b. $50\%,\ \ \frac{39}{80}$

   c. $-\frac{5}{3},\ \ -\frac{3}{2}$

   d.

3. List a fraction bigger than, and smaller than $\frac{4}{15}$ with denominator of 17.

   $$\frac{\quad}{17} < \frac{4}{15} < \frac{\quad}{17}$$

4. Use the appropriate sign $<, >$, or $=$, to make the statements below a true statement.

   a. $-23.5\underline{\quad} - 2.5$

   b. $0.002\ \underline{\quad}0.0025$

   c. $456.89\underline{\quad} 4.5689$

   d. $223.7\ \underline{\quad}\ \frac{2237}{10}.$

1.5 Representing Real Numbers on a Number Line and Complex Numbers in the Complex Plane

Lecture

🖥 Plotting Numbers on a Number Line

http://www.youtube.com/watch?v=BohmHn8NgOA   (14 min)

Number Line

One can represent real numbers as points on a number line as follows. Draw a line (which you can think of as an infinite tape measure) on which we can mark a reference point and label it. We can choose to label our reference point with any real number we wish, like zero for example, and then imagine moving on this line towards infinity on either side of the reference point. If you draw your line horizontally, then going to the right of the reference point is considered the positive direction and going to the left of the reference point is considered the negative direction. If you draw your line vertically, then going up from the reference point is considered the positive direction and going down from the reference point is considered the negative direction. Your reference point does not have to be zero. It could be any number. Wherever the reference point is marked, a nearby point is marked to determine the scale of the number line (this distance between tick marks is usually a power of 10 such as $\frac{1}{10}, 1, 10, 100 \ldots$). Other positions on the number line are reached by moving left or right in those increments.

We will use the term **increment** to represent the distance between two adjacent tick marks.

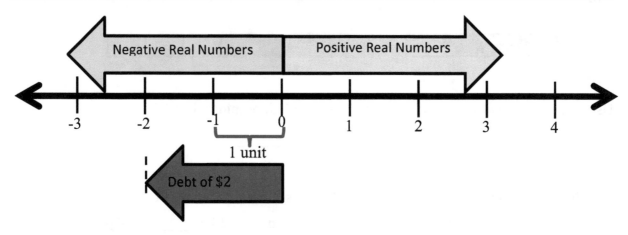

So for example, if the line is marked in increments of 1 unit, then starting at the reference point you will mark the tick mark to the right of the reference point as one unit greater than the reference point. If the reference point was marked as zero, the next tick mark to the right would be marked as 1, the one to the right of that would be 2 and so on, the next tick mark to the left of zero would be marked as -1 and to the left of that would be -2 and so on.

If the line is marked in increments of 5000 units, then starting at the reference point you will mark the tick mark to the right of the reference point as 5000 additional units. So if your reference point was marked as zero, the next tick mark to the right would be marked as 5000, the one to the right of that would be 10,000 and so on. The next tick mark to the left of zero would be marked as −5000 and to the left of that would be −10,000 and so on.

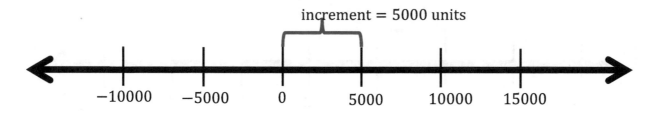

increment = 5000 units

−10000   −5000   0   5000   10000   15000

If the line is marked in increments of 12001 units, then starting at the reference point you will mark the tick mark to the right of the reference point 12001 additional units. So if your reference point was marked as −2001, the next tick mark to the right would be marked as 10,000.

Question: Label the additional tick marks shown on the number line below.

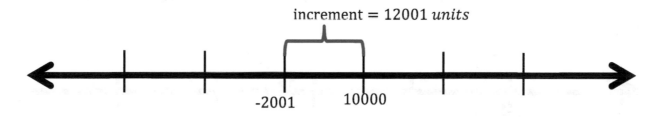

increment = 12001 *units*

-2001   10000

If you draw your number line vertically you can represent numbers similarly. (Most often you see a vertical representation of the real number line when you are using measuring cups, thermometers and so on.)

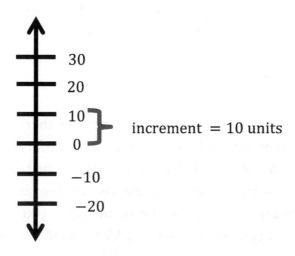

30
20
10
0 } increment = 10 units
−10
−20

We plot rational numbers of the form $\frac{a}{b}$ in exactly the same way as for plotting integers.

Label the tick marks using increments of $\frac{1}{b}$ units from the reference point (or increments of $\frac{1}{any\ multiple\ of\ b}$ $units$) as shown below.

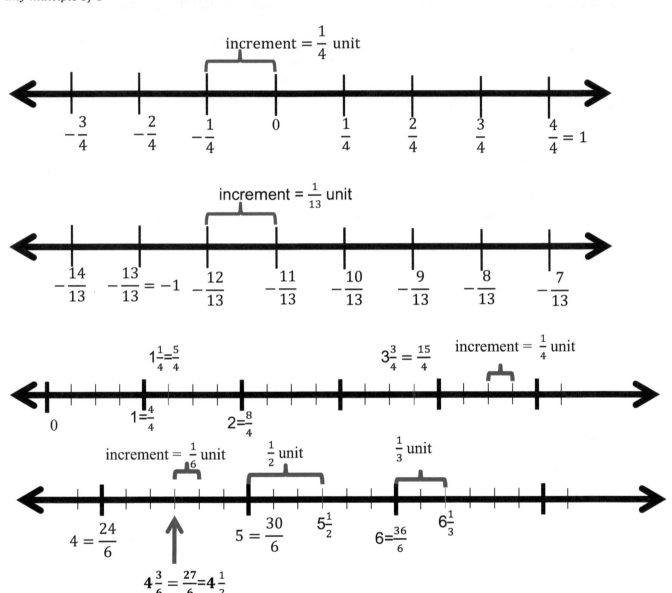

At times in addition to your tick marks that show the basic scale there may be a need to have a subscale to show smaller increments on the number line to represent numbers in between the two major tick marks as shown above. This shows up on measuring tapes and rulers and meter sticks. A standard one foot ruler and or tape measure has markings at increments of 1/16th, ¼th , and ½ of an inch as well as at one foot intervals. On metric rulers you can see the centimeter markings along with 1/10th of a centimeter marking which is a millimeter. A meter stick is divided into "tenths" and then "hundredths" (centimeters) and then "thousandths" of a meter (millimeters). The main point is that finer divisions of the metric system correspond to moving one or more place values right in the decimal representation of a number.

We will now discuss representing terminating decimals on a number line. We start with a number line where the increment is the power of ten equal to the place value of the right most digit of the decimal number. For the number -2.7 we make the increment $\frac{1}{10}$, and for -2.13576, the increment is set to $\frac{1}{10^5}$ as shown on the number lines below.

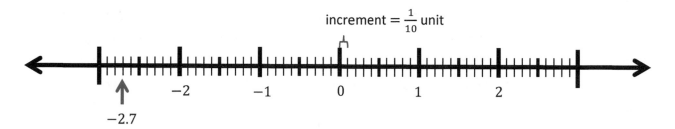

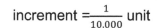

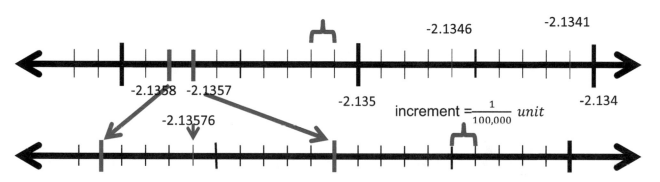

Notice that we have not shown you how to place irrational numbers on the number line yet. Since all irrational numbers have a non-repeating decimal representation you can only approximate where they lie on a number line using the method above. You can do a geometric construction to plot some of these numbers on the number line, like $\sqrt{2}$. But we will not discuss this aspect of irrational numbers in this book.

We can see that every point on the number line can be accounted for in this way by a decimal number. We keep zooming in to read off more and more decimal places. It is amazing to note that if we looked at just the irrational numbers on a number line they would also appear to occupy the entire number line.

Now some of us may be wondering "What about complex numbers?". We haven't shown you how to visualize these numbers yet. So now put on your mathematician hat and think for a moment if you were to represent complex numbers what would you do? Remember that real numbers can all be represented as a position on a number line and also each position corresponds to a decimal number. Thus, there is no room on the number line for the complex numbers. You also know that the complex numbers are of the form $a + bi$ where a and b are real numbers and are called the real part and imaginary part respectively. We really want you to think about this so the answer will be provided at the end of the next set of video log questions. This is where your consciousness comes into play. Engage yourself in this kind of thinking and it will train your brain to problem solve without you even realizing it. This will give you a taste of what it is like to play with mathematics and ponder on questions you do not know answers to. If you do think of an answer and it is not the answer in the book, this does not mean your answer is not valid. Talk it through with a mathematician to see if your reasoning skills are valid. Remember making mistakes is not a negative attribute. This is how we learn to do mathematics and not just memorize what someone else has told us.

For problems 1-11 plot the numbers so that each of them falls on their own tick mark. Be sure to specify the scale or increment you are using for your number line.

1   Plot the numbers $-4,\ -3,\ 3,\ 4$ on the same number line.

2   Plot the numbers $1.4,\ 1.5,\ 1.8$ on the same number line.

3   Plot the numbers $1.41,\ 1.43,\ 1.48,\ 1.5$ on the same number line.

4   Plot -3.15 and -3.115 on the same number line.

5   Plot 5 and 5000 on the same number line.

6   Plot the numbers $\frac{1}{4},\ \frac{2}{4},\ \frac{3}{4},\ \frac{7}{4}$ on the same number line.

7   Plot $\frac{4}{5}, \frac{2}{5}$, and $-1\frac{2}{5}$ on the same number line.

8   Plot $-\frac{4}{7}, -\frac{12}{7}$, and $-\frac{15}{7}$ on the same number line.

9   Plot the numbers $\frac{11}{6}, \frac{5}{6}, -\frac{3}{6}$, and $-\frac{7}{6}$

10 Plot $\frac{11\pi}{6}, \frac{5\pi}{6}, -\frac{3\pi}{6}$, and $-\frac{7\pi}{6}$ and π on the same number line. (Use $\pi/6$ as the increment.)

11 Plot $\frac{2}{3}, -\frac{1}{6}$, and $3\frac{1}{2}$ on the same number line.

12 For each of the number line positions marked with arrows below, determine its decimal or fraction as a mixed number representation.

   a.

   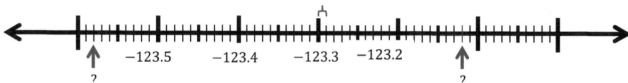

   b.

   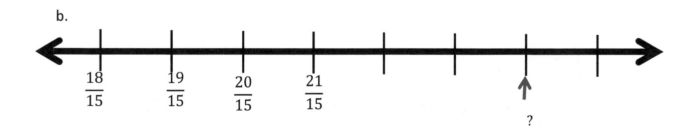

c.

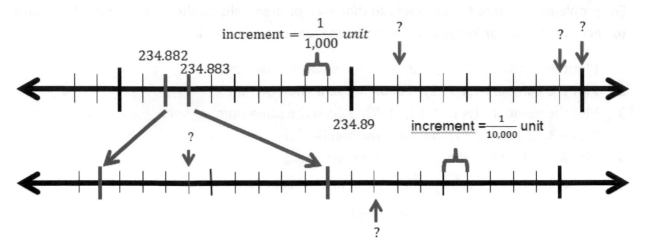

d.

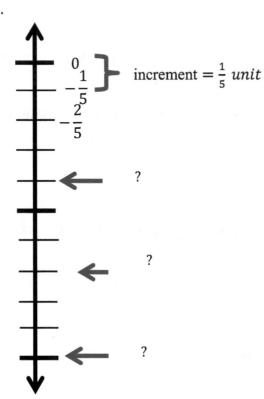

13 Is there a way to plot the numbers $\sqrt{2}$, 5000, and $\frac{11}{2}$ on the same number line so that each of them will get their own tick mark? Explain your reasoning.

14 Show the relative positions of the numbers $\sqrt{2}$, 50, and $\frac{11}{2}$ on the same number line without the necessity that all of these must fall on their own tick mark.

15 Show the relative positions of the numbers -4.11, -4.111, and -4.1111 on the same number line without the necessity that all of these must fall on the same tick mark.

Plotting Complex Numbers

Perhaps you already thought of this, but since complex numbers look like they are made of two real numbers one in the real part and one in the imaginary part, we could use two number lines to represent them.

Here is one way to it. Take two number lines perpendicular to each other, mark their point of intersection as your reference point (called the origin) and label it as $(0,0)$. This horizontal number line is referred to as the **real axis** and the vertical line as the **imaginary axis**. Complex numbers are then plotted just like you plot coordinates in a rectangular coordinate system (which will be discussed in detail in module 4). For example, to plot the number $3 + 2i$, you will move 3 right from the origin, and then 2 up and connect the origin to the point at $(3,2)$. All complex numbers can be drawn this way and the collection of all the complex numbers forms the **complex plane**.

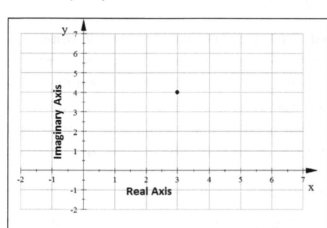

Complex Number plotted as a point in the complex plane

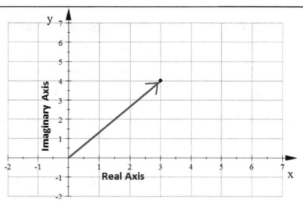

Complex Number plotted as a vector in the complex plane

Video Log 1.5b

1. Plot the complex numbers below.
    a. $2 + 5i$
    b. $-4 - 2i$
    c. 3
    d. $-3i$
    e. $-2 + 3i$

Lecture

🖥 Scientific Notation

http://www.youtube.com/watch?v=4lM8zwi0kWY **(10 min)**

When dealing with very large or very small numbers, it is cumbersome to write and read many zeros as placeholders and they must be counted carefully to know the exact value of the number. For example, the U.S. Debt in 2016 was approximately $19000000000000, and the diameter of an E. coli bacterium is approximately 0.0000012m. The U.S. debt number when expanded in terms of place values looks like:

$$1 \times 10^{13} + 6 \times 10^{12} + 0 \times 10^{11} + 0 \times 10^{10} \dots + 0 \times 10^2 + 0 \times 10 + 0 \times 1$$

Scientific Notation uses the largest place value with a nonzero digit as a reference and writes the number as a decimal number between one and ten multiplied by ten to the power of the place value of the digit that is now in the unit's place value. Thus the U.S. debt in scientific notation is $\$1.6 \times 10^{13}$. Often we think of large numbers in terms of millions, billions and trillions etc. which can easily be adapted from scientific notation. For example a trillion is 10^{12} and thus the U.S. debt is $\$1.6 \times 10^{13} = \underline{1.6 \times 10} \times 10^{12} = 16 \times 10^{12}$ or 16 trillion dollars.

Expanding the diameter of an E. coli we have $0.0000012m = 0 + 0 \times \frac{1}{10} + 0 \times \frac{1}{10^2} \dots + 1 \times \frac{1}{10^6} + 2 \times \frac{1}{10^7}$. The largest place value with a nonzero digit is $\frac{1}{10^6}$ or 10^{-6} (we will work with exponents more thoroughly later). Thus in scientific notation, the size of an E. coli is $1.2 \times 10^{-6}m$. The reference place value here is $10^{-6}m$ which is called a micron and thus an E. coli is approximately 1.2 microns in diameter. If one goes three place values smaller by dividing by 10 three more times, we get to nanometer (nm) units as $10^{-9}m$. Thus we could also say that an E. coli is 1200 nm in diameter.

Converting a Number in Scientific Notation to Decimal Notation

If a number is written in scientific notation, to convert it to decimal notation observe the power of ten on the number and move the decimal point that many places to the left when the power of ten is negative, and that many places to the right if the power of ten is positive. Finally, put in zeros for any of the place values between the new and old decimal location that don't have a digit assigned to them.

Converting a Number in Decimal Notation to Scientific Notation

To convert a number from its decimal to scientific notation form, we move the decimal point so it is one place to the right of the first nonzero digit and the power of ten depends on whether you moved the decimal point left or right. The power will be negative if you moved right and positive if you moved left. Another way to think of this would be that in the scientific notation the power or exponent on ten is positive for large numbers and negative for very small numbers.

Scientific Notation	Decimal Notation
3.46×10^{-5}	0.0000346
3.46×10^{5}	346000.
5.1×10^{-2}	0.051
5.1×10^{3}	5100

Examples

1. Distance to the sun in meters is $149,600,000,000m$. In scientific notation it would be written as $1.496 \times 10^{11}m$.
2. Length of a virus in meters is $0.0000000023m$. In scientific notation this would be written as $2.3 \times 10^{-9}m$
3. The size of a carbon atom is approximately $1.5 \times 10^{-10}m$, which in decimal notation would be written as 0.00000000015m .
4. The population of the world is approximately 7.3×10^{9} people or in decimal notation would be written as 7,300,000,000 .

Rounding

We use numbers in all aspects of our life to measure quantities, e.g. distances that we drive, price paid for a car, cholesterol levels, golf scores, square footage of a home. While some of these measures are known with precision, (a golf score is an exact number) most measurements are only known approximately (depending on the accuracy of the measuring devices used to measure these quantities) and we usually round off to some nearest unit or fraction of a unit.

A person may say that they are 5′ 11″ or maybe 5′ 11 ½″ tall, and someone pays 22 grand for a new car. What do the statements above indicate about the actual measures of the quantities? What do they suggest as a range of the actual height and amount paid for the car might be? The 5′ 11″ suggests the height is between 5′10.5″ and 5′11.5″, while the 5′11 ½ "suggest a height between 5′ 11¼ " and 5′11¾". In the first case the height was rounded to the nearest inch, while in the second to the nearest half inch. The car price of 22 grand suggests the actual cost may have been anywhere between 21,500 and 22,500 dollars and it was rounded to the nearest thousands place.

When rounding we may indicate to what degree of accuracy by saying e.g., to the nearest tenth of a mile, or to the nearest ¼ inch or nearest $100. To visualize this, we consider our unrounded number sitting on a number line which is marked with hash marks at units of accuracy indicated, e.g. tenths of a mile or $100 units. Then we round by selecting the number on the tick mark nearest to the unrounded number. For numbers exactly halfway between tick marks we could round up or down, two conventions are commonly used. One is to round up or to the right on a number line or alternatively one can round to the even digit. Thus rounding 0.75 and −5.345 to the nearest tenth gives the numbers 0.8 and −5.3 using either convention.

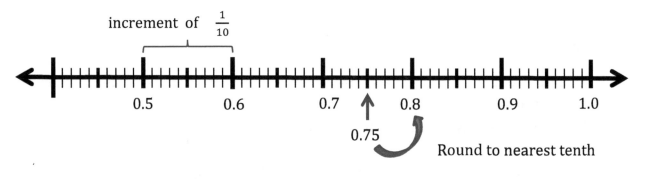

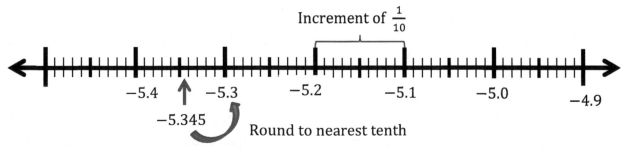

Often when using English units of measure, we round to the nearest eighth or quarter of an inch. When these measurements are obtained on a tape measure, we very naturally use our visual perception to round or approximate a measurement by going to the nearest hash mark on the ruler. In recording measured data from laboratory experiments, care must always be taken to record numbers to indicate the level of accuracy that they were measured to. For example, if the length of a pendulum is measured to be $100\ cm$ long, but the measurement was really only known to be between 99.5cm and $100.5\ cm$, then we'd record the number as 100. cm which indicates the accuracy of measurement as $100cm$ $\pm 0.5cm$. Another way to indicate the accuracy of measurements is to state explicitly what the tolerance of confidence is. Thus we may have measured a pendulum to be $1.052 \pm 0.003m$ when we have confidence to within $0.003m$ (or $0.3\ cm$ or $3\ mm$) in the actual length. Indicating the accuracy of experimental measurements is critically important when these are used to compute other quantities. For example if the length, width, and height of a box are all measured to three digits of accuracy, then the product of these numbers which gives the volume of the box should be reported to no more than three digits of accuracy and not the 12 digits or so that a calculator display will show you.

Examples of rounding:

1. My bathroom scale read 172.5, 170.0, 171.5, 173.0, 172.5 lbs. on five consecutive days. What is the scale rounding these numbers to and within what range do you expect the actual weight was on day three?
2. Milk that is labeled 1% means that by weight it has 1% butterfat. This percentage is actually rounded to the one's place. What is the possible range of actual % butterfat for this milk? Also what is the % butterfat range for skim milk which means 0% butterfat?

Solutions

1. The scale seems to read to the nearest $0.5\ or\ 1/2$ lb. Thus on day 3, the actual weight was somewhere between 171.25 and 171.75.
2. Rounding the % to the one's place means the actual percentage was between 0.5% and 1.5%. For skim milk the actual percentage fat must be between 0.0 and 0.5% fat since it can't be negative.

Video Log 1.5c
1. Write the following two numbers in Scientific Notation
   a. 450.1297
   b. 0.009075
2. Write the following two numbers in Decimal Notation
   a. 1.0087×10^8
   b. 7.89×10^{-6}

3. Round the numbers below-
    a. 3.486 to the nearest tenth
    b. 3.4468 to the nearest tenth
    c. 3.556 to the nearest hundredth
    d. 325.68 to the nearest hundreds
    e. 325.68 to the nearest tens
    f. -135 to the nearest tens. (Hint: You might want to draw a number line to help you with this one.)

4. If the number 89.46 was the answer to the problem of rounding to the nearest hundredths, list at least two possible original numbers that could lead to this answer.

5. Determine if the rounding of the number 175.246 to the nearest tenths as shown below is valid or not. Explain what happened.

$$175.246 \rightarrow 175.25 \rightarrow 175.3$$

Since 6 is bigger than 5 we round the 4 to a 5, then since we want to round to nearest tenths we will round the 2 to a 3 since the hundredths place now is a 5. So 175.246 rounded to a nearest tenths would be 175.3.

6. If your favorite Granola bar or Candy bar says it has 0 gm. of Trans fats, do you think that is accurate? If not, what could be the case? Explain.

7. While you are driving, your car's digital speedometer reads 25 mph. Do you think that the speed is exactly 25 mph? What factors should you be aware of? What kind of rounding is taking place?

8. How do you interpret a bathroom scale reading of 135.6 lbs., when the scale only displays the last digit as an even number?

9. Find an instance in biology, astronomy, or any other field of your interest where scientific notation and rounding is useful.

1.6 Natural Number Exponents and Properties of Exponent
Lecture

💻 Exponents

http://www.youtube.com/watch?v=QlnQTDKNH_Q (9 min)

Exponent Notation

Over the centuries since algebra has been around, several conventions have been used to denote repeated multiplication by the same number. Superscripts or "exponents" have become the accepted way to indicate how many times a quantity is to be multiplied. Thus multiplying by the number 10 three times is denoted as $10 \times 10 \times 10 = 10^3$. The formula for the area of a circle, $A = \pi r^2$, says that the area is obtained by multiplying π by r two times, i.e., $A = \pi \times r \times r$. Note that the exponent "2" only applies to the quantity or object that it is directly above. This quantity r is called the base of the exponential expression. If one wanted to use exponents to describe $(\pi \times r) \times (\pi \times r)$, we could write $(\pi \times r)^2 = (\pi r)^2$ in which case the base would be πr.

Earlier when we wrote counting numbers in expanded notation we expressed them using powers of ten. For example the number $324 = 3 \times 10^2 + 4 \times 10^1 + 4 \times 10^0$.

Recall that $10^n = \underbrace{10 \times 10 \times \ldots \times 10}_{n \text{ times}}$

Definition of counting number exponents

In general, for any real number a and a counting number n, $a^n = \underbrace{a \times a \times \ldots \times a}_{n \text{ times}}$ where you multiply n copies of the factor a.

Historical note: The word power was originally used only for the result of an exponentiation. In $2^3 = 8$, 8 is a power, sometimes called a power of 2. Recently some people have started calling the 3 a power. The confusion may be because people historically would also say 8 is the third power of 2.

Examples:

1. $2^3 = 2 \times 2 \times 2 = 8$, here <u>base</u> = **2** and <u>exponent</u> = **3**

2. $(-5)^3 = (-5) \times (-5) \times (-5) = -125$, here <u>base</u> = -5, <u>exponent</u> = **3**

    As you can see in example 2 the exponent belongs to the number -5.

---

3 $-4^2 = -4 \times 4 = -16$, here <u>base</u> = **4**, <u>exponent</u> = **2**

By convention -4^2 means $-(4^2) = -(4 \times 4) = -(16) = -16$. That means that the exponent only belongs to the number 4 and the $-$ sign is the sign of the number 4^2.

4 $a^2 = a \times a$, here <u>base</u> = a, <u>exponent</u> = **2**

5 $-(f(x))^3 = -(f(x) \times f(x) \times f(x))$, here <u>base</u> $= f(x)$, <u>exponent</u> $= $ **3**

6 $(ab)^5 = ab \times ab \times ab \times ab \times ab$, here <u>base</u> = (ab), <u>exponent</u> = **5**

7 $(a^2c^3)^4 = (a^2c^3) \times (a^2c^3) \times (a^2c^3) \times (a^2c^3)$, here <u>base</u> = (a^2c^3), <u>exponent</u> = **4,**

but it also has other bases and exponents given by <u>base</u> = a, <u>exponent</u>= **2,** <u>base</u> = c, <u>exponent</u> $= $ **3**.

Practice Questions

		Base/s	Exponent/s
1.	$-\left(\dfrac{2}{3}\right)^4$		
2.	$(g(x))^4$		
3.	$\left(\dfrac{1}{3}\right)^2$		
4.	$(c^2 d^3)^5$		
5.	$(a + b)^2$		
6.	$-\left(-\dfrac{x + 1}{y}\right)^2$		
7.	$-(3x - 2)^2$		
8.	$(-b)^4$		
9.	5^4		
10.	$-(-7)^4$		
11.	-7^4		
12.	7^4		
13.	$(-7)^4$		
14.	$-(a + b)^4$		

Solutions to the practice problems

		Base	Exponent
1.	$-\left(\dfrac{2}{3}\right)^4$	$\dfrac{2}{3}$	4
2.	$(g(x))^4$	$g(x)$	4
3.	$\left(\dfrac{1}{3}\right)^2$	$\dfrac{1}{3}$	2
4.	$(c^2d^3)^5$	(c^2d^3)	5
		c	2
		d	3
5.	$(a+b)^2$	$a+b$	2
6.	$-\left(-\dfrac{x+1}{y}\right)^2$	$-\dfrac{x+1}{y}$	2
7.	$-(3x-2)^2$	$3x-2$	2
8.	$(-b)^4$	$-b$	4
9.	5^4	5	4
10.	$-(-7)^4$	-7	4

11.	-7^4	7	4
12.	7^4	7	4
13.	$(-7)^4$	-7	4
14.	$-(a+b)^4$	$a+b$	4

Playing

So let us now investigate what happens if we play with this new object and try to make complex mathematical sentences with these objects.

Lecture

🖥 Product Rule of Exponents

  http://www.youtube.com/watch?v=qS2yuBEXcxk (9 min)

Product Rule of Exponents

  1. $2^3 \times 2^4 = ?$

        When a mathematician encounters a problem not seen before they go back to the meaning of the symbols. In this problem we can see that we will end up with

        $2^3 \times 2^4 = (2 \times 2 \times 2) \times (2 \times 2 \times 2 \times 2) = 2^7$

  2. $3^2 \times 3^5 = ?$

        $3^2 \times 3^5 = (3 \times 3) \times (3 \times 3 \times 3 \times 3 \times 3) = 3^7$

        A mathematician always tries to be efficient and so just looking at these two examples you can see a pattern emerge.

        Here are more examples to help you combine exponents efficiently-

3. $10^2 \times 10^4 = (10 \times 10) \times (10 \times 10 \times 10 \times 10) = 10^6 = 10^{2+4}$

4. $4^{22} \times 4^{100} =?$ Use the previous examples to see if you got the answer to this problem.

5. $(10^2)^4 = 10^2 \times 10^2 \times 10^2 \times 10^2$ we can see that another way we could write this is

$$(10^2)^4 = 10^2 \times 10^2 \times 10^2 \times 10^2 = 10^{2+2+2+2} = 10^8 \text{ or } (10^2)^4 = 10^{2\times4} = 10^8$$

Practice Examples

For all the problems use the patterns observed above to write the answer in the form of one base raised to one exponent or in the form a^n. The convention is that $a^2 a^3 = a^2 \times a^3 = a^5$. Remember what the base's and exponent's meanings are before writing the answer. Becoming conscious of the meaning of the symbols that are in front of you is what will allow you to reason what the correct meaning is rather than simply memorizing rules.

1. $(5x + 7)^8 (5x + 7)^3$

2. $(3^2 3^5)^2$

3. $\left(-\dfrac{2t - 5}{3y + 4}\right)^{10} \left(-\dfrac{2t - 5}{3y + 4}\right)^{7}$

4. $((2x + 4)^4)^3$

5. $(g(x))^4 (g(x))^3$

6. $-(c^2 c^3)^4$

Answers to Practice Problems

1. $(5x + 7)^8 (5x + 7)^3 = (5x + 7)^{11}$

2. $(3^2 3^5)^2 = 3^{14}$

3. $\left(-\dfrac{2t-5}{3y+4}\right)^{10}\left(-\dfrac{2t-5}{3y+4}\right)^{7} = \left(-\dfrac{2t-5}{3y+4}\right)^{17}$

4. $((2x+4)^4)^3 = (2x+4)^{12}$

5. $(g(x))^4(g(x))^3 = (g(x))^7$

6. $-(c^2c^3)^4 = -c^{20}$

Video Log 1.6a

1. Write the product below in the exponential notation as a^n. For example, $5 \times 5 \times 5 \times 5 = 5^4$.

   a. $7 \times 7 \times 7$

   b. $-6 \times 6 \times 6$

   c. $(-3) \times (-3) \times (-3) \times (-3)$

   d. $-3 \times -3 \times -3 \times -3$

   e. $\dfrac{2}{3} \times \dfrac{2}{3} \times \dfrac{2}{3}$

   f. $-\dfrac{2}{3} \times \dfrac{2}{3} \times \dfrac{2}{3}$

   g. $a \times a \times a \times a$

   h. $(x+y) \times (x+y)$

2. Identify base and exponents below.

	Base/s	Exponent/s		Base/s	Exponent/s
a. 2^3			d. $(-7)^2$		
b. a^{12}			e. -7^2		
c. $(5x+3)^4$			f. $-a^2$		

3. Evaluate the following.

   a. 2^3

   b. -3^2

   c. $(-3)^2$

   d. -3^3

   e. $(-7)^2$

   f. -7^2

4. Fill the table below.

Example	Base	Exponent	Write in English words how you would read the problem out loud	Expanded form	Evaluate
2^3					
$(-5)^3$					
-4^2					

5. Write the numbers in the exponential notation as a^n. For example, $125 = 5^3$

   a. 8

   b. 25

   c. -16

   d. 27

   e. 4

   f. $\frac{1}{32}$

   g. $-\frac{1}{32}$

   h. -25

6. Fill the blanks below with either $<, >$, or $=$ sign without actually evaluating if possible.

   a. -10^2_____$(-10)^2$

   b. $(-3)^2$_____ 3^2

   c. $(-5)^3$_____ 5^3

   d. -5^3_____ $(-5)^3$

   e. $\left(\frac{1}{2}\right)^3$_____ 2^3

   f. -3^2_____$\left(\frac{1}{3}\right)^2$

   g. $2^3 \times 3^2$_____ 6^3

   h. $-2^2 \times 3^2$_____ 6^3

7. Use the patterns observed in this section to write each expression in the form of one base raised to one exponent or in the form a^n. Remember what the base and exponent's meanings are before writing the answer.

a. $\left(\frac{2}{3}\right)^3 \left(\frac{2}{3}\right)^5$

b. $(3x - 2)^5 (3x - 2)^4$

c. $-(c^2 c^3)^4$

d. $(3^2 3^5)^2$

e. $\left(-\frac{x+1}{y}\right)^6 \left(-\frac{x+1}{y}\right)^5$

f. $(x^5)^3$

g. $(5^4)^3$

h. $\left(\frac{1}{3}\right)^2 \left(\frac{1}{3}\right)^7$

i. $5^{14} 5^3$

j. $(-b)^{10} (-b)^{12}$

k. $(-7a)^2 (-7a)^{11}$

l. $(g(x))^4 (g(x))^3$

m. $((2x + 4)^4)^3$

n. $(3.5^2)^4$

8. For the problems below fill in the missing bases and exponents so that their product is the given answer.

a.	b.
$\boxed{a}^{2} \times \boxed{a}^{\boxed{4}} = a^6$	$\boxed{}^{\boxed{}} \times \boxed{}^{\boxed{}} = (-5x)^7$

c.	d.
$\boxed{2x+4}^{\boxed{3}} \times \boxed{2x+4}^{\boxed{4}} = (2x + 4)^7$	$\boxed{\frac{1}{4}}^{\boxed{2}} \times \boxed{\frac{1}{4}}^{\boxed{7}} = \left(\frac{1}{4}\right)^9$

Mathematicians' use of notation is very efficient, and observed patterns lead to generalized statements that then have to be proven true. Once they are proven, these statements gain the status of being called rules, laws, or theorems. Our general observations so far can be characterized as two Laws of Exponents.

General Observations: For all counting numbers n, m, and all real numbers a,

Product Rule: $a^m a^n = a^{n+m}$

Power Rule 1: $(a^m)^n = a^{mn}$

The next set of observations will help us simplify other combinations of bases and exponents efficiently.

Lecture

🖥 Quotient Rule of Exponents

http://www.youtube.com/watch?v=SgEyb7s1Vcw (5 min)

Quotient Rule

Examples

1. $$\frac{10^6}{10^2} = \frac{10 \times 10 \times 10 \times 10 \times 10 \times 10}{10 \times 10}$$

We have seen that if we multiply or divide numerator and denominator by the same number, it creates an equivalent fraction. Thus we can divide numerator and denominator in this example by ten twice to make the denominator 1. Sometimes division by a number in the numerator and denominator is referred to as "canceling a common factor" and is denoted by putting a slash through the number. It is important for you to remember to not just say cancel out the common factor but to say divide both numerator and denominator by the common factor. This becomes more important when the numerator and denominator consists or two or more terms being added or subtracted.

$$\frac{10^6}{10^2} = \frac{10 \times 10 \times 10 \times 10 \times \cancel{10}^{1} \times \cancel{10}^{1}}{\underset{1}{\cancel{10}} \times \underset{1}{\cancel{10}}} = \frac{10^4}{1} = 10^4 = 10^{6-2}$$

2. $$\frac{x^8}{x^3} = \frac{x \times x \times x \times x \times x \times x \times x \times x}{x \times x \times x}$$

We divide numerator and denominator by x three times to get one in the denominator.

$$\frac{x^8}{x^3} = \frac{x \times x \times x \times x \times x \times \cancel{x}^{1} \times \cancel{x}^{1} \times \cancel{x}^{1}}{\underset{1}{\cancel{x}} \times \underset{1}{\cancel{x}} \times \underset{1}{\cancel{x}}} = \frac{x^5}{1} = x^5 = x^{8-3}$$

Many students simply memorize these laws, but it is better at the beginning to think about what makes sense simply in terms of the definition of an exponent. Then if one is confused about which "rule" to apply, you can fall-back on what an exponent means to arrive at the correct meaning.

More examples involving rules of exponents for products, quotients and powers of powers are given below for your exploration.

Practice Examples

For all the problems use the patterns you observed above (Or make your own patterns.) to simplify each expression in the form of one base raised to one exponent or in the form a^n.

1. $\left(\dfrac{10^6}{10^2}\right)^3$

2. $\dfrac{5^{14}}{5^3}$

3. $\dfrac{(2a-b)^5}{(2a-b)^2}$

4. $-\left(\dfrac{d^{12}}{d^2}\right)^2$

5. $\dfrac{(-b)^{12}}{(-b)^3}$

Solutions

1.
$$\left(\frac{10^6}{10^2}\right)^3 = 10^{12}$$

2.
$$\frac{5^{14}}{5^3} = 5^{11}$$

3.
$$\frac{(2a-b)^5}{(2a-b)^2} = (2a-b)^3$$

4.
$$-\left(\frac{d^{12}}{d^2}\right)^2 = -d^{20}$$

5.
$$\frac{(-b)^{12}}{(-b)^3} = (-b)^9 = -b^9$$

General Observations: For all counting numbers m, n and all non zero real numbers a,

Quotient Rule: $\dfrac{a^m}{a^n} = a^{m-n}$

Note: *This particular observation should make you think. Remember in all the examples we did so far, we had the numerator exponent bigger than or equal to the denominator exponent. What happens when the numerator exponent is smaller than or equal to the denominator exponent? Explore that on your own for now and later on we will discuss it more thoroughly.*

Video Log 1.6b

1. *For all the problems use the patterns observed above to write the answer in the form of one base raised to one exponent or in the form a^n. The convention is that $a^2 a^3 = a^2 \times a^3 = a^5$. Remember what the base's and exponent's meanings are before writing the answer.*

a. $\dfrac{5^{14}}{5^3}$

b. $\dfrac{(-7a)^{11}}{(-7a)^2}$

c. $\dfrac{(3x-2)^5}{(3x-2)^4}$

d. $\dfrac{(a+b)^3}{(a+b)^2}$

e. $\dfrac{(g(x))^7}{(g(x))^3}$

f. $\dfrac{(-b)^{15}}{(-b)^3}$

g. $\left(\dfrac{2^{10}}{2^4}\right)^3$

h. $\left(\dfrac{x^6}{x^2}\right)^3$

i. $-\left(\dfrac{c^{13}}{c^3}\right)^2$

2. For the problems below fill in the missing bases and/or exponents on either the numerator or the denominator so that their quotient is the given answer.

a.
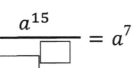
$$\frac{a^{15}}{\boxed{}} = a^7$$

b.
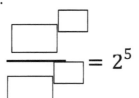
$$\frac{\boxed{}}{\boxed{}} = 2^5$$

c.
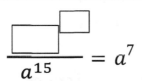
$$\frac{\boxed{}}{a^{15}} = a^7$$

d.
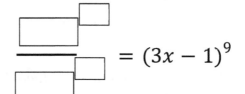
$$\frac{\boxed{}}{\boxed{}} = (3x-1)^9$$

1.7 Negative and Zero Exponents

Lecture

💻 Zero and Negative Exponents

http://www.youtube.com/watch?v=3_pnpRr93hA (14 min)

Next we extend the basic definition of counting number exponents to zero and negative number exponents in such a way as to preserve all the rules of exponents that work for the natural numbers.

Zero as An Exponent

Playing

1. Consider the following and observe what happens-

$$1 = \frac{8}{8} = \frac{2^3}{2^3}$$

If we want our observations to be consistent then we would need to also accept that

$$1 = \frac{8}{8} = \frac{2^3}{2^3} = 2^{3-3} = 2^0$$

What this would suggest to us is that to have our previous discussion be consistent we would have to define that for any nonzero real number a, $\boldsymbol{a^0 = 1}$. This allows us to extend our previous exponent notation to whole numbers.

> *Note: With this observation we extend the idea of powers to those with zero exponents. Another way to see what to do with a 0 exponent is to notice the following. If we expand a decimal number e.g., $3247 = 3 \times 10^3 + 2 \times 10^2 + 1 \times 10^1 + 7 \times 10^?$, then the pattern suggest that the question mark exponent should be zero, and since $7 \times 10^? = 7 \times 1$, we should have that $10^0 = 1$. This meaning from decimal numbers says that multiplying a digit by 10^n means we multiply the digit by 10, n times. Looking at it another way, if we multiply e.g., the digit 7 by 10 zero times or not at all, then the 7 in fact stays the same. Thus multiplying by 10^0 should be the same as multiplying by 1 and that $7 \times 10^0 = 7 \times 1 = 7$ and thus $10^0 = 1$. This interpretation allows whole number exponents to follow the same rules as the counting number exponents.*

Negative Exponents

1. Now consider the following two examples and observe what happens-

$$\frac{10^2}{10^6} = \frac{\overset{1}{\cancel{10}} \times \overset{1}{\cancel{10}}}{\underset{1}{\cancel{10}} \times \underset{1}{\cancel{10}} \times 10 \times 10 \times 10 \times 10} = \frac{1}{10^4} \text{ , whereas } 10^{2-6} = 10^{-4}$$

$$\frac{1}{10^{-3}} = \frac{1 \cdot 10^3}{10^{-3} \cdot 10^3} = \frac{10^3}{10^0} = \frac{10^3}{1} = 10^3 \quad or \quad \frac{1}{10^{-3}} = \frac{10^3}{1}$$

These examples suggest that to be consistent, we should define negative exponents to mean that for any nonzero real number, a, $a^{-n} = \frac{1}{a^n}$. This extends our notation of exponents to negative integers.

In other words, a base raised to a negative exponent in a numerator is the same as that base moved to the denominator with the exponent sign changed. Also a base raised to a negative exponent in the denominator is the same as that base moved to the numerator with the sign of the exponent switched to positive. Thus we can move a base across the fraction bar by changing the sign of the exponent.

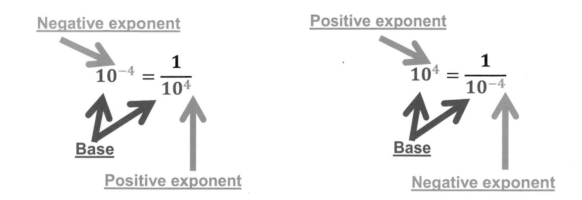

All of our previous observations and laws also hold true for integer exponents. This is one of the important features in mathematics. When we extend our original notation of exponents to include more numbers, we need to explore if the previous rules stay or do we need to modify them for the new exponents. We will continue to point this out to you when it occurs.

Note: *The negative exponent definition also agrees with the result of the quotient property when the bottom power of a common base is larger than the top power. For example we know that $\frac{a^3}{a^5} = \frac{1}{a^2}$ simply by dividing the top and bottom by a three times, while using the quotient rule to simplify we obtain $\frac{1}{a^2} = \frac{a^3}{a^5} = a^{3-5} = a^{-2}$ and thus $a^{-2} = \frac{1}{a^2}$. It is important to be clear about what negative means in the base and in the exponent. A negative exponent simply means divide by the base a certain number of times, while a negative base means we multiply or divide by that negative base a given number of times.*

To evaluate for example 3^{-2} we would first have to write it as

$$3^{-2} = \frac{1}{3^2} = \frac{1}{3 \times 3} = \frac{1}{9}$$

To evaluate for example $\frac{1}{3^{-2}}$ we would first have to write it as

$$\frac{1}{3^{-2}} = 3^2 = 3 \times 3 = 9$$

Once you rewrite your negative exponents in such a way that the base is raised to a positive power we can then evaluate and make sense of what negative exponents really mean.

Zero Power Definition: $a^0 = 1$ for any base $a \neq 0$.

Negative Power Definition: $a^{-n} = \frac{1}{a^n}$ and $\frac{1}{a^{-n}} = a^n$, for any nonzero base a, and any counting number n.

1. Write the product below in the exponential notation with negative exponent as either a^{-n} or $\dfrac{1}{a^{-n}}$. For example, $\dfrac{1}{5} \times \dfrac{1}{5} \times \dfrac{1}{5} \times \dfrac{1}{5} = \dfrac{1}{5^4} = 5^{-4}$, or $5 \times 5 \times 5 \times 5 = 5^4 = \dfrac{1}{5^{-4}}$, or $\dfrac{1}{5 \times 5 \times 5 \times 5} = \dfrac{1}{5^4} = 5^{-4}$

a. $\dfrac{1}{7 \times 7 \times 7}$

b. $-\dfrac{1}{7 \times 7 \times 7}$

c. $\dfrac{1}{(-3) \times (-3) \times (-3) \times (-3) \times (-3)}$

d. $\dfrac{1}{3} \times \dfrac{1}{3} \times \dfrac{1}{3}$

e. $\dfrac{1}{3} \times \dfrac{1}{3} \times \dfrac{1}{3}$

f. $8 \times 8 \times 8 \times 8 \times 8$

g. $-8 \times 8 \times 8 \times 8 \times 8$

h. $\dfrac{1}{a \times a \times a \times a \times a \times a \times a}$

i. $a \times a \times a \times a \times a \times a \times a$

2. Identify base and exponents below. If there are multiple bases and exponents, write all of them.

	Base/s	Exponent/s		Base/s	Exponent/s
a. 2^{-3}			d. $(-7)^{-2}$		
b. a^{-12}			e. -7^{-3}		
c. $(5x+3)^{-4}$			f. $-a^{-2}$		
d. $-(-7)^{-9}$			g. $-(c^2)^{-4}$		

3. Fill the table below.

Example	Base	Exponent	Write in English words how you would read the problem out loud	Expanded form	Evaluate
2^{-3}					
$\dfrac{1}{2^{-3}}$					
$(-3)^{-2}$					
-3^{-2}					
$(-3)^{-2}$					
-3^2					
$\dfrac{1}{-3^{-2}}$					
$\dfrac{1}{(-3)^{-2}}$					
-31^0					
$(-31)^0$					
$\dfrac{1}{(-31)^0}$					
$\dfrac{1}{-31^0}$					

4. Write the numbers in the exponential notation as a^{-n} or a^n. For example, $\dfrac{1}{125} = 5^{-3}$ and $125 = 5^3$

a. $\dfrac{1}{8}$

b. $-\dfrac{1}{25}$

c. $\dfrac{1}{-9}$

d. 27

e. 49

f. $\dfrac{1}{32}$

g. $-\dfrac{1}{32}$

h. -25

Summary of Laws of Exponents

For all integers $n, m,$ and all non zero real numbers a,

Product Rule: $a^m a^n = a^{n+m}$

Power Rule 1: $(a^m)^n = a^{mn}$

Negative exponent: $a^{-n} = \dfrac{1}{a^n}$ Or $\dfrac{1}{a^{-n}} = a^n$

Quotient Rule: $\dfrac{a^m}{a^n} = a^{m-n}$ also $\dfrac{a^m}{a^n} = \dfrac{1}{a^{n-m}}$

Zero exponent: $a^0 = 1$

Now that you understand negative exponents and are comfortable identifying base and exponents, we can work more on the meaning of when the base is a negative real number.

Note : *A negative exponent does NOT make the quantity positive or negative; it simply moves the base to the numerator or denominator.*

Consider the following examples to understand how negative base and negative exponents interact with each other.

We will work with several examples so there is no confusion on what the roles of the base and the exponent are.

Examples

1. -3^2

    The base $= 3$, and exponent $= 2$, that means we have to first evaluate $3^2 = 3 \times 3 = 9$. You would read this as negative of 3 to the second power. This will give us a way to evaluate the original problem as follows: $-3^2 = -3 \times 3 = -9$. This problem demonstrates that in the problem -3^2 you can think of it as having imaginary parentheses as shown below, and the negative sign can be thought of as following along on the outside: $-(3^2) = -(3 \times 3) = -(9)$. Or another way to look at this is that the negative sign will follow along during the computation of 3^2 as shown below.

2. -3^{-2}

    The base $= 3$, and exponent $= -2$, that means that we have to first evaluate $3^{-2} = \dfrac{1}{3^2} = \dfrac{1}{3 \times 3} = \dfrac{1}{9}$. The original problem with the minus out front is $-3^{-2} = -\dfrac{1}{9}$. You would read this as negative of 3 to the negative second power. This problem demonstrates that in the problem -3^{-2} you can think of it as having imaginary parentheses as shown below, and the negative sign can be thought of as following along on the outside: $-(3^{-2}) = -\left(\dfrac{1}{3^2}\right) = -\left(\dfrac{1}{3 \times 3}\right) = -\left(\dfrac{1}{9}\right)$.

    Or another way to see this, is that the negative sign will follow along during the computation of 3^{-2} as shown below.

    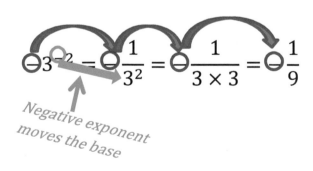

3. $(-3)^2$

The base $= -3$, and exponent $= 2$, that means that we have to first evaluate $(-3)^2 = (-3) \times (-3) = 9$. You would read this as negative 3 to the second power. So you can see that this time the negative sign is with the base and so has to follow the base how many ever times the exponent indicates.

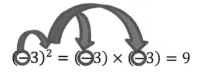

4. $(-2)^3$

The base $= -2$, and exponent $= 3$, that means that we have to first evaluate $(-2)^3 = (-2) \times (-2) \times (-2) = -8$. So you can see that again this time the negative sign is with the base and so has to follow the base three times as the exponent indicates.

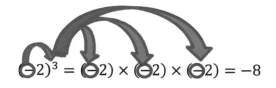

5. $(-5)^{-2}$

What we want you to develop is an understanding of the symbols and not just rote memorization of the rules. If you learn to process the symbols and really think about what they mean, you will gain confidence in working with exponents. Without looking at the work below see if you can successfully solve this question. Then check if your work agrees with what is shown below.

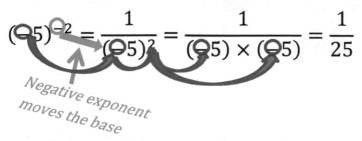

$$(-5)^{-2} = \frac{1}{(-5)^2} = \frac{1}{(-5) \times (-5)} = \frac{1}{25}$$

Negative exponent moves the base

The base = -5, and exponent = -2. You can see that this time the negative sign is with the base and so has to follow the base how ever many times the exponent asks for it. But since the exponent is negative you have to convert it so it becomes a positive exponent before we can evaluate it.

6. $(-3)^{-3}$

The base = -3, and exponent = -3. You can see that this time the negative sign is with the base and so has to follow the base how ever many times the exponent asks for it. But since the exponent is negative you have to convert it so it becomes a positive exponent before we can evaluate it.

$$(-3)^{-3} = \frac{1}{(-3)^3} = \frac{1}{(-3) \times (-3) \times (-3)} = \frac{1}{-27}$$

Negative exponent moves the base

7.
$$-\frac{1}{3^2}$$

The base $= 3$, and exponent $= 2$, that means we have to first evaluate $3^2 = 3 \times 3 =$ 9. The original problem would then be solved as follows: $-\frac{1}{3^2} = -\frac{1}{3 \times 3} = -\frac{1}{9}$.

You can think of imaginary parentheses as shown below, and the negative sign can be thought of as following along on the outside of the parentheses

$-\left(\frac{1}{3^2}\right) = -\left(\frac{1}{3 \times 3}\right) = -\left(\frac{1}{9}\right)$. And another way to look at is that the negative sign

will follow along during the computation of $\frac{1}{3^2}$ as shown below.

$$\ominus\frac{1}{3^2} = \ominus\frac{1}{3 \times 3} = \ominus\frac{1}{9}$$

8.
$$-\frac{1}{3^{-2}}$$

The base $= 3$, and exponent $= -2$. The original problem would then can be looked at as having the imaginary parentheses if it helps you read the problem correctly as

$$-\left(\frac{1}{3^{-2}}\right) = -(3^2) = -(3 \times 3) = -(9) = -9$$

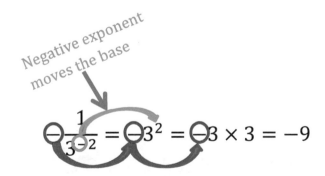

Negative exponent moves the base

$$\ominus\frac{1}{3^{-2}} = \ominus 3^2 = \ominus 3 \times 3 = -9$$

9. $\dfrac{1}{(-3)^{-2}}$

The base $= -3$, and exponent $= -2$. $\dfrac{1}{(-3)^{-2}} = (-3)^2 = (-3) \times (-3) = 9$

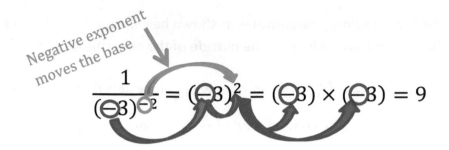

10. $\dfrac{1}{(-2)^3}$

The base $= -2$, and exponent $= 3$, that that means that we have to first evaluate $(-2)^3 = (-2) \times (-2) \times (-2) = -8$.

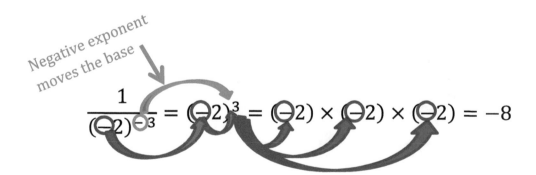

11. $\dfrac{1}{(-2)^{-3}}$

The base $= -2$, and exponent $= -3$.

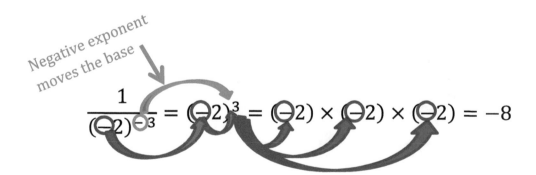

Practice Problems

Simplify the following so that your answers have no negative exponents and then evaluate your answer so that there are no exponents. Assume all variables are nonzero real numbers. Evaluate each number that is raised to an exponent. For the bases that involve variables, leave your answer so the variable is raised to a positive exponent.

1. -4^{-2}

2. 3^2

3. $\dfrac{1}{3^{-2}}$

4. $-\dfrac{1}{3^{-2}}$

5. 2^{-4}

6. $(-4)^{-2}$

7. a^{-5}

8. $\dfrac{7^2}{7^{-1}}$

9. $\dfrac{(-d)^{-4}}{(-d)^{15}}$

10. $(2^{-2})^{-3}$

11. $\left(\dfrac{3^{-1}}{3^2}\right)^{-2}$

Solutions

1. $-4^{-2} = -\dfrac{1}{16}$

2. $3^2 = 9$

3. $\dfrac{1}{3^{-2}} = 9$

4. $-\dfrac{1}{3^{-2}} = -9$

5. $2^{-4} = \dfrac{1}{16}$

6. $(-4)^{-2} = \dfrac{1}{16}$

7. $a^{-5} = \dfrac{1}{a^5}$

8. $\dfrac{7^2}{7^{-1}} = 7^3 = 343$

9. $\dfrac{(-d)^{-4}}{(-d)^{15}} = \dfrac{1}{(-d)^{19}} = -\dfrac{1}{d^{19}}$

10. $(2^{-2})^{-3} = 2^6 = 64$

11. $\left(\dfrac{3^{-1}}{3^2}\right)^{-2} = 3^6 = 729$

1. Evaluate the following.

   a. 2^{-3}

   b. -3^{-2}

   c. $(-3)^{-2}$

   d. $(-3)^2$

   e. -3^{-3}

   f. $(-7)^{-2}$

   g. -7^2

   h. -7^{-2}

   i. 129^0

2. Fill the blanks below with either $<, >$, or $=$ sign without actually evaluating if possible.

   a. -10^2_____$(-10)^{-2}$

   b. $(-3)^2$_____-3^2

   c. 5^{-3}_____5^3

   d. -5^{-3}_____5^3

   e. $\left(\frac{1}{2}\right)^3$_____$2^{-3}$

   f. $2^{-3} \times 3^{-2}$_____6^{-3}

   g. $-2^{-2} \times 3^{-2}$_____6^{-3}

   h. 365^0_____-365^0

3. For all the problems use the patterns observed so far to write the answer without any negative exponents in the form a^n or $\frac{1}{a^n}$, where n is a counting number, and a is the base. For example, -4^{-12}, could be written as $-4^{-12} = -\frac{1}{4^{12}}$; whereas $\frac{(f(x))^{-3}}{(f(x))^5}$, could be written as $\frac{(f(x))^{-3}}{(f(x))^5} = (f(x))^{-3-5} = (f(x))^{-8} = \frac{1}{(f(x))^8}$. Remember to show all your reasoning. Assume that all variables are such that in the final answer the denominators end up being nonzero real numbers.

a. -3^{-2}	g. $\frac{5^3}{5^{-14}}$	l. $\frac{(g(x))^{-7}}{(g(x))^3}$
b. $(-3)^{-2}$	h. $(-3^{-5})^2$	m. $\frac{(3x-2)^4}{(3x-2)^{-5}}$
c. a^{-7}	i. $\left(\frac{x^2}{x^{-6}}\right)^3$	n. $\frac{(-7a)^{-11}}{(-7a)^2}$
d. -2^{-4}	j. $-\left(\frac{c^{-3}}{c^{13}}\right)^2$	o. $\left(temp(x)\right)^{-5}$
e. $(2^{-4})^{-3}$	k. $\frac{(a+b)^2}{(a+b)^3}$	p. $\frac{(-b)^{-3}}{(-b)^{12}}$
f. $\frac{1}{5^{-14}}$		

4. *Simplify each exponential expression using the properties of exponents. Write your answers without any negative exponents in the form a^n or $\frac{1}{a^n}$, where n is a counting number.*

a. $2^3 \times 2^5$

b. $3^{10} \times 3^2$

c. $(-5)^3 \times (-5)^4$

d. $-a^3b^5a^5b^8$

e. $(6^2)^4$

f. $(-x^2)^5$

g. $\frac{4^9}{4^3}$

h. $\frac{x^9}{x^5}$

i. $-\left(\frac{123}{96768}\right)^0$

j. $\frac{1}{-2^{-3}}$

k. $\frac{a^2b^5}{a^{-8}b^3}$

l. $\frac{(a^2)^3b^5}{a^3b^{-10}}$

m. $-\frac{8x^4y^{-2}z^{-4}}{2x^4y^2z^5}$

5. Find all entries in the right column i.-xi. that match each entry in the left column a.-f.

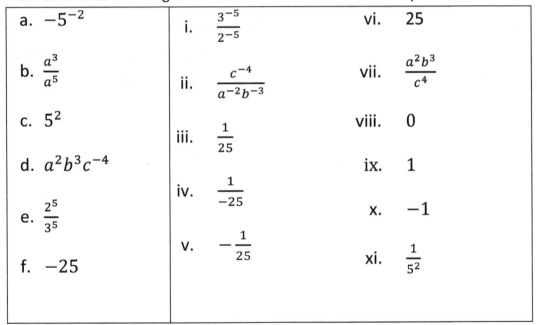

a. -5^{-2}

b. $\frac{a^3}{a^5}$

c. 5^2

d. $a^2b^3c^{-4}$

e. $\frac{2^5}{3^5}$

f. -25

i. $\frac{3^{-5}}{2^{-5}}$

ii. $\frac{c^{-4}}{a^{-2}b^{-3}}$

iii. $\frac{1}{25}$

iv. $\frac{1}{-25}$

v. $-\frac{1}{25}$

vi. 25

vii. $\frac{a^2b^3}{c^4}$

viii. 0

ix. 1

x. -1

xi. $\frac{1}{5^2}$

You might be wondering right now where all this will be used. We will discuss that in Module 4 but for now just know that in science problems, it is often necessary to multiply or divide two or more expressions with one or more common bases. We use the definitions for integer exponents and the properties above to simplify products, quotients, and exponents, or powers. Here simplify means to combine all the multiplications and divisions of each base raised to exponents, so that in the end, the exponents are all positive and each base should appear only one time in the product or quotient. This makes computation more efficient and makes it easier for the reader to see what the end results are.

1.8 Rational Exponents and Radicals
Lecture

⬚ Rational Exponents

http://www.youtube.com/watch?v=GJVtvQ2bm8M (13 min)

Rational Exponents

Playing

So far we have worked with integer exponents. We will now extend the ideas of exponents to rational exponents, much like we extended number sets from the Natural, to Whole, to Integer to Fractions. We start by playing with the idea of fractional powers and how to make sense of a base raised to an exponent that is a fraction.

For example let us start with thinking about $32^{\frac{1}{5}}$, and what it should mean? Think about it before reading on. This will help you to gain an insight into fractional exponents.

We know that 2^5 means multiply the base 2, five times or that $2^5 = 2 \times 2 \times 2 \times 2 \times 2 = 32$. When we write $32 = 2^5$, this means multiplying by 32 is the same as multiplying by 2 five times. Then $32^{\frac{1}{5}}$ should mean multiply by 2 ($\frac{1}{5}$ of five times) or simply multiply by 2 once. In other words we want to have the meaning of $32^{\frac{1}{5}} = (2^5)^{\frac{1}{5}} = 2$. This gives a starting point for understanding fractional exponents.

Fractional Exponents

Why should we even want to think of fractional exponents? Consider this -

When the side of a square or cube is known, the area of the square and volume of the cube are computed by the formulas below.

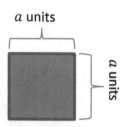

a units

a units

Area of the square

$A = a^2$ square units,

Length of the side $= a$ units

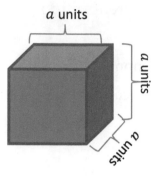

a units

a units

a units

Volume of the cube

$V = a^3$ cubic units,

Length of the side $= a$ units

If A and V are positive real numbers then

➤ $A^{\frac{1}{2}}$ units can be looked at as length of the side of a square whose area is A square units.

➤ $V^{\frac{1}{3}}$ units can be looked at as the length of a side of a cube whose volume is V cubic units.

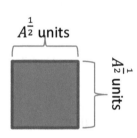

$A^{\frac{1}{2}}$ units

$A^{\frac{1}{2}}$ units

Area of the square A square units

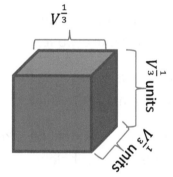

$V^{\frac{1}{3}}$

$V^{\frac{1}{3}}$ units

$V^{\frac{1}{3}}$ units

Volume of the cube V cubic units

For example if the area of a square is $9cm^2$, what would be the length of each of the sides?

Answer:

$3^2 = 9$ so the side of the square must be $3cm = 9^{1/2}cm$.

We would like to think of $9^{\frac{1}{2}} = 3$.

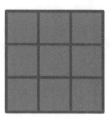

Here is another example where the volume of a cube is $8\ cm^3$, what is the length of the side of this cube?

Answer:

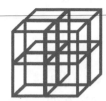

$2^3 = 8$ so the side of the cube must be 2 units.

Another way to think of this would be $8^{\frac{1}{3}} = 2$.

We know that we can think of $25^{\frac{1}{2}}$ as a number that when multiplied by itself two times it should be equal to 25, which suggests that $25^{\frac{1}{2}} = 5$ or -5 and so we have to be careful in our definition. We define $25^{\frac{1}{2}} = 5$ and this (the positive number) is called the principle square root of 25.

Definition: For any counting number n and a real number a, $a^{\frac{1}{n}}$ is the real number that when multiplied by itself n times results in the number a (if n is an even counting number, we must have that a is a nonnegative real number).

Note: Also $a^{\frac{m}{n}}$ is equal to $a^{\frac{1}{n}}$ multiplied by itself m times, i.e. $a^{\frac{m}{n}} = \left(a^{\frac{1}{n}}\right)^m$. It is also true that $a^{\frac{m}{n}} = (a^m)^{\frac{1}{n}}$. When $m > n$ we can write the exponent as a mixed number and simplify the whole number part via the product rule, e.g., $a^{\frac{9}{4}} = a^{2\frac{1}{4}} = a^2 a^{\frac{1}{4}}$. In this way we can always simplify a base to a rational exponent as a base to a natural number times a base raised to a proper fraction. We will work with this more in module 2.

Examples
Simplify the following so the rational exponents are proper fractions.

1. $3^{\frac{5}{3}}$

    We write $\frac{5}{3} = 1\frac{2}{3}$ and have $3^{\frac{5}{3}} = 3^1 \cdot 3^{\frac{2}{3}} = 3 \cdot 3^{\frac{2}{3}}$

2. $8^{\frac{1}{2}}$

    We write $8 = 2^3$ and thus $(2^3)^{\frac{1}{2}} = 2^{1\frac{1}{2}} = 2^1 \cdot 2^{\frac{1}{2}} = 2 \cdot 2^{\frac{1}{2}}$

3. $a^{\frac{13}{4}}$

We write $\frac{13}{4} = \frac{12}{4} + \frac{1}{4} = 3 + \frac{1}{4}$ and have $a^{\frac{13}{4}} = a^3 a^{\frac{1}{4}}$.

Video Log 1.8a

1. Evaluate each of the exponential expressions

   a. $9^{\frac{1}{2}}$ d. $25^{\frac{1}{2}}$ g. $(-8)^{\frac{1}{3}}$

   b. $16^{\frac{1}{2}}$ e. $49^{\frac{1}{2}}$ h. $(a^2)^{\frac{1}{2}}$

   c. $-9^{\frac{1}{2}}$ f. $27^{\frac{1}{3}}$

2. Simplify so that the base is raised to a natural number times a base to a proper fraction.

   a. $3^{\frac{6}{5}}$ b. $32^{\frac{1}{3}}$ (Note that $32 = 2^5$.)   c. $y^{\frac{23}{3}}$

3. Fill in the missing base below.

a. _____$^{1/2} = 6$	b. _____$^{1/3} = 2$	c. _____$^{1/5} = a$

We next introduce **radical notation** which is another way to represent a base raised to a fraction exponent.

Radicals

Lecture

🖥️ Radical Notation

http://www.youtube.com/watch?v=B0zdWX3CzFE (8 min)

In general if a is a non-negative real number, and n is a counting number, we denote $a^{\frac{1}{n}} = \sqrt[n]{a}$ and define it as a number that when raised to the exponent n gives the answer a. When $n = 2$ it is conventional to write $\sqrt{a}$ without the little 2 and call it the square root. This name makes sense in that $A^{\frac{1}{2}} = \sqrt{A}$ is the length of the side of a square with area equal to A. Likewise, $\sqrt[3]{V} = V^{\frac{1}{3}}$ is called the cube root of V. If n is an odd counting number, we can have a be any real number. So from prior examples we know that $\sqrt{25} = 5$, $\sqrt[3]{-8} = -2$.

If the area of a square is 81 square feet, then the side length is given by $a = (81\ ft^2)^{\frac{1}{2}} = 9\ ft$. This "9" is called the **square root** of 81 since it is the "root" or solution to the problem of finding the side-length of a square with area of 81. Historically, radical notation was used to denote square roots before fractional exponents were invented. Thus $81^{\frac{1}{2}} = \sqrt{81} = 9$. This radical symbol $\sqrt{\ }$ is called the square root radical and it means the same thing as taking the number under the radical sign to the one half power. Thus to find the side length of a square so that the area would be $5\ ft^2$ we'd have $a = (5\ ft^2)^{\frac{1}{2}} = \sqrt{5 ft^2} \approx 2.236\ ft$. (This number can be obtained on a calculator by evaluating "5^(1/2)" or by using the square root key.)

A cube that is two feet by two feet by two feet has volume of $V = 2^3 ft^3 = 8 ft^3$ and $a = (V)^{\frac{1}{3}} = (8\ ft^3)^{\frac{1}{3}} = \sqrt[3]{8 ft^3} = 2\ ft$. A cubical box with volume of 2 cubic feet has side length of $a = \sqrt[3]{2 ft^3} \approx 1.26\ ft$.

> **Note:** *Since working with radicals and exponents with fractional exponents is the same, we know all our exponent laws from before should apply and this fact will be dealt with fully in module 2 when we combine radicals through multiplication and division. We will now work through many examples of this concept of fractional exponents and their equivalent radicals to get comfortable with their meaning.*

Definition: An nth root or radical $\sqrt[n]{a}$ is defined in terms of fractional exponents by $\sqrt[n]{a} = a^{\frac{1}{n}}$.

In the exponential notation $a^{\frac{1}{n}}$, the number a is the base and $\frac{1}{n}$ is the exponent

In the radical notation $\sqrt[n]{a}$,

➤ The symbol $\sqrt[n]{\ }$ is called the radical sign denoting the nth root.

- The quantity a is called the <u>radicand</u>. The radicand is the expression that sits inside a radical. It is equivalent to the base in the exponential form.
- n, is called the <u>index</u> of the radical. In the exponential notation it is the denominator of the exponent ($\frac{1}{n}$).
- When the index is 2 we call it the square root and leave the 2 out and use just the radical symbol $\sqrt{\ }$. When the index is n, we say it is the nth root.

It is important in working with radicals that you understand the radicand and the index just like you got used to identifying the base and the exponent when working with the exponential notation.

For example

		Radicand	Index	How to read it
1.	$\sqrt{25}$	25	2	Square root of 25
2.	$\sqrt[3]{64}$	64	3	Cube root of 64
3.	$-\dfrac{1}{\sqrt[5]{7}}$	7	5	Negative 1 over 5th root of 7
4.	$\sqrt[4]{3-4a}$	$3-4a$	4	4th root of $3-4a$
5.	$\sqrt[7]{x^3}$	x^3	7	7th root of x cubed

Identify the <u>radicand</u> and the <u>index</u> in the radical expressions below, and write in words how you would read the expression.

		Radicand	Index	Write in English words how you would read the problem out loud
1.	$\sqrt[7]{a+b}$			
2.	$\sqrt[3]{(g(x))}$			
3.	$\sqrt[5]{-b}$			
4.	$\sqrt{6}$			
5.	$-\dfrac{1}{\sqrt[6]{12}}$			
6.	$\sqrt[3]{225}$			
7.	$\sqrt[5]{\dfrac{1}{7}}$			
8.	$\sqrt{3x}$			
9.	$3\sqrt{x}$			

Below are examples of how you can use radical notation to represent fractional exponents and vice versa.

Radical Notation		
Exponential Notation		
	$a^{\frac{1}{2}}$	$=$	$\sqrt{a}$ (square root of a)
	$a^{\frac{1}{3}}$	$=$	$\sqrt[3]{a}$ (cube root of a)
	$a^{\frac{1}{5}}$	$=$	$\sqrt[5]{a}$ (fifth root of a)
	$\left(\dfrac{1}{a}\right)^{\frac{1}{2}}$	$=$	$\sqrt{\dfrac{1}{a}}$
$a^{-\frac{1}{3}} = \dfrac{1}{a^{\frac{1}{3}}}$		$=$	$\dfrac{1}{\sqrt[3]{a}}$
	$a^{\frac{2}{5}}$	$=$	$\sqrt[5]{a^2}$
$a^{\frac{7}{2}} = a^{3\frac{1}{2}}$		$=$	$a^3\sqrt{a}$

Practice Problems

Convert the exponential notation into radical notation and radical notation into exponential notation.

1. $3^{\frac{1}{6}}$

2. $\sqrt[5]{\dfrac{1}{x}}$

3. $(x + y)^{\frac{1}{2}}$

4. $8^{-\frac{1}{3}}$

5. $\sqrt{a + b}$

6. $\sqrt[5]{a^2}$

7. $\left(\sqrt{(5)}\right)^3$

Rewrite the exponential notation using the radical notation.

1. $3^{\frac{1}{5}}$

3. $(2-3x)^{\frac{1}{4}}$

5. $123^{\frac{1}{2}}$

2. $a^{-\frac{1}{3}}$

4. $(ab)^{\frac{1}{7}}$

6. $4^{1/3}$

Rewrite the radical notation using the exponential notation.

1. $\sqrt[5]{2}$

3. $\sqrt{3-2x}$

5. $\sqrt[3]{25}$

2. $\frac{1}{\sqrt[3]{x}}$

4. $\sqrt[7]{ab}$

6. $-\sqrt{6}$

Solutions to Practice Problems

Convert the exponential notation into radical notation and radical notation into exponential notation.

1. $3^{\frac{1}{6}} = \sqrt[6]{3}$

2. $\sqrt[5]{\frac{1}{x}} = \left(\frac{1}{x}\right)^{\frac{1}{5}}$

3. $(x+y)^{\frac{1}{2}} = \sqrt{x+y}$

4. $8^{-\frac{1}{3}} = \frac{1}{8^{\frac{1}{3}}} = \frac{1}{\sqrt[3]{8}}$

5. $\sqrt{a+b} = (a+b)^{\frac{1}{2}}$

6. $\sqrt[5]{a^2} = (a^2)^{\frac{1}{5}} = a^{\frac{2}{5}}$

7. $\left(\sqrt{(5)}\right)^3 = \left(5^{\frac{1}{2}}\right)^3 = 5^{\frac{3}{2}}$

Rewrite the exponential notation using the radical notation.

1. $3^{\frac{1}{5}} = \sqrt[5]{3}$

2. $a^{-\frac{1}{3}} = \frac{1}{a^{\frac{1}{3}}} = \frac{1}{\sqrt[3]{a}}$

3. $(2-3x)^{\frac{1}{4}} = \sqrt[4]{2-3x}$

4. $(ab)^{\frac{1}{7}} = \sqrt[7]{ab}$

5. $123^{\frac{1}{2}} = \sqrt{123}$

6. $4^{1/3} = \sqrt[3]{4}$

Rewrite the radical notation using the exponential notation

1. $\sqrt[5]{2} = 2^{\frac{1}{5}}$
2. $\frac{1}{\sqrt[3]{x}} = x^{-1/3}$
3. $\sqrt{3 - 2x} = (3 - 2x)^{\frac{1}{2}}$
4. $\sqrt[7]{ab} = (ab)^{\frac{1}{7}}$
5. $\sqrt[3]{25} = 25^{1/3} = (5^2)^{1/3} = 5^{2/3}$
6. $-\sqrt{6} = -6^{\frac{1}{2}}$

Video Log 1.8c

1. Rewrite the exponential notation using the radical notation.

   a. $3^{\frac{1}{2}}$

   b. $5^{\frac{1}{3}}$

   c. $7^{\frac{1}{5}}$

   d. $x^{\frac{1}{5}}$

   e. $5^{\frac{4}{3}}$

   f. $x^{-\frac{1}{5}}$

   g. $(3 + 5x)^{\frac{1}{7}}$

   h. $(ab)^{\frac{1}{3}}$

   i. $5^{\frac{11}{3}}$

   j. $4^{-1/3}$

2. Rewrite the radical notation using the exponential notation.

   a. $\sqrt[5]{7}$

   b. $\frac{1}{\sqrt[5]{a}}$

   c. $\sqrt{4 + 9a}$

   d. $\sqrt[3]{ab}$

   e. $\sqrt[3]{2^{11}}$

   f. $-\sqrt{5}$

3. Fill in the missing radicand.

   a. $\sqrt{\underline{\hspace{2cm}}} = a^{\frac{1}{2}}$

   b. $\sqrt{\underline{\hspace{2cm}}} = 5$

   c. $\sqrt[3]{\underline{\hspace{2cm}}} = 2$

   d. $\sqrt[3]{\underline{\hspace{2cm}}} = a^{\frac{1}{3}}$

Examples

Evaluate the following. Your final answer should be without an exponent or a radical. Assume all variables are nonzero positive real numbers.

1. $\sqrt[5]{2^5}$

2. $\dfrac{1}{\sqrt[3]{x^3}}$

3. $\sqrt{25}$

4. $\sqrt[3]{8}$

5. $-\sqrt{16}$

6. $\sqrt{-16}$

Solutions

1.
$$\sqrt[5]{2^5} = 2$$

2.
$$\frac{1}{\sqrt[3]{x^3}} = \frac{1}{x}$$

3.
$$\sqrt{25} = 5$$

4.
$$\sqrt[3]{8} = 2$$

5.
$$-\sqrt{16} = -4$$

6.
$$\sqrt{-16} = 4i, \text{ since } \sqrt{16} = 4 \text{ and } \sqrt{-1} = i.$$

Convert each radical to an improper rational exponent and then convert the proper fractional part of the exponent back to a radical.

1. $\sqrt[3]{16}$

2. $\sqrt{x^7}$

3. $\dfrac{2}{\sqrt[3]{x^8}}$

4. $\sqrt{32}$

Solutions

7. We have $16 = 2^4$, and $\sqrt[3]{16} = (2^4)^{\frac{1}{3}} = 2^{\frac{4}{3}} = 2^{1\frac{1}{3}} = 2 \cdot 2^{\frac{1}{3}} = 2\sqrt[3]{2}$.

8. $(x^7)^{\frac{1}{2}} = x^{\frac{7}{2}} = x^{3\frac{1}{2}} = x^3 x^{\frac{1}{2}} = x^3 \sqrt{x}$.

9. $\dfrac{2}{(x^8)^{\frac{1}{3}}} = \dfrac{2}{x^{\frac{8}{3}}} = \dfrac{2}{x^{2\frac{2}{3}}} = \dfrac{2}{x^2 x^{\frac{2}{3}}} = \dfrac{2}{x^2 (x^2)^{\frac{1}{3}}} = \dfrac{2}{x^2 \sqrt[3]{x^2}}$.

10. We have $32 = 2^5$, and $\sqrt{32} = (2^5)^{\frac{1}{2}} = 2^{\frac{5}{2}} = 2^{2\frac{1}{2}} = 2^2 \cdot 2^{\frac{1}{2}} = 4\sqrt{2}$.

Notice that if we had something like $\sqrt{5}$, we cannot evaluate it exactly. You can use your calculator to get an approximate value but you can also use your estimation skills and knowledge of exponents to know what the approximate value of $\sqrt{5}$ will be. See examples below.

Lecture

▣ Estimating Radicals

http://www.youtube.com/watch?v=hMWQUtQuTKI (5 min)

Examples

Estimate the value of the following to the nearest tenths.

1. $\sqrt{5}$

    Notice that $4 < 5 < 9$ and so $\sqrt{4} < \sqrt{5} < \sqrt{9}$, or that $2 < \sqrt{5} < 3$. So we know that the decimal estimate of $\sqrt{5}$ is going to have a 2 in the units place. We can find more digits by doing the same process. For example notice that $2.1^2 = 4.41$, $2.2^2 = 4.84$, $2.3^2 = 5.29$, which shows us that $2.2 < \sqrt{5} < 2.3$. This establishes that the tenths place digit for the decimal estimate of $\sqrt{5}$ is 2.

2. $\sqrt{47}$

    Notice that $36 < 47 < 49$ and so $\sqrt{36} < \sqrt{47} < \sqrt{49}$, or that $6 < \sqrt{47} < 7$, so the units place of $\sqrt{47}$ is going to have to be 6. To obtain the tenths place digit we compute $6.9^2 = 47.61$, $6.8^2 = 46.24$ which shows that $\sqrt{47}$ is between 6.8 and 6.9 or that the tenth place digit of the decimal expansion of $\sqrt{47}$ is 8.

3. $\sqrt[3]{9}$

    Notice that $8 < 9 < 27$ and so $\sqrt[3]{8} < \sqrt[3]{9} < \sqrt[3]{27}$, or that $2 < \sqrt[3]{9} < 3$. Therefore the units place of $\sqrt[3]{9}$ has to be 2. We can find more digits by doing the same process. For example, notice that $2.0^3 = 8$ and $2.1^3 = 9.261$. Thus the tenths place in $\sqrt[3]{9}$ is zero. Continuing this one more digit, we compute $2.08^3 = 8.998912$, and $2.09^3 = 9.129329$, and hence the hundredths place value digit of the decimal expansion of $\sqrt[3]{9}$ is 8.

The above examples provide support for properties of radicals that correspond to exponent laws. We will investigate this more fully in module two.

Examples

1. Arrange the numbers in the problems below in ascending order.

$$3^{\frac{1}{2}}, \ 3^{-2}, \ \sqrt{3}, \ -3^2, \ (-3)^2, \ \sqrt{3^3}, \frac{1}{3^{-2}}, \ \frac{-1}{3^{-\frac{1}{2}}}, \ \left(-\sqrt{3}\right)^{-1}$$

2. Use the appropriate symbols $<, >, or \ =$ to fill in the blanks below.

a. $\sqrt{4}$ _____ $\frac{1}{2^{-1}}$

b. $\sqrt{5}$ _____ 2.1

c. -5^{-1} _____ -5

d. -4^2 _____ 16

Solutions

1. *Simplifying all the numbers and so that they have positive exponents and then evaluating them if possible will allow to order the numbers as we want. The numbers listed can be rewritten as*

$$3^{\frac{1}{2}}, \ 3^{-2} = \frac{1}{3^2} = \frac{1}{9}, \ \sqrt{3}, \ -3^2 = -9, \ (-3)^2 = 9,$$

$$\sqrt{3^3} = 3^{\frac{3}{2}} = 3^{1\frac{1}{2}} = 3\sqrt{3}, \quad \frac{1}{3^{-2}} = 3^2 = 9, \frac{-1}{3^{-\frac{1}{2}}} = -3^{\frac{1}{2}} = -\sqrt{3},$$

$$\left(-\sqrt{3}\right)^{-1} = \frac{1}{-\sqrt{3}} = -\frac{1}{\sqrt{3}}$$

Now -9 is the smallest, and $-3^{\frac{1}{2}} = -\sqrt{3}$ is smaller than $-\frac{1}{\sqrt{3}}$. The smallest positive number is the $\frac{1}{9}$ followed by $3^{\frac{1}{2}}$ (also listed as $\sqrt{3}$), and then $3 \cdot 3^{\frac{1}{2}}$, and the largest number is $(-3)^2 = 9$. Thus the original list in increasing order is:

$$-3^2, \ -\frac{1}{3^{-\frac{1}{2}}}, \ -\left(\sqrt{3}\right)^{-\frac{1}{2}}, \ 3^{-2}, \ 3^{\frac{1}{2}}, \ \sqrt{3^3} \ , \ \frac{1}{3^{-2}}$$

---

2. *Use the appropriate symbols* $<, >,$ *or* $=$ *to fill in the blanks below.*

a. $\sqrt{4} = \dfrac{1}{2^{-1}}$, *since* $\dfrac{1}{2^{-1}} = 2^1 = 2$ *and* $\sqrt{4} = 2$

b. $\sqrt{5} > 2.1$, *since* $5 > 2.1^2 = 4.41$

c. $-5^{-1} > -5$, *since* $-5^{-1} = -\dfrac{1}{5} > -5$

d. $-4^2 < 16$, *since* $-4^2 = -4 \times 4 = -16$

Video Log 1.8d

1. Evaluate the following. Your final answer should be without a radical. Assume all variables are nonzero positive real numbers.

a. $\sqrt{9}$

b. $\sqrt{10000}$

c. $\sqrt{400}$

d. $\dfrac{1}{\sqrt[3]{27}}$

e. $\sqrt[5]{b^5}$

f. $-\sqrt{36}$

g. $-\dfrac{1}{\sqrt{4}}$

h. $\sqrt{-9}$

i. $\sqrt{x^2}$

j. $\sqrt{y^6}$

k. $\sqrt[3]{y^6}$

l. $\sqrt[6]{x^6}$

m. $\sqrt[5]{b^5}$

n. $\dfrac{1}{\sqrt[3]{a^3}}$

o. $-\sqrt{b^{10}}$

p. $-\dfrac{1}{\sqrt{b^2}}$

q. $\sqrt{\dfrac{49}{9}}$

r. $\dfrac{\sqrt[3]{27}}{\sqrt[3]{8}}$

2. Fill in the missing index, radicand, or both.

a. $\sqrt{} = a^3$

b. $\sqrt[3]{} = m^4$

c. $\sqrt[6]{} = x^3$

d. $\sqrt[5]{} = c$

e. $\dfrac{1}{\sqrt[3]{}} = \dfrac{1}{b^3}$

f. $\sqrt{} = 10$

g. $\sqrt{\dfrac{}{}} = \dfrac{5}{4}$

h. $\sqrt{} = x^3$

i. $\sqrt{} = x^5$

3. Evaluate the following. Your final answer should be without a radical. Assume all variables are nonzero positive real numbers. Remember radicals are just fractional exponents and therefore the previous product, and quotient rules apply. Simply your answer completely and a fraction must be written in the lowest terms.

a. $\sqrt{25x^2}$	h. $-\dfrac{1}{\sqrt{a^6b^2}}$	n. $\sqrt{\dfrac{4a^8}{9b^2}}$
b. $\sqrt{4y^6}$	i. $\sqrt{4a^8b^4}$	o. $\sqrt[3]{\dfrac{8a^3b^{12}}{27c^9}}$
c. $\sqrt[3]{8y^6}$	j. $\dfrac{2a}{\sqrt{36a^4}}$	
d. $\sqrt[6]{64x^6}$	k. $-\sqrt{9a^8y^{12}}$	
e. $\sqrt[5]{32b^5}$	l. $\sqrt{4a}\sqrt{4a}$	
f. $\dfrac{1}{\sqrt[3]{27a^3}}$	m. $\sqrt{2a}\sqrt{4a}\sqrt{2a^2}$	
g. $-\sqrt{49b^{10}}$		

4. Fill in the missing index, radicand, or both.

a. $\sqrt{} = a^3b^2$

b. $\sqrt[3]{} = 3m^4$

c. $\sqrt[6]{} = 2a^2x^3$

d. $\sqrt[5]{} = ac$

e. $\dfrac{1}{\sqrt[3]{}} = \dfrac{1}{2x}$

f. $\sqrt{} = 10$

g. $\sqrt{\dfrac{}{}} = \dfrac{2a^2b^3}{c^{10}}$

h. $\sqrt{} = x^3y^5$

i. $\sqrt{} = 4a^5$

5. Evaluate the following. Assume all variables are nonzero positive real numbers. Remember radicals are just fractional exponents and therefore the previous product, and quotient rules apply. Write your final answer in the simplest form so that the exponents inside a radical are less than the index of the radical. A fractional answer must be written in the lowest terms.

a. $\sqrt{8a^5}$	e. $\dfrac{2a}{\sqrt[3]{8a^3}}$	i. $\sqrt[5]{a^7y^{11}}$
b. $5\sqrt{4a^3b^{10}}$	f. $-\sqrt{45a^7y^{11}}$	j. $\dfrac{\sqrt{a}}{\sqrt{a^3}}$
c. $7ab\sqrt[3]{a^3b^6c^5}$	g. $\sqrt{4a}\sqrt{8a}$	
d. $\sqrt{18a^3b^4c^5}$	h. $\sqrt[3]{-24a^7y^{11}}$	

6. Find the tenths place digit of each radical below.

a. $\sqrt{7}$ c. $\sqrt{10}$

b. $\sqrt[3]{25}$

7. Find all entries in the right column i.-x. that match each entry in the left column a.-f.

a. $\sqrt{2}$	i. 2^{-2}	vii. $2^{\frac{1}{2}}$
b. 8	ii. 2^{-3}	viii. $\sqrt{32}$
c. $4\sqrt{2}$	iii. 2^3	ix. $-\dfrac{1}{2^{-\frac{1}{2}}}$
d. -4	iv. -2^2	x. $-\sqrt{2}$
e. $\dfrac{1}{4}$	v. $(-2)^2$	
f. $\dfrac{1}{\sqrt{2}}$	vi. $2^{-\frac{1}{2}}$	

8. For each number in the left column, state whether it is less than, equal to, or greater than the number at the top of each column. Follow the example in the first row.

	$2^{\frac{1}{2}}$	2^3	-2^2	$\dfrac{1}{\sqrt{2}}$	$4\sqrt{2}$	$-\dfrac{1}{2^{-\frac{1}{2}}}$
$\sqrt{2}$	=	<	>	>	<	>
$\dfrac{1}{2^2}$						
-4						
4						
$\sqrt{32}$						
$2^{-\frac{1}{2}}$						
$\dfrac{1}{2^{-\frac{1}{2}}}$						
$-\sqrt{2}$						

1.9 Polynomials
Lecture

🖥 Polynomials

https://www.youtube.com/watch?v=GjpAlev8o8E **(14 min)**

Recall that when we studied the expanded form of whole numbers, we could generalize them in a variety of ways. One way is to replace the powers of ten with powers of a variable base. For example, the number $347 = 3 \cdot 10^2 + 4 \cdot 10 + 7 \cdot 10^0$. In this number the digits $3, 4,$ and 7 are called the coefficients, and we can generalize this into a "polynomial" by replacing the base ten with a variable say x as follows: $3x^2 + 4x + 7$. In general replacing all bases in our decimal number system with one or more variable terms raised to different whole number exponents and replacing the coefficients with any real numbers makes this object into a polynomial. It turns out that polynomial objects like this are very useful, e.g., for describing paths of baseballs, pricing strategies to optimize profits, chaotic processes and much more.

Definition: A polynomial with real coefficients consists of a sum of one or more terms that are each the product of a real number called the **coefficient of the term**, and one or more variables raised to whole number powers. Polynomials with one, two or three terms are called monomials, binomials, and trinomials respectively. It is possible for a term to not have any variables and this is called a constant term.

In a polynomial with one variable the highest exponent of the variable is called the <u>degree</u> of that polynomial. In a polynomial with multiple variables the degree of each term is the sum of all exponents on all the variables in that term. For example in the polynomial $3x^2y^5 + 4x^3y^2 - 3$ the degree of the second term $4x^3y^2$ is equal to $3 + 2 = 5$. The degree of the polynomial is the highest degree of all terms. A term without any variable has degree zero and is called the constant term. Usually we write polynomials from left to right in decreasing degree of terms.

Examples:

$$3x^2 + 4x + 7, \quad 9x^5 - 3x^4 + 2, \quad \frac{9}{5}C + 32, \quad x^2y^4 - x^2y^2 + 5x - y,$$

$$\frac{4}{3}\pi r^3 + \pi r^2 l, \quad z^2 - 3y^3z.$$

The degree of $3x^2 + 4x + 7$ is two. The degree of $9x^5 - 3x^4 + 2$, is five. The degree of $\frac{9}{5}C + 32$ is one. The degree of $x^2y^4 - x^2y^2 + 5x - y$ is six. The degree of $z^2 - 3y^3z$ is four.

There are times when mathematicians also work with polynomials with complex numbers for coefficients and these are called complex polynomials.

In this class we will work primarily with polynomials in one variable and having real coefficients which in general form can be written as $a_n x^n + a_{n-1} x^{n-1} + a_{n-2} x^{n-2} + \cdots a_2 x^2 + a_1 x + a_0$. Here the a_k is the coefficient of x^k, where k is a whole number $0, 1, 2, \ldots, n$.

For the second polynomial example above, the coefficients are $a_5 = 9, a_4 = -3, a_3 = 0, a_2 = 0, a_1 = 0, a_0 = 2$.

The use of subscripts on coefficients like a_3 is a clever way to not run out symbols (there are only 26 letters) and also to connect the coefficient to the corresponding power of x.

Practice examples

Explain why each expression below is not a polynomial.

1. $3\sqrt{x}$

2. $\dfrac{2}{x^2} + 3x - 3$

3. $\dfrac{3}{x - 2}$

4. $2^x + 5x$

Answers

1. $3\sqrt{x}$

   The x is raised to the exponent ½ which is not a whole number. Note that $\sqrt{2}x$ is a polynomial with coefficient $\sqrt{2}$.

2. $\dfrac{2}{x^2} + 3x - 3$

   The division by x^2 corresponds to x^{-2} which is again a non-whole number exponent.

3. $\dfrac{3}{x - 2}$

   The denominator is a polynomial, but the original expression is not the sum of terms with whole number powers; it is a quotient of polynomials.

4. $2^x + 5x$

   Here the first term has x as an exponent but the exponents must be whole numbers.

Rational Expressions

Recall that rational numbers consist of fractions of integers. When we extend this to fractions where both the numerator and denominator are polynomial expressions, these objects are called rational expressions. Some examples are given below and they show up in various formulas in science.

$$\frac{2x-3}{x^2+1}, \qquad \frac{3x^2-2x+4}{x^2-4}, \qquad \frac{PV}{nRT}, \qquad \frac{GMm}{R^2}$$

Algebraic Expressions

If we combine sums, differences, products, quotients, integer and fractional powers to variables and coefficients, we obtain what is called an algebraic expression. The main extension that we obtain from rational expressions is the inclusion of radicals or fractional powers of variable expressions combined with polynomials, e.g., $\frac{\sqrt{2x^2+3x-2}}{\sqrt{x}+2x-3}$.

Video Log 1.9a

1. Determine the degree of the polynomial and other information asked of you for each question below.

a. $3x^5 - 4.3x^4 + 5x^2 - 7x + \sqrt{2}$ Degree of the polynomial_____ Leading coefficient _____ Coefficient of degree 2 term _____ Coefficient of degree 3 term _____ b. $x^5 - x^{10} + \frac{1}{2}x^{12} - \frac{7}{\sqrt{3}}x - 10.\overline{23}$ Degree of the polynomial_____ Leading coefficient _____ Coefficient of degree 5 term _____ Constant term _____	c. $31x^5y^3 - 4.3x^4y^2 + \frac{5}{37}x^2y^7 - 7x - 3y + \frac{1}{2}$ Degree of the polynomial_____ Leading coefficient _____ Coefficient of degree 9 term _____ d. $\sqrt{3}x^6 - 0.003x^3$ Degree of the polynomial_____ Leading coefficient _____

2. Determine whether the expressions below are polynomial, or rational expressions, or neither.

   a. $\sqrt{2} - 5x^{12} + 10x - 15x^2$

   c. $6.1x^3y^2 - \frac{x^6}{5} + 7$

   b. $\frac{3x-1}{x^2-4}$

   d. $-5t^{21} + 10t^{-3} - 15$

3. Create a polynomial in the variable x that is degree four, has three terms and the second degree term has the coefficient of $\sqrt[3]{5}$.

4. Create a degree 6 polynomial with 5 terms in the variables x and y where all the terms are of degree six.

Playing

Lecture

🖥 Translating Words Part 1

http://www.youtube.com/watch?v=Ff-bOPs5iz4 (13 min)

🖥 Translating Words Part 2

http://www.youtube.com/watch?v=xVKV_9OsNeQ (6 min)

All of the algebraic objects we've studied are used extensively in describing and modeling experiments and relationships in the natural and social sciences. We thus need to be able to translate from words, observed patterns, or relations into mathematical expressions.

The ability to translate a real life situation into mathematical expressions, equations or inequalities requires us to use variables for unknown quantities. We will start with translating words to algebraic expressions. In later modules you will see how this ability helps in solving real world problems.

To represent unknown quantities we make use of variables. Depending on the context of the situation, the variables can represent real or complex number values. Sometimes we have to restrict our variable values to whole numbers, or positive real numbers so that the variable accurately represents the possible outcomes of the situation being represented.

The table below shows some conversion of words into mathematical operations.

	Words	Expression	Example
1.	"Twice" a quantity	$2 \times x$	Draw a rectangle in which the length of a rectangle is twice the width. Here the variable x must be a positive real number since it represents the width of a rectangle.
2.	"Two more than a quantity"	$A + 2$	Eric has 2 more marbles than Anu. Represent the number of marbles they each have using appropriate variables. Let Anu's marbles be represented by A, then Eric has $A + 2$ marbles. Here the variable A represents a whole number since we are using it to represent number of marbles.
3.	"30 more than twice the quantity"	$2T + 30$	Julie was adding water to a tank at a rate of $2\ Liters/hour$. The tank had 30 $Liters$ already in it at the time she began adding water. Write an expression representing the amount of water in the tank after some number of hours. Let T represent the number hours Julie was adding water. Then $2T + 30$ Liters is the amount of water in the tank after T hours.
4.	"Twice as much as 3 more than the quantity"	$2(p + 3)$	Asha paid twice as much as three dollars more than the price Usha paid for her plane ticket because she waited until the last day to purchase her plane ticket. Let p represent the price of Usha's plane ticket. Than Asha's plane ticket costs $2(p + 3)$.

5.	"half of a quantity"	$\frac{1}{2}G$	Dan's car's fuel gauge shows that his gas tank is half full. Represent the number of gallons of fuel in Dan's car. Let G represent the capacity of the fuel tank in Dan's car. Dan's car has $\frac{1}{2}G$ gallons of gas.
6.	"37% of a quantity"	$0.37P$	Mary bought a shirt for 37% of the original price. Represent the sale price of Mary's. Let P represent the original price Mary's shirt. Then the sale price is $0.37P$.
7.	"x times as much as y"	xy	Represent the area of an arbitrary rectangle. Let x, and y represent the length and width respectively of a rectangle. (Using variables for length and width allows us to talk about any rectangle.) The area of the rectangle with these dimensions is xy square units.
8.	"x more than y"	$y + x$	Premium coffee at a convenience store always costs fifty cents more than the generic brand. State the price for a cup of premium coffee in terms of the generic price in cents and in dollars. Let G represent the price of a generic cup of coffee. The cost for a premium cup is given by: $G + 50$ or by $G + 0.5$ where G is the generic price given in cents or in dollars respectively .
9.	"x less than y"	$y - x$	Joe's salary was $12,500 dollars less than Patti's salary. Express Joe's salary in terms of Patti's. Let P represent Patti's salary. Then Joe's salary is given by $P - 12,500$.

10.	"r % of y"	$\frac{r}{100} \times y$	A store was having a sale where all items were marked down 15%. Write an expression that represents how much a general item was marked down.
			Let y be the original price of any general item. Then the amount of the markdown is given by $\frac{15}{100} \times y = 0.15 \times y$.
11.	"r percent more than y"	$y + \frac{r}{100} \cdot y$	The restaurant bill for groups is computed by adding a 22% as a tip.
			If we denote the original bill as y, then with the added tip is final amount due is given by $y + \frac{22}{100} \cdot y$ $\ or\ y + 0.22y$
12.	"r percent less than y"	$y - \frac{r}{100} \cdot y$	Paul's salary was 5% less than Rose's salary. Write an expression for Paul's salary in terms of Rose's.
			Let R represent Rose's salary. Then Paul's salary is Rose's minus 5% of Rose's, i.e., $R - 0.05R$.
13.	"x **is** at least as much as y"	$x \geq y$	Keith earns at least as much as Paul does.
			Let K and P represent Keith's and Paul's salaries. The above statement can be expressed as $K \geq P$.
14.	"x is at most as much as y"	$x \leq y$	The electric bill is at most as much as the phone bill.
			Let E represent the electric bill and P the phone bill. Algebraically, the above statement can be written as $E \leq P$.

Write an expression for each of the situations in examples below.

1. The length of a rectangle is two more than the width. Express the value of the length in terms of the width w.

2. The sale price of the shirt is 25% off of the regular price. Express the sale price in terms of the regular price R.

3. The price of gasoline increased by 15% from 2012 to 2013. Express the amount of the increase per gallon in terms of C which represents the 2012 cost of a gallon.

4. Write an expression for the perimeter of the polygon in terms of x, and y.

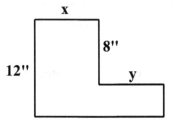

5. Sue walked for two thirds of the distance of the whole race. Express the distance Sue walked in terms of the total length of the race L.

6. The current price of a quart of maple syrup is 35% more than it was in 2008. Express the current price of maple syrup in terms of the 2008 price of M dollars per quart.

7. Joe bikes at least ten miles more than twice the distance he runs each week. Express this as an inequality where B and R represent the number of miles Joe bikes and runs each week.

8. A 48 inch plank has x inches cut off of it. Express the length of the plank remaining in terms of x.

9. Express as an algebraic expression. The product of eight more than a **number** and 11. Use x to represent the **number.**

10. Jean has $120 dollars to spend on food for a party. Give an expression for how much she has yet to spend after paying x dollars at the local Deli.

11. Jim is 5 years older than Bob and Karl is half of Bob's age. Write an expression for the sum of the three men's ages in terms of Bob's age B.

12. Glenn is two years younger than his brother Bob. Give an expression for Glenn's age in terms of Bob's age B.

There are many other places where algebraic expressions are used. Sometimes a connection between two algebraic expressions is made using equations. We will study more on equations in Module 3, but we introduce some basic formulas to find area, perimeter, and other such geometric measures below. We know some of this might be a review for you, but you will get to see an array of formulas with algebraic expressions showing you a part of their potential. See examples below.

Geometric Formulas and Examples

1. **Perimeter of a polygon** is the total length of the boundary surrounding a polygon.

Note: In general for any polygon just add up the lengths of all the sides of the polygon to get the perimeter.

Examples

2. Perimeter of a rectange of length x and width h is given by

$P = x + h + x + h = 2x + 2h$ units

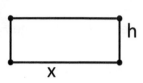

The perimeter of the given rectangle is $5 + 2 + 5 + 2 = 14$ units.

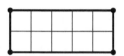

The perimeter of the given shape is
$2 + 3 + 1 + 1 + 1 + 2 + 1 + 1 + 1 + 2 + 2 + 2 + 2 + 2 + 2 + 5 = 30\ units$

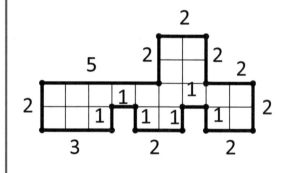

3. **Circumference of a circle** of radius R is given by $C = 2\pi R$ or $C = \pi D$, where D is the diameter of the circle or twice the radius and $\pi \approx 3.14$ is a constant.

Note: You can think of this as 3 strings as long as the diameter would almost reach around the circle.

Circumference of the given circle of radius 15 inches is $2\pi(15\ inches) = 30\pi\ inches \approx 94.2 inches$ *Note: The computations above are based on using the approximation of $3.14\ for\ \pi.$*	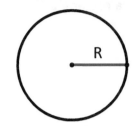

4. **Area** of a two dimensional shape is the number of square units the shape occupies.

5. **Area of a rectangle** of length x and width h is given by $A = xh$ squared units.	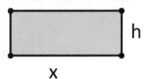
Area of the rectangle is $5 \times 2\ cm^2 = 10\ cm^2$	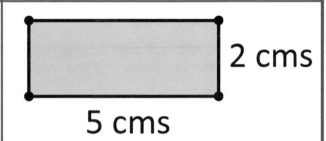
6. **Area of a square** of length l is given by $A = l^2$ squared units.	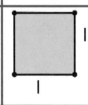

7. **Area of a parallelogram** of base x and height h is given by xh.

To understand why this formula works, look at how the picture is cut and put back together to form a rectangle.

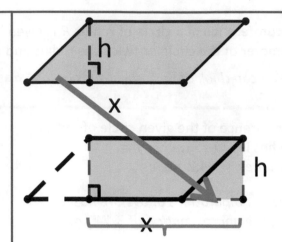

Area of the parallelogram is $4 \times 5\ yd^2 = 20\ yd^2$ since the height is perpendicular to the base which is 5 yds.

Note: It is important to know what information is given and what information in a problem is superfluous or not needed.

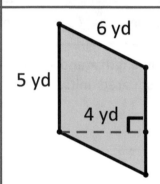

8. **Area of a triangle** with base x and height h is given by $A = \frac{1}{2}xh$.

This works because the area of any triangle is half that of a parallelogram that is constructed by creating a copy of the triangle and rotating it 180 degrees and joining the two triangles along the congruent side as shown.

The area of a triangle is half of the parallelogram.

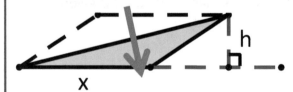

Area of the triangle is

$$\frac{1}{2}(7 \times 4)in^2 = \frac{1}{2}(28)\ in^2 = 14\ in^2$$

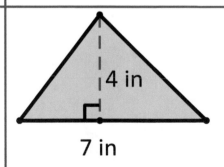

9. **Area of a trapezoid** with the two base lengths, a, b and height of h, is given by
$A = \frac{1}{2}(a + b)h$

This formula can be derived by breaking the trapezoid into smaller known polygons like triangles and rectangles.

Area of the trapezoid is

$$\frac{1}{2}(3 + 6)(4)in^2 = \frac{1}{2}(9)(4)\ in^2$$
$$= 18\ in^2$$

10. **Area of a circle** of radius R is given by $A = \pi R^2$ squared units

Area of the circle is $\pi(3^2) \approx 28.26\ cm^2$

11. **Surface area** of a 3 dimensional solid is the total external area of all the surfaces that enclose the solid.

12. **Surface area of a rectangular prism** of length x, width y, and height z is given by $A = 2xy + 2yz + 2xz$

The rectangular prism has 6 surfaces all made up of rectangles. The bottom/top rectangles both have area of xy squared units, the two left/right rectangles both have area of xz squared units, and the front/back rectangles both have area yz squared units. So the sum of all these areas gives the total surface area indicated by the formula.

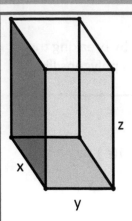

The surface area of the rectangular prism is

$$A = (2 \times 2 \times 4 + 2 \times 2 \times 7 + 2 \times 4 \times 7) \, ft^2$$
$$= (16 + 28 + 56) ft^2$$
$$= 100 \, ft^2$$

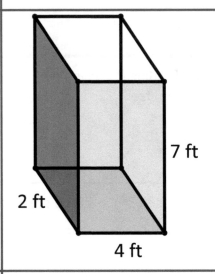

7 ft

2 ft

4 ft

13. **Surface area of a Cylinder** of radius r and length l is given by $A = 2\pi r^2 + 2\pi rl$. The $2\pi r^2$ is the area of the circular top and bottom, i.e., two circles. For the side, think of a tin can with the top and bottom removed. Make a cut parallel to the length of the can and then flatten this metal out into a rectangle. Its dimensions will be the can length times the distance around the rim of the can which is $2\pi r$. Thus the area of the lateral surface of the cylinder is $(2\pi r \times l)$.

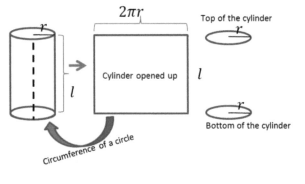

$A = 2\pi \cdot 2^2 + 2\pi \cdot 2 \cdot 12$ $\quad = 8\pi + 48\pi$ $\quad = 56\pi \; ft^2$	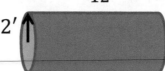 12' 2'

14. Volume is the amount of space in cubic units bounded by a closed shape 3-dimensional object.

15. Volume of a rectangular prism of length x, width y, and height z is given by $V = xyz$	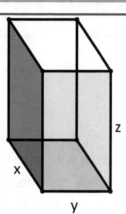 z x y
The volume of the rectangular prism is $V = (2 \times 4 \times 7)\; ft^3 = 56 \; ft^3$	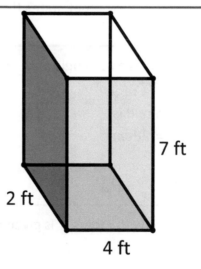 7 ft 2 ft 4 ft
16. Volume of a cube of length x is given by $\quad V = x^3$ You can see that the cube is a rectangular prism with the length, width and height all equal in measure.	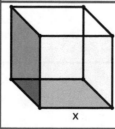 x

Volume of the cube is $$V = (5 \times 5 \times 5)ft^3 = 125\ ft^3$$	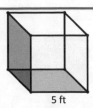 5 ft
17. Volume of a Cylinder of length l and radius r is given by $V = \pi r^2 l$.	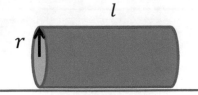 l r
$$V = \pi \cdot 2^2 \cdot 12$$ $$= 48\pi\ ft^3$$	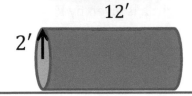 $12'$ $2'$

18. **Volume of a pyramid or a cone** with base area of B, and height h, is given by $V = \frac{1}{3}Bh$. We use an area formula for the base from above and substitute into this formula to get the volume. It is possible to slice a rectangular prism into three pyramids of equal volume. This supports the formula above that states the volume of a pyramid is a third of the volume of a prism.

The base of this pyramid is a rectangle with area of $(7 \times 4)cm^2 = 28\ cm^2$. The volume of the pyramid is $V = \frac{1}{3}(28 \times 3)cm^3 = 28cm^3$	Rectangular Pyramid 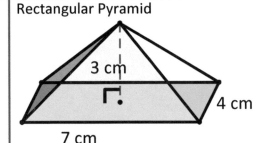 3 cm 4 cm 7 cm
19. **Volume of a sphere** with radius R is given by $$V = \frac{4}{3}\pi R^3$$	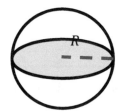
Volume of a sphere is $\frac{4}{3}\pi(3^3)in^3 = 113.04\ in^3$	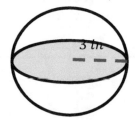

		Summary of the geometry formulas represented using algebraic expressions
1.		Perimeter of a polygon is the sum of all its lengths
2.		Perimeter of a rectangle of length l and width w is given by $P = 2l + 2w$
3.		Circumference of a circle of radius R is given by $C = 2\pi R$ or $C = \pi D$, where D is the diameter of the circle or twice the radius. *Note: You can think of this as almost 3.14 of strings as long as the diameter would fit along the circle.*
4.		Area of a rectangle of length x and width h is given by $A = xh$.
5.		Area of a square of length x is given by $A = x^2$
6.		Area of a parallelogram of base x and height h is given by $A = xh$
7.		Area of a triangle base x and height h is given by $A = \frac{1}{2}xh$
8.		Area of a trapezoid that with the two base lengths a, b and height of h, is given by $A = \frac{1}{2}(a + b)h$
9.		Area of a circle of radius r is $A = \pi r^2$
10.		Surface area of a rectangular prism of length x, width y, and height z is given by $A = 2xy + 2xz + 2yz$
11.		Surface area of a cylinder of radius r and length l is given by $A = 2\pi r^2 + 2\pi r l$.
12.		Volume of a rectangular prism of length x, width y, and height z is given by $V = xyz$
13.		Volume of a cylinder of length l and radius r is given by $V = \pi r^2 l$
14.		Volume of a cube of length x is given by $V = x^3$
15.		Volume of a pyramid or cone with base area of B, and height h, is given by $V = \frac{1}{3}Bh$
16.		Volume of a sphere with radius R is given by $V = \frac{4}{3}\pi R^3$

	Find the following
1.	Find the perimeter of the polygon. 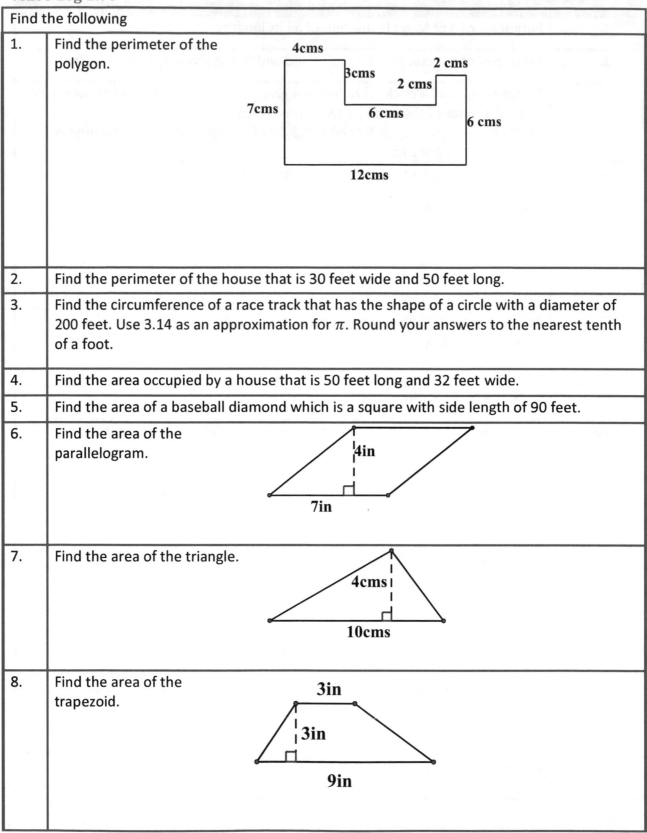
2.	Find the perimeter of the house that is 30 feet wide and 50 feet long.
3.	Find the circumference of a race track that has the shape of a circle with a diameter of 200 feet. Use 3.14 as an approximation for π. Round your answers to the nearest tenth of a foot.
4.	Find the area occupied by a house that is 50 feet long and 32 feet wide.
5.	Find the area of a baseball diamond which is a square with side length of 90 feet.
6.	Find the area of the parallelogram.
7.	Find the area of the triangle.
8.	Find the area of the trapezoid.

9.	Find the surface area and volume of a matchbox (shaped as a rectangular prism) that is 2cms by 4cms by 5cms.
10.	Find the volume of a model pyramid that has a square base of 4feet by 4feet and is 6 feet tall.
11.	Find the volume of a conical pile of sand (sand pile in shape of an inverted cone) that has a base diameter of 6 feet and is 2 feet tall. Use 3.14 as an approximation for π. Round your answers to the nearest tenth of a cubic foot.
12.	Find the volume of a grapefruit with diameter of 9 cm. Assume that a grapefruit is a perfect sphere. Use 3.14 as an approximation for π. Round your answers to the nearest tenth of a cubic cm.
13.	Find the volume and total surface area of a cylindrical pontoon that is two feet in diameter and 20 feet long.
14.	A rectangular swimming pool is 30 feet long and 15 feet wide. A contractor is to replace a ceramic tile deck that is six feet wide surrounding the pool. Determine how many square feet of decking material is needed.
15.	Draw at least three rectangles all with the same perimeter of 40 units. Also compute the area of each and speculate on what the largest area might be.
16.	Draw at least three rectangles all with area of 24 square units. Also compute the perimeter of each and speculate which rectangle of area 24 square units would have the smallest perimeter.

1.10 Functions

Function Notation
Lecture

💻 Introduction to Functions

http://www.youtube.com/watch?v=GHR4QiPoBi8 (11 min)

We very often consider how different things are related in many situations in every-day life. Some examples include: each person is related to their biological mother; the price of gas in $\frac{\$}{gal}$ is related to time; temperature in Fahrenheit degrees is related to temperature in Celsius degrees; your height in inches is related to your age in years; the profit of an automaker is related to the annual car sales; the number of movie ticket sales at a theater is related to the ticket price. Many of these relationships can be quantified using numerical measures of each related quantity, e.g. the height of a person in inches on his birthday is related to his age in years, or the relationship between Fahrenheit and Celsius temperatures is given by the equation $°F = \frac{9}{5}°C + 32$ for any value of °C.

The connections between different quantities can be referred to as **relations**.

Oftentimes we think of a direction in the relation in that when the value of one quantity (called an input) is known, this determines a value of the second quantity (called an output).

A **function** is a directed relation where every individual input has a unique output.

We will focus on relations between two items or characteristics that are connected to each other. For example, think of the students in a class and their height in inches. We could represent these data as a set of ordered pairs or as a table.

A={(Robert,72),(Sarah,61), (Matt,70), (Robin,61),(Sarah, 65)}

Name of Student	Height in Inches
Robert	72
Sarah	61
Matt	70
Robin	61
Sarah	65

In the data pairs above, two people could have different names and have the same height. Also two people can have the same name but different heights, or two could have the same height and the same name with a larger class. The way this data is presented suggests that the name of the person is the "input", while the height of that person is the "output".

Clearly the relation above is not a function, since the single input "Sarah" has two different outputs 61" and 65". Note that if the input column included middle initial, e.g., B={(Robert A, 72),(Sarah K, 61), (Matt L, 70), (Robin P , 61),(Sarah M, 65)}, then each input has a single output and B would be a functional relation of the form $(name, height)$. However the relation B in the other direction from height to name would not be a function since in that direction, the input of 61" yields two different names!

Consider the sister relationship where any person with one or more sisters is the input and that person's sister(s) is the output. Since there are people who have more than one sister, this is not a function relationship. Next, consider the biological mother relationship where any person is an input and the output is that person's biological mother. Explain why this is a function. Note if we reverse the direction of this Mother relation, it is not a function, i.e., starting with an input of a mother with more than one child, that mother would give rise to at least two different outputs (her children).

Another way to express some relations and functions is through an equation with two variables. For example, $y = 3x + 1$, where the input x is any real number, and y is the corresponding output number. This is a relation between x and y that is a function since for any value of the input x, there is only one output, namely $y = 3x + 1$. We'd say this equation represents a function from x to y. In the relation $y^2 = x$, where input x is any nonnegative real number, y is not a function of x, since the input of $x = 4$ will yield two different outputs $y = 2$, $y = -2$.

In order to distinguish two different functions like $y = 3x + 1$ and $y = x - 5$, we need a notation that clearly describes the two "y"s as being different. We use the notation $f(x) = 3x + 1$ and $g(x) = x - 5$ where we are giving names of f and g to these two different functional relations. We would read that as "f of x is $3x + 1$" and "g of x is $x - 5$". We could also write this as e.g., $y = f(x) = 3x + 1$ which identifies the function equation $y = 3x + 1$ with the function name f. It is very important to make sure you learn to read and process this notation correctly. Many students who make mistakes in working with functions confuse the notation $f(x)$ with f times x. Remember that the notation $f(x)$ is NOT read as f times x. You can think of it as $f(\_\_\_)$, and the blank can be filled in with many different inputs.

In the notation $f(x) = 3x + 1$, f is the name of the function, and x is called the input or argument, $f(x)$ refers to the output. This statement simply says that the function f computes its outputs by multiplying an input by 3 and then adding 1.

Domain and Range of a Function

The collection of all the input x values we can have in a function so that the output is well defined is called the **domain** of the function. The collection of all the output values of a function is called the **range** of the function.

Working with Domain and Range of a Function or a Relation

Playing

Remember there cannot be a function or a relation without having a domain and range. In mathematics we are always trying to use our imagination to see what all possibilities are in every new scenario.

Some questions to ask are

1. What kinds of sets of objects we can be used for domains and ranges. Try to come up with functions for each of the domains: {All the houses in the city you live in}, {All the employees at the school you are attending}, {All the days in time since you were born}.
2. Do functions have to have one input and one output, or could we have multiple inputs and one unique output? For example can you think of a function perhaps given by an equation where the output depends on two separate real numbers as inputs?

Before you continue reading, spend some time just thinking and trying to answer these questions. There are many different answers. Try being creative and see what you can come up with.

A function of one variable means the input can be described by just one variable, e.g., $f(x) = 3x + 1$. When a function has multiple inputs and one output we call it a function of several variable. For example, the volume of a box is a function of three variables, its length l, its width w and its height h and we might write this as $V = f(l, w, h) = l \cdot w \cdot h$. The domain of a function can be anything you want it to be from a finite set of objects to infinite sets. We will mostly work with functions of a single variable in this book.

Next we develop some notation and conventions on how work with functions efficiently. Any letter really can represent the single input. For example, we may use letters like $x, or\ t$ to represent an input to a function. Similarly we use a different letter to represent the corresponding single output, e.g., y, or z might represent the output of a function. The functional relationship itself will often be denoted by the letter f or some other appropriate letter. A statement like $y = f(x)$ simply says that y represents an output, x an input and they are related by the function called f. (Remember that this is not saying to multiply f by x!) To define what this relationship is, we'd have to elaborate on the meaning of y and x and how y and x are related perhaps by some equation. We can also look at the function notation as follows where the object x is transformed by the application of the function f to become a new object called $f(x)$ (read as f of x)

$$x \xrightarrow{f} f(x)$$

This notation is credited to the mathematician Leonard Euler and was developed around 1734.

To denote what kind of function we are working with mathematicians may use the notation shown below. Writing $f: \mathbb{R} \to \mathbb{R}$ to means we have a real number as an input and also a real number as the output. Such a function is called a real valued function of one variable. Writing $f: \mathbb{R} \times \mathbb{R} \to \mathbb{R}$ to mean the function f is taking an ordered pair of real numbers and transforming them into a real number. Such a function is called a real valued function of two variables. Functions can have as many input variables as needed. Writing $f: \mathbb{R}^n \to \mathbb{R}$ to means we have an n-tuple as an input and output is a real number.

We can represent functions in many ways. Below are some of the ways.

a) Using function notation as described above.
    1 $f(x) = x^2$
       Here the domain is set of all real numbers and range is set of all non-negative real numbers.
    2 $f(x, y) = x^2 + y^2$
       Here the domain is the set of tuples of the type (x, y) with x and y both real numbers and the range is the set of all non-negative real numbers.
    3 $f(t) = 2t - 5$
       Here the domain is set of all real numbers and range is the set of all real numbers.

b) As a set of objects. For example,
    1. $f: \{(2, -1), (4,2), (3,2), (0,4)\}$.
       Read this is as when input is 2 output is -1, input is 0 output is 4 and so on. Here the domain is the set $\{2,4,3,0\}$ and the range is the set $\{-1,2,4\}$ as you can see we did not write the number 2 in the range twice.
    2. $f: \{(x, y) | y = x^2, x \in R\}$. Read this as f is the function that is a collection of all ordered tuples of the type (x, y) in which $y = x^2$ and x is a real number. Here the domain is the set of all real numbers and range is set of all non-negative real numbers.

c) As formulas or equations in two or more variables. For example,
    1. $y = x^2$
       Here the domain is the set of all real numbers and range is set of all non-negative real numbers.
    2. $z = x^2 + y^2$ Here the domain is the set of tuples of the type (x, y) with x and y both real numbers and the range is the set of all non-negative real numbers.

d) As English sentences modeling scenarios. For example,
    1. Linda's parents loaned her 12,480 dollars interest free for her college tuition and books. Linda promised to pay her parents back 80 dollars a week until the loan is completely paid off. Write an equation that will allow Linda a quick overview of how much money she owes her parents in a particular week before it is all paid off.
       The equation would look like Amount owed by Linda $12480 - 80 \times$ $(number\ of\ weeks)$
       Here domain is all whole numbers less than or equal to $\frac{12480}{80} = 156$ and range is all whole between zero and 12480 which are multiples of 80.
    2. The period of a pendulum is proportional to the square root of its length. Here domain is set of all non-zero real numbers and range is also set of non-zero real numbers.

e) As graphs.

1.

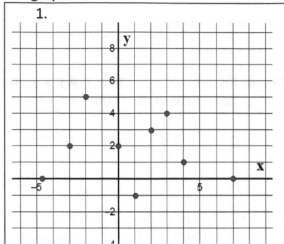

Input is the x coordinate of the point and output is the y coordinate of the point. For example input of -2 will give you output of 5 since $(-2,5)$ is a point plotted above. Here domain is $\{-5,-3,-2,0,1,2,3,4,7\}$ and range is $\{-1,0,1,2,3,4,5\}$.

2.

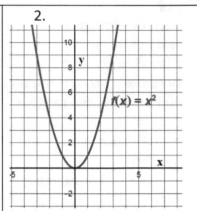

Input is the x coordinate of a point on the graph of the function $f(x) = x^2$, then output is the y coordinate of that point. For example input of -2 will give you output of 4 since $(-2,4)$ is a point on the graph above. Here the domain is the set of all real numbers and range is set of all non-negative real numbers.

Playing

If we say $f(x) = 3x + 1$, then that means that we really have

$$f(\underline{\hspace{1cm}}) = 3 \times (\underline{\hspace{1cm}}) + 1$$

That means if you are asked to evaluate the following you must replace the blank above with whatever takes its place in the notation

$$f(\underline{\uparrow}) = 3 \times (\underline{\uparrow}) + 1$$
$$f(COLD) = 3 \times (COLD) + 1$$

$$f(2) = 3 \times (2) + 1 = 6 + 1 = 7$$
$$f(100) = 3 \times (100) + 1 = 300 + 1 = 301$$
$$f(a) = 3(a) + 1 = 3a + 1$$

$$f(a + h) = 3(a + h) + 1$$

See if you can use these examples to work on the following practice problems.

Practice Examples

1. $y = M(x)$ The output y is the biological mother of the input x. Also, $M(Paul\ Martin) = Marcella\ Martin$ which says that this "biological mother of person" function takes as input $x =$ Paul Martin and his biological mother is $y =$ Marcella Martin. Could there be inputs other than $x =$ *Paul Martin* that make $M(x) = Marcella\ Martin$?

2. $°F = T(°C) = \frac{9}{5}°C + 32$. This statement is a description of the $°C \rightarrow °F$ conversion function. The input is the temperature in $°C$, the output is the temperature in $°F$ and the name of the function is T. In this course our functions usually will be defined in this way, i.e. $y = f(x) =$(some algebraic formula involving x). Also note that a function is the relation between input and output and that $f(x) = \frac{9}{5}x + 32$ is the same function as $T(°C) = \frac{9}{5}°C + 32$ since they have all the same ordered pairs.

3. $V = \frac{4}{3}\pi r^3$ is the volume formula when the radius of a ball is known. This is a polynomial function. We might call this function simply V in which case we'd have $V = V(r) = \frac{4}{3}\pi r^3$ where we use the same variable to denote an output and the name of the relationship. Likewise, the *area of a circle* function can be expressed as $A = A(r) = \pi r^2$.

4. The height of a baseball might be given by $y = h(t) = 2 + 160t - 16t^2$ where y is the height above the ground in feet and t is the number of seconds after the ball is hit by the bat and h is the name of this relationship between time and height. This is also an example of a polynomial function. This notation allows us to easily describe the height at several different times, e.g. $h(2) = 258$ says that when the input is 2 seconds, the height is 258 feet. Other questions can also be stated easily using this notation, e.g., "determine when $h(t) = 100$" says that the output of the height function is 100 and we are to find the input t when this happens. You could try guessing and checking to find out that this happens at $t \approx 0.66 sec, and\ t \approx 9.34\ sec$. More direct methods of doing this will be developed in Module 3.

5. Another type of function that is often useful is called an exponential function where the input is actually in the exponent. For example $P(t) = 6(1.012)^t$ might be used as a model of the world's population t years after 2000 where the output is in billions of people. $P(25) = 6(1.012)^{25} \approx 8.085 \; billion.$ That means the prediction for number of people in the year 2025 is 8.085 billion people.

6. Let $f(x) = 7x^2 + 1$ and $g(t) = \sqrt{t} + 7$. Then
    a. $f(4) = 7 \cdot 4^2 + 1 = 7 \cdot 16 + 1 = 113$
    b. $f(a+h) = 7 \cdot (a+h)^2 + 1$
    c. $f(-2) = 7 \cdot (-2)^2 + 1 = 7 \cdot 4 + 1 = 29$
    d. $g(a+1) = \sqrt{a+1} + 7$
    e. $g(4) = \sqrt{4} + 7 = 9$
    f. $f(3) + g(a) = 7 \cdot (3)^2 + 1 + \sqrt{a} + 7 = 63 + 1 + \sqrt{a} + 7 = 71 + \sqrt{a}$

7. $S(c)$=social security number of person c. Here all U.S. citizens or legal aliens in the U.S. is the domain, and all the social security numbers given out forms the range of the function.

8. For all real numbers x, we define a new object called **absolute value** of x (denoted as $|x|$) to mean the distance from the number x to zero on a number line. For example $|-2| = 2$ and $|2| = 2$.
    So $Absolute(t) = |t|$ represents the absolute value function. And
    $Absolute \; (-3.1) = 3.1,$
    $Absolute(0) = 0,$
    $Absolute(-100) = 100$
    $Absolute(100) = 100.$
    $Absolute(-1200) = 1200$
    $Absolute(1400) = 1400$

Vertical Line Test:
The graph of a relation is a function if and only if any vertical line intersects the graph in one or less points.

Examples

1. Below y **is** a function of x as it passes the vertical line test.

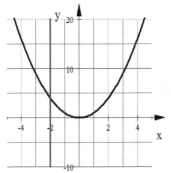

As you can see from the graph above any vertical line will intersect the graph in only one point.

2. Below y **is not** function of x as it does not pass the vertical line test.

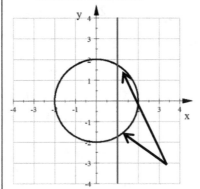

3. Below y **is** a function of x as it passes the vertical line test.

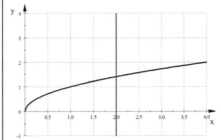

As you can see from the graph above any vertical line will intersect the graph in only one point.

Types of Functions
Lecture

🖥 Functions

http://www.youtube.com/watch?v=AORKWOJWM4A (5 min)

A list of commonly used functions with special names is given below.

Name of the function	Examples
Constant Function: Output is the same constant no matter what the input.	1. If $f(x) = 5$, $f\left(\frac{2}{3}\right) = 5$, $f(100) = 5$ $f(-3456) = 5$ $f(a + h) = 5$
Square root function: Output is the nonnegative square root of the input. The domain is all non-negative real numbers.	2. If $g(x) = \sqrt{x}$, $g\left(\frac{2}{3}\right) = \sqrt{\frac{2}{3}}$, $g(100) = \sqrt{100} = 10$ $g(3456) = \sqrt{3456}$ $g(a + h) = \sqrt{a + h}$
Exponential Function: The input x is a real number, and the output is the value of the number a^x for a fixed positive real number $a \neq 1$.	3. If $E(x) = 2^x$ $E\left(\frac{2}{3}\right) = 2^{\frac{2}{3}}$, $E(100) = 2^{100}$ $E(-3456) = 2^{-3456}$ $E(a + h) = 2^{a+h}$
Polynomial Function: The input is a real number, the output is the value of polynomial when inserting the input number for the variable.	4. $P(x) = 3x^2 - 5x + 7$ $P(2) = 3(2^2) - 5(2) + 7$ $\qquad = 3(4) - 10 + 7$ $\qquad = 12 - 10 + 7 = 9$, or $P(2) = 9$ $P(0) = 3(0)^2 - 5(0) + 7 = 7$ $P(a + h) = 3(a + h)^2 - 5(a + h) + 7$
Rational Function: As the word suggests this function is a fraction that has polynomials for its numerator and denominator. The inputs are all real numbers so that the denominator remains non-zero	5. $R(x) = \frac{3x+1}{x-1}, x \neq 1$ *(need to have x cannot equal 1 to make the function well defined)* $R(4) = \frac{3(4) + 1}{4 - 1} = \frac{12 + 1}{3} = \frac{13}{3}$ $R(a + h) = \frac{3(a + h) + 1}{a + h - 1}$

1. Think of two relations where the domain is all the students in your current math class one which is a function and the other which is not a function. Describe clearly what the output is for each of your relations and explain why one is a function and the other is not.

2. Consider the relation between set A being $\{1,2,3,....365\}$ and set B being the official high temperature at Madison, WI on that day in 2016 degrees Fahrenheit.
   a. Explain whether or not this relation is a function when A is the domain
   b. Explain whether or not the relation is a function when B is the domain.

3. Create a function so that the input is a real number and output is a constant of 5. Write your answer in function notation.

4. Let $f(x) = 3x + 1$, $g(t) = \sqrt{5}$, $R(s) = \frac{3s+4}{s-6}$, and $h(a) = \sqrt[3]{a}$, find the value of

   a. $f(5)$ d. $R(1)$ g. $g(-5)$

   b. $g(100)$ e. $-h(8)$ h. $R(0)$

   c. $f(a)$ f. $h(1)$ i. $g(a+h)$

Extra Credit Questions

5. Can you think of a function $f(x)$ for which no matter what x is, the output is always 1? What would the function formula look like?

6. Can you think of a function $g(x)$ so that for any two real numbers a and b, if $a < b$, then $g(a) < g(b)$?

7. Can you think of a function $h(x)$ so that for any two real numbers a and b, if $a < b$, then $h(a) > h(b)$?

This completes module one. We started out with number systems, beginning with counting numbers and extending on through whole numbers, integers, fractions, rational and irrational numbers, real numbers, decimal numbers, and complex numbers. We also looked at numbers as ratios, and percentages. We then introduced the notation of a base and exponent. Then we extended from whole number to fractional exponents and the corresponding equivalent radical notation for fractional exponents. Finally we described polynomials, rational expressions and functions.

In the next module we extend arithmetic operations of addition, subtraction, multiplication and division on numbers to these mathematical objects and also standard conventions for simplifying them.

Module 2: Arithmetic of Algebraic Objects

Introduction

In this module we review the basic ideas of addition, subtraction, multiplication and division of integers and decimal numbers and extend these ideas to establish the arithmetic of all the algebraic objects we introduced in module one, i.e., Complex Numbers, Polynomials, Rational Expressions, Radical Expressions, and Functions.

So far we have developed the terminology and notation to represent many different mathematical objects. Now we will learn how to form new objects by combining one or more of these objects in various ways much like kids create assemblies using all of their toys. Any time we encounter more than one object, the human tendency is to combine these objects in a particular order depending on their specific attributes. Some objects just can't be combined with others. Some objects can be converted by using equivalent forms so that they can be combined with others.

In what follows we will establish what types of algebraic objects can be meaningfully combined using different operations. In all of this, it is most important to have consistent rules across different objects and pay careful attention to what attributes we are using to compare or combine objects. The attribute of critical interest when combining different objects is their <u>unit</u>, e.g., an object representing area $4ft^2$, or length $4\,ft$, or velocity $50\frac{ft}{s}$ or time $3\,hrs$ can only be combined with certain other objects in certain ways.

In this module we study the arithmetic operations for combining two or more objects within a specific structure of the set of objects we are working on. The field of study in mathematics called Abstract Algebra studies a variety of different operations and how they create a certain structure on the collection of objects that are studied. The discussion in this module will lay a necessary foundation to access the higher level abstraction in calculus and other higher-level courses in mathematics.

2.1 Addition as Combining "Like" Units

You may want to watch the lectures below before starting to read the next section.

Lecture

💻 Identifying Like Units

http://www.youtube.com/watch?v=Zqzb5VpogNs (6 min)

Before we go into the definition of what addition is or what the meaning of addition is, we would like you to think about in your own words what addition is.

In our everyday use of numbers we always use them to measure how much there is of some quantity, e.g., time, distance, or how many of some type of thing there are. When numbers are used in this manner they always have some kind of unit attached to them.

Definition: Addition is a **binary operation** and is denoted by the $+$ sign, which means it acts on **two** objects with specific rules. The objects themselves are called <u>addends or summands</u>, and each must have the same units in order to be combined through addition.

For example combining two finite collections of distinct objects into a new collection represents addition of counting numbers. When you can start with counting numbers you might get a sense of how they are built on this concept of addition. If you think of the counting number one, it refers to a way to represent a collection of a single unit. The counting number two refers to a way to represent a collection of objects that is one additional unit more than the number of objects required to represent one. In this manner we count upwards using the process of addition.

Like Units

In order for this concept of addition to be meaningful, the two numbers involved must refer to the same unit. Thus the saying "you can't add apples and oranges." Two apples plus three apples is five apples, and two oranges plus three oranges is five oranges. But two oranges plus three apples is?? This last statement could be given meaning if the unit is understood to be a piece of fruit, in which case two oranges plus three apples is really "two pieces of fruit together with three pieces of fruit gives a sum of five pieces of fruit."

You can add two or more objects only if they have the same units. The use of $+$ notation to denote addition actually began in the 1500's. Almost 5000 years ago there is evidence of using the preposition "to" for addition and "from" for subtraction.

Practice Examples
Answer true or false for the examples shown below.
1. $5ft + 15ft = 20ft$
2. $5ft + 6in = 11$
3. $5ft + 6in = 60in + 6in = 66in$
4. $10cm + 5cm^3 = 15cm^4$

Solutions
1. True, both terms have the same units which are the same as the units on the sum.
2. False, the units are different on the 5 and the 6.
3. True, $1ft = 12in$, $5ft = 60in$.
4. False, units of distance and volume can't be added.

Video Log 2.1a

Answer whether the statements below are true or false.
1. $5in + 3in = 8$
2. $5in + 3 = 8$
3. $5in + 3in + 7in = 15in$
4. $5ft + 3in + 4in = 12$
5. $5ft + 3in + 4in = 60in + 3in + 4in = 67in$

Like Units

It is important to learn how to interpret the mathematical objects you saw in Module 1. For example when we say '2 *apples*' we think of a collection of two apples. If we say '$2x$' it has the same meaning as the '2 *apples*' except now we are thinking of it as a collection of two x's. When you first learned how to add counting numbers, you started by counting your way up from the first number as many as the second number. Thus, in the problem $2 + 3$, we start at the number 2 and count three up so that would be 3,4,5 and since we ended on 5 our answer to the question $2 + 3$ would be 5. This allows us to count other things in the same manner, for example, consider a basket with two apples and you added three additional apples to the basket. How many apples are then in the basket? The problem can be rewritten as '2 *apples* + 3 *apples*', and we could count up 3 more apples giving us a total of 5 *apples* in the basket. So an apple is a unit in the problem just discussed. Similarly then, we can say $2x + 3x = 5x$ so x is acting like a unit, or in $2\sqrt{x} + 3\sqrt{x} = 5\sqrt{x}$ we have that $\sqrt{x}$ acts as a unit. So it is important that you learn to identify objects with the same unit.

Practice Examples

1. Identify the like terms in each deck below and write one expression to represent how many of each of the units your deck has. For example, $x^2 = \frac{1}{x^{-2}} = x \cdot x$ are all equivalent forms of x^2, and so if I had the four cards on the left as shown below, my answer would be $11x^2$. As another example, $1m = 100cm = 0.001km$ are all equivalent forms of $1m$, and so if I had the cards as shown on the right below, my answer would be 75m. So the expression representing my cards would be

$$2x^2 + \frac{3}{x^{-2}} + 5x \cdot x + \frac{1}{\frac{1}{x^2}} + 200cm + 0.07km + 3m = 11x^2 + 75m$$

Deck Cards Sorted out

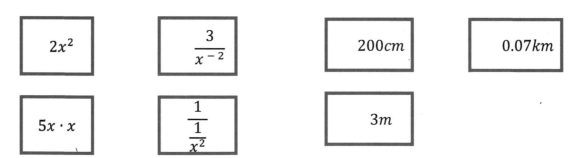

This exercise is to show you that you can use your instincts to decide which objects share the same units and then check if your instinct has good sound mathematical reasoning. You might think this above exercise pointless but it serves a purpose in your cognitive processing of what objects can be combined through addition.

You can see why mastery of Module 1 is necessary so you can identify objects with the same units before actually doing the addition process. You will get more practice as we go through this module in determining like units and at times converting an object to an equivalent object so you can perform arithmetic operations on it.

Video Log 2.1b

1. Identify the like terms in each deck below and write one expression to represent how many of each of the units your deck has.

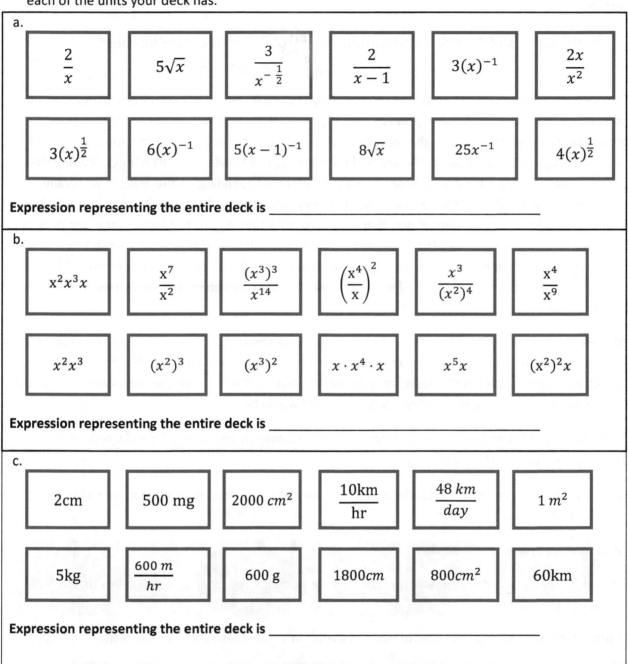

a.

$\dfrac{2}{x}$	$5\sqrt{x}$	$\dfrac{3}{x^{-\frac{1}{2}}}$	$\dfrac{2}{x-1}$	$3(x)^{-1}$	$\dfrac{2x}{x^2}$
$3(x)^{\frac{1}{2}}$	$6(x)^{-1}$	$5(x-1)^{-1}$	$8\sqrt{x}$	$25x^{-1}$	$4(x)^{\frac{1}{2}}$

Expression representing the entire deck is _____

b.

$x^2 x^3 x$	$\dfrac{x^7}{x^2}$	$\dfrac{(x^3)^3}{x^{14}}$	$\left(\dfrac{x^4}{x}\right)^2$	$\dfrac{x^3}{(x^2)^4}$	$\dfrac{x^4}{x^9}$
$x^2 x^3$	$(x^2)^3$	$(x^3)^2$	$x \cdot x^4 \cdot x$	$x^5 x$	$(x^2)^2 x$

Expression representing the entire deck is _____

c.

2cm	500 mg	$2000\ cm^2$	$\dfrac{10\text{km}}{\text{hr}}$	$\dfrac{48\ km}{day}$	$1\ m^2$
5kg	$\dfrac{600\ m}{hr}$	600 g	$1800cm$	$800cm^2$	60km

Expression representing the entire deck is _____

2. *Create a deck of cards for which the reduced expression is below. Your deck must have a minimum of 6 cards. All cards must be distinct terms (enough so that there are a variety of representations of each of the three terms).*

$$5\sqrt{x} + 30x^4 - 7x^{\frac{1}{3}}$$

Properties of Addition
Lecture

🖥 Properties of Addition and Introduction to Adding Decimal Numbers

http://www.youtube.com/watch?v=b12XsziOpJA (10 min)

The addition operation between two or more real numbers has several important properties that we don't often think about, but these properties justify many of our standard methods for doing arithmetic. Consider for example that you are buying milk and eggs at a store. The cashier might add up your bill by adding the cost of milk first and then the eggs, or maybe the cost of eggs first and then the milk. Do you expect the bill of these items to be different depending on the order in which the items were added? Of course we don't, or we'd be very careful about how we place the items at the checkout counter. This example reflects that the cost of milk then eggs is the same as the cost of eggs then milk. We can use variables to represent the cost of our milk and eggs, so that we can talk about this property more generally and extend it to other objects besides grocery items. Let m stand for the cost of milk and e stand for the cost of eggs. Then what is described above can be written in mathematical language as $m + e = e + m$.

You can see this property when you think of our apple example from before - if you had two apples in a basket and then added three more apples to the basket the basket would have five apples. If you started with three apples in the basket and then added two additional apples in the basket, you would have five apples in the basket. Another way to say that would be

$2 apples + 3 apples = 3 apples + 2 apples = 5 apples$. Similarly we can say $2x + 3x = 3x + 2x = 5x$ or $2\sqrt{x} + 3\sqrt{x} = 3\sqrt{x} + 2\sqrt{x} = 5\sqrt{x}$

This property of real numbers extends to all the mathematical objects you have learned so far and can be written as follows.

Commutative Property of Addition

If a and b are any two mathematical objects we have studied so far, then $a + b = b + a$ (a and b are referred to as summands).

In other words: Changing the order of two summands in a sum doesn't change the result.

Terminology: Addition is commutative.

Remembering the names of the properties is going to be important. Cognitively it will help you rationalize your steps when you are working with mathematical problems. Being able to articulate, speak and write correctly in mathematics as we mentioned in Module 0 is extremely important. This kind of training will help you become more aware and conscious of your reasoning. We recommend you add the name of this property and what it means to your list at the end of your notebook as mentioned in the Module 0.

A natural question that may come to your mind is: What can we do if we have more than two mathematical objects to be added? Does the order in which you add these numbers matter? To think of this, let us start with three counting numbers. Consider the situation where Laura and her husband Paul are going to a recycling yard to get paid for aluminum cans, milk jugs, and newspaper. Let c stand for the amount of money received for the cans, m for the amount for the milk jugs, and n for the amount for the newspaper. In one scenario, Paul takes the cans and Laura the milk jugs and newspaper, and then they combine the money received. The total amount of money received in this scenario would be written as $c + (m + n)$. Another scenario would be for Paul to take both the cans and the milk jugs and Laura just the newspaper. The total amount of money received in this second scenario would be indicated by $(c + m) + n$. Our intuition is that in both scenarios, Laura and Paul would receive the same total amount for their recyclables.

Similarly $(3apples + 2apples) + 4apples$ suggests that you add the three apples and the 2 apples first to give you five apples and then add an additional 4 apples giving you a total of 9 apples. But if we had $3apples + (2apples + 4apples)$ we first add the 4 apples to the 2 apples giving us 6 apples and then adding that to the 3 apples giving us 9 apples. So again we have $(3apples + 2apples) + 4apples = 3apples + (2apples + 4apples)$. In the same fashion we also have:

$$(3x + 2x) + 4x = 3x + (2x + 4x) \text{ or } \left(3\sqrt{x} + 2\sqrt{x}\right) + 4\sqrt{x} = 3\sqrt{x} + \left(2\sqrt{x} + 4\sqrt{x}\right).$$

This addition property of real numbers extends to all the mathematical objects you have learned so far and can be written as follows.

Associative Property of Addition

If $a, b,$ and c represent any three mathematical objects we have studied so far that have a common unit, then

$(a + b) + c = a + (b + c)$.

In other words: Changing the grouping of the summands in a sum doesn't change the result.

Terminology: Addition is associative.

This property not only gives us a way to add more than two numbers, we can use it to our advantage when adding large numbers. For example, consider the problem $(246 + 897) + 3$. Instead of doing this problem, if we were to add $246 + (897 + 3)$, it might make our work easier since $897 + 3 =$

900, and it might be easier to add $246 + 900 = 1146$. An even simpler example is when adding 7+8, we can think of 8 as 3+5, and then $7 + 8 = 7 + (3 + 5) = (7 + 3) + 5 = 15$.

Note: *The commutative and associative property of addition allow us to add any number of objects and in any order.*

To see that, let's take a look at addition of 3 whole numbers $2, 3, and\ 7$. We can't add all the numbers at once, but we show that we can add them in any of six possible orders. To add numbers in the order 2, 3, 7, we will have to use $(2 + 3) + 7 = 5 + 7 = 12$. To add numbers in the order 2, 7, 3 we will have to use $(2 + 3) + 7 = 2 + (3 + 7) = 2 + (7 + 3) = (2 + 7) + 3 = 9 + 3 = 12$ (associative and commutative property of addition, then associative property of addition). To add numbers in the order 3, 2, 7 we have to use: $(2 + 3) + 7 = (3 + 2) + 7 = 5 + 7 = 12$ (commutative property of addition). To add numbers in the order 3, 7, 2, we will have to use $(3 + 2) + 7 = 3 + (2 + 7) = 3 + (7 + 2) = (3 + 7) + 2 = 10 + 2 = 12$ (associative, commutative, and associative property of addition respectively). To add numbers in the order 7, 2, 3 we will have to use $(2 + 3) + 7 = 7 + (2 + 3) = (7 + 2) + 3 = 9 + 3 = 12$ (commutative, associative property of addition). Finally, to add numbers in the order 7, 3, 2 we will have to use $7 + (2 + 3) = 7 + (3 + 2) = (7 + 3) + 2 = 10 + 2 = 12$ (commutative then associative property of addition). In this manner we can see that we can add three numbers in any order and get the same result. A mathematician would extend these observations to a more general statement than just adding three terms. In a finite sum (that means adding a finite number of terms) of mathematical objects you have learned so far, the order in which you add them does not matter. This fact is based on using the commutative and associative properties of addition.

If we add zero to any real number, you know the number remains unchanged. This also happens to all the mathematical objects we have studied so far.

Additive Identity:

If we let a represent any mathematical object that we have studied so far, $a + 0 = a$ and $0 + a = a$.

In other words: Adding 0 to any mathematical object leaves that mathematical object unchanged.

Terminology: The number 0 is the additive identity.

This property may seem a bit useless, but it turns out to be an extremely important property in our decimal numeration system. It allows us to add or subtract expressions that have terms with different units. For example, to add $(3mi + 185yd + 6in) + (8mi + 2ft)$, we can write it as $(3mi + 185yd + 0\ ft + 6in) + (8mi + 0yd + 2ft + 0in)$. This allows us to quickly see how each of the units are lined up. We can group the like units together which easily shows us that $(3mi + 185yd + 0\ ft + 6in) + (8mi + 0yd + 2ft + 0in) = 11mi + 185yd + 2ft + 6in$.

Here zero was used as a place holder for the missing units. It also allows us to prove some other properties that are discussed a little later.

1. Identify all the properties of real numbers that justifies each equation a.-d. Please enter the property number i-iii in the box provided below. Properties to select from are listed below.

i. Commutative property of addition	ii. Associative property of addition
iii. Additive identity of addition	

Equation	Property	Equation	Property
a. $5 + x = x + 5$		b. $513 + 0 = 513$	
c. $3 + (7 + 8) = (3 + 7) + 8$		d. $12 + (3 + 8) = (12 + 8) + 3$	

2. Evaluate the following. When necessary rearrange the terms in the sums below using the commutative and associative properties of addition so that the sum is as easy as possible without a calculator. Explain specifically which properties you used and why.
    a. $89456 + 0$
    b. $(875 + 20) + 80$
    c. $(40 + 793) + 60$
    d. $350 + 467 + 566 + 434 + 233 + 650$

3. What is the largest number you could get from adding two single digit numbers?

4. Can there be a carryover of more than 1 when adding 2 decimal numbers? Explain why or why not.

5. Jen worked $2\ hr\ 45\ min$ at the library and $3hr\ 20min$ as a hotel receptionist and $1hr\ 15min$ as a lifeguard. What is the total number of hours and minutes she worked?

6. State the property of addition that justifies each statement.

    a. $y + (3 + x) = y + (x + 3)$

    b. Getting a free item at the grocery store does not change the total bill.

    c. $3\sqrt{x} + \left(4\sqrt{x} + 3\right) = (3\sqrt{x} + 4\sqrt{x}) + 3$

7. Find the perimeter of a track that consists of two horizontal segments of 100 yards and two semicircular portions each of diameter 100 yards as shown in the picture. Use 3.14 as an approximation of π. Recall that a circle's perimeter or circumference is given by $C = 2\pi r = \pi D$.

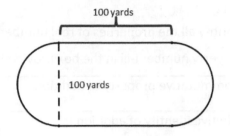

100 yards

100 yards

Lecture

🖥 Addition of Decimal Numbers, Polynomials, Radical Expressions, and Functions

http://www.youtube.com/watch?v=Xwwy9_-NQ0M   (14 min)

Lining up the like units helps us add many different objects together and is the basis behind addition of decimal numbers. Sometimes a group of one unit forms another unit (For example 12 one-inch units combine to make a one-foot unit). This also shows up when adding decimal numbers and with other unit conversion problems you will see later.

Practice Examples

Perform the following additions.

1. $5\,ft\,3\,in + 2\,ft\,11\,in$

2. $(2\,weeks + 3\,days + 5\,hours + 23\,minutes)$
    $+ (4\,weeks + 6\,days + 19\,hours + 53\,minutes)$

3. $489 + 235$

4. Find the perimeter of the polygon and state the units that are being combined.

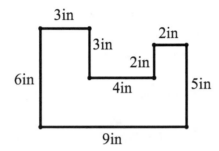

5. Identify the property of addtion that justifies the equation. Select from: Commutative
    Property; Associative Property; and Additive Identity Property of addition.
    a. $2 + (3 + x) = (2 + 3) + x$
    b. $3x + (5 + 2x) = 3x + (2x + 5)$
    c. $5x + 0 = 5x$

Attempt these problems yourself before looking at the answers below.

Solutions

To solve these problems you can write them one under the other so that the units are lined up. This
helps you understand how you can only add like units and that some units can be grouped to form
another unit.

1. $5\,ft\,3\,in + 2\,ft\,\,11\,in.$

    To solve this problem remember
    that $1ft = 12in$, and that we can
    only add like units.

	ft	in			ft	in
	5	3			5	3
+	2	11		+	2	11
					1	
	7	14	➡		8	~~1ft~~ 2

$14in = 12\,in + 2\,in$ To combine like units the
$\quad\quad = 1\,ft + 2\,in$ $1ft$ in the in column has to
be carried over into the ft
column.

Answer: $5\,ft\,3\,in + 2\,ft\,11\,in = 8\,ft\,2\,in$

2.

$(2\ weeks + 3\ days + 5\ hours + 23\ minutes) + (4\ weeks + 6\ days + 19\ hours + 53\ minutes)$

Remember that $7 days = 1 week, 24 hours = 1 day, 1 hour = 60 minutes$

Let the variables stand for $w = weeks, d = days, h = hours, m = minutes.$

So our problem now looks as $(2w + 3d + 5h + 23m) + (4w + 6d + 19h + 53m)$

In order to add like units, we have to use the commutative and associative properties of addition so we can add the terms in any order we want. So for example, the weeks go together, the days go together, and so on.

$$(2w + 3d + 5h + 23m) + (4w + 6d + 19h + 53m)$$
$$= (2w + 4w) + (3d + 6d) + (5h + 19h) + (23m + 53m)$$
$$= (2 + 4)w + (3 + 6)d + (5 + 19)h + (23 + 53)m$$
$$= 6w + 9d + 24h + 76m$$

$76m = 60m + 16m = 1h + 16m$

$$= 6w + 9d + 1d + 1h + 16m$$

$9d = 7d + 2d = 1w + 2d$

$$= 6w + 1w + 2d + 1d + 1h + 16m$$

$$= 7w + 3d + 1h + 16m$$

(The work below shows another way to show your steps using the carry-over principle.)

	$w = Weeks$	$d = Days$	$h = Hours$	$m = Minutes$
	2	3	5	23
+	4	6	19	53
	6	9	24	76
	$6 + 1$	$7 + 2 + 1$	$24 + 1$	$60m + 16m$
	$= 7w$	$= 1w + 3d$	$= 1d + 1h$	$= 1h + 16m$
	7	3	1	16

Final Answer: $7 weeks\ 3 days\ 1\ hour\ 16\ minutes$

Perhaps if we had time measurement aligned with our decimal number system, we'd have ten hour days, ten minute hours and ten day weeks. It would be hard to force this upon our solar system with its approximately 365 days in a one year cycle.

3. We start by writing the numbers 489 and 235 so the place values are visible.

Hundreds	Tens	Ones
4	8	9
2	3	5
6	11	14
$6 + 1$ ⬅	$10 + 1 + 1$ ⬅	$10 + 4$
$= 7\text{hundred}$	$= 1\text{hundred}+2\text{tens}$	$= 1\text{ten}+4\text{ones}$
7	2	4

(with a + sign on the left of the second row)

4. To find the perimeter of the polygon, we simply sum the lengths of each of the sides and the unit is inches. Thus $P = (3 + 3 + 4 + 2 + 2 + 5 + 9 + 6)in = 34in$

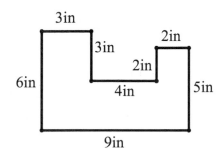

5.
   a. $2 + (3 + x) = (2 + 3) + x$ This is by the associative property of addition.

   b. $3x + (5 + 2x) = 3x + (2x + 5)$ This is by the commutative property of addition.

   c. $5x + 0 = 5x$ This is by the additive identity property.

In both the above examples we added the same kind of objects, i.e., distance with distance, and time with time, but the addends were each a combination of different sized units e.g., of time or of length. We used bundling of smaller units into larger groups much like in the standard algorithm for adding decimal numbers except the rate of bundling varies for minutes, hours, days and weeks. We start with the smallest unit terms, add these and bundle up if there are enough to make a larger group size, and then combine the next larger group etc. This means you move right to left when working with decimal number addition similar to the problems above.

Addition Algorithm for Decimal Numbers and Polynomials

The standard method for adding decimal numbers follows the above examples. The key concept for adding decimal numbers is that the bundling occurs in groups of ten. Recall that in a decimal number, each digit has its own unit based on its place (as we saw in chapter one). For example, in the number 123.58, the digit 8 is in the hundredths place, the 5 is in the tenths place, the 3 is in the ones place, and so on. Also remember that ten hundredths make one group of tenths, ten tenths make one group of ones, ten ones make one group of tens, and so on. So to add decimal numbers, 'add only like terms' means you add the digits in the hundredths places together, the digits in the tenths places together, and so on. Keep in mind that when the addition of digits yields a number bigger than 9, then we have

to bundle ten of the place value to make one of the place value to the left. That means we have to move from right to left as that is how our digits are placed (this is to make it more efficient so that we do not have to change digits again as we proceed). For example, if we wanted to add 123.58 + 594.47, then we first add the 8 hundredths to the 7 hundredths to obtain 15 hundredths. Note that we can view 15 hundredths as (10 + 5) hundredths, and bundle the 10 hundredths to equal 1 tenth (the associative property of addition is used here!). So 15 in hundredths, you can see that the digit 1 is how many tenths we have. A similar method would work for adding 12,358 + 59,447.
See below

$$
\begin{array}{r}
\overset{1\ \ \overset{1}{}\ \ \overset{1}{}}{1\,2\,3.5\,8} \\
+\,5\,9\,4.4\,7 \\
\hline
7\,1\,8.0\,5
\end{array}
\qquad
\begin{array}{r}
\overset{1\ \ \ \ \overset{1}{}\overset{1}{}}{1\,2,3\,5\,8} \\
+\,5\,9,4\,4\,7 \\
\hline
7\,1,8\,0\,5
\end{array}
$$

We can extend this to addition of three or more decimal numbers. The only difference is that you combine more than just two groups of each place value and may have to bundle up more than one group of the next place value higher. For example **23.86 + 36.52 + 45.89** is added as below:

$$
\begin{array}{r}
\overset{1\ \ 2\ \ 1}{2\,3.8\,6} \\
3\,6.5\,2 \\
+\quad\ \ 4\,5.8\,9 \\
\hline
1\,0\,6.2\,7
\end{array}
$$

Practice Examples
Add the following decimal numbers.

1. $24 + 65$

2. $265 + 528$

3. $76 + 87$

4. $0.00568 + 5.897$

5. $56987.45 + 8795.579$

Solutions

1. $24 + 65$

You can do this in two different ways as shown below.

$24 + 65$

$= (20 + 4) + (60 + 5)$

$= (20 + 60) + (4 + 5)$

$= 80 + 9 = 89$

```
      Tens   Ones
        2    4
   +    6    5
   _____
        8    9
```

2. $265 + 528$

Again you can use the ways shown above or pick one you like best. The only thing to watch out for is to make sure you add like place values.

```
    1
   265
 + 528
 _____
   793
```

3. $76 + 87$

```
   1
   76
 + 87
 ____
  163
```

4. $0.00568 + 5.897 = 0.00568 + 5.89700 = 5.90268$

Or

```
    11
  0.00568
+ 5.89700
_____
  5.90268
```

5. $56987.45 + 8795.579 = 56987.450 + 08795.579 = 65773.029$

Or

```
  11111 1
  56987.450
+ 08785.579
_____
  65773.029
```

Playing

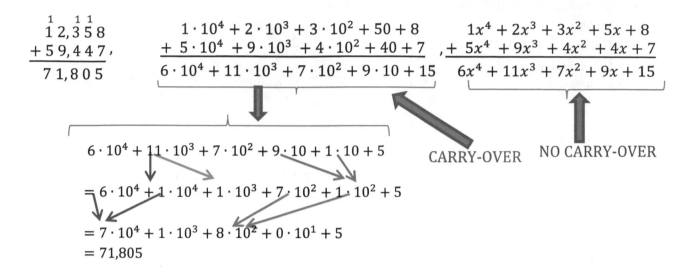

$$6 \cdot 10^4 + 11 \cdot 10^3 + 7 \cdot 10^2 + 9 \cdot 10 + 1 \cdot 10 + 5$$

$$= 6 \cdot 10^4 + 1 \cdot 10^4 + 1 \cdot 10^3 + 7 \cdot 10^2 + 1 \cdot 10^2 + 5$$

$$= 7 \cdot 10^4 + 1 \cdot 10^3 + 8 \cdot 10^2 + 0 \cdot 10^1 + 5$$

$$= 71{,}805$$

> **Note:** *We can extend the method of adding decimal numbers to adding polynomials and other mathematical objects; e.g., $(x^4 + 2x^3 + 3x^2 + 5x + 8) + (5x^4 + 9x^3 + 4x^2 + 4x + 7)$, where the like units are identified with their common power of x. The only difference in adding polynomials compared to decimal numbers is that we do not get a carry-over as there is no equivalency between a certain number of x making a number x^2.*

Another way to see this addition is to put both numbers in expanded form and combine terms with like units (same powers of ten) grouping it as: $\left(1 \times 10^2 + 2 \times 10 + 3 \times 1 + 5 \times \frac{1}{10} + 8 \times \frac{1}{10^2}\right) +$ $\left(5 \times 10^2 + 9 \times 10 + 4 \times 1 + 4 \times \frac{1}{10} + 3 \times \frac{1}{10^2}\right) = (1+5) \times 10^2 + (2+9) \times 10 + (3+4) \times 1 +$ $(5+4) \times \frac{1}{10} + (8+3) \times \frac{1}{10^2}$. Again rearrangement is allowed via the commutative and associative properties of addition. The beauty of adding numbers this way is that we only really need to know how to add numbers from zero to nine, which is why that is heavily emphasized in elementary school.

If we had adopted a base-five system, we'd only need to add the numbers zero to four, but this would be at the expense of having to use many more digits and place-values when dealing with large numbers. In fact computers use the binary number system so the only digits available are zero and one and it takes a ten-digit binary computer number to express the number 1023.

1. Perform the additions below without using a calculator. Pay attention to the bundling at each place value where it is required.

a. $36 + 21$	e. $(3x + 6) + (2x + 1)$
b. $23 + 77$	f. $(2x + 3) + (7x + 7)$
c. $269 + 374$	g. $(2x^2 + 6x + 9) + (3x^2 + 7x + 4)$
d. $3489 + 896$	h. $(3x^3 + 4x^2 + 8x + 9) + (8x^2 + 9x + 6)$
What are the differences or similarities between a & e, between b & f, between c & g, and between d & h?	
i. $4507.89 + 103.54$	m. $(4507x + 0.89) + (103x + 0.54)$
j. $2482 + 55 + 797$	n. $(2x^4 + 4x^3 + 8x + 2) + (5x + 5) + (7x^2 + 9x + 7)$
k. $32.9 + 14.7 + 19.8$	o. $(3x + 2.9) + (x + 4.7) + (x + 9.8)$
l. $73,407 + 1020$	p. $(7x^4 + 3x^3 + 4x^2 + 7) + (x^3 + 2x)$
What are the differences or similarities between i & m, between j & n, between k & o, and between l & p?	

2. First round each number to the hundreds place then add to approximate the sum below.
   $1439 + 1263 + 845$.

3. Use the addition algorithm on $785 + 963$, except work from left to right. What problem arises from doing it this way?

4. Write an expression using addition of at least two mathematical objects whose sum is given below.

   a. 58.65

   b. 7089

   c. $17x + 23$

   d. $8x^4 + 12x^3 + 5x^2 + 7x + 10$

Additional Examples of "Like Units"

Other types of numbers and algebraic objects introduced in Module One can be added by considering algebraic objects as units and combining objects of the same type.

Remember you can only add terms with like units and after adding like terms remember to keep the units intact. For example, $2\sqrt{7} + 13\sqrt{7} = (2 + 13)\sqrt{7} = 15\sqrt{7}$. In this example we have 2 of a quantity and you are adding 13 of the same quantity to it, giving you 15 of that quantity. Below are more examples of adding "like terms".

$2x + 13x = (2 + 13)x = 15x$, or $2x^{\frac{2}{3}} + 13x^{\frac{2}{3}} = (2 + 13)x^{\frac{2}{3}} = 15x^{\frac{2}{3}}$, $2cm + 13cm = (2 + 13)cm = 15cm$, or $2apples + 13apples = (2 + 13)apples = 15apples$. You can see that in all these problems you ended up having 15 of a particular unit and only the unit is what changed from problem to problem. The mathematical principle of addition remained the same. This is the power of mathematics. Once you learn how to do something like adding $2apples + 13apples = 15apples$ in the lower grades, that logic carries through to higher level problems like $2\sqrt{x+1} + 13\sqrt{x+1} = 15\sqrt{x+1}$.

If you miss little details like these early on, it can have a ripple effect throughout your mathematics learning. So do pay careful attention to the details and become conscious of your learning and processing of symbols. Learn to articulate your reasoning and do not just robotically work the problem.

We now apply the method shown above to add more complex expressions. For example, if you are adding $2\sqrt{7} + 3\sqrt[3]{5} + 15\sqrt{7} + 7\sqrt[3]{5}$, we first identify the like-unit terms and then remember to keep the units intact after adding. We will circle the like units below so you can see what they are (if you use this method of circling your units or underlying them, just remember do not cancel terms out as a way to identify like terms, as that would not be accurate). Some students have the habit of canceling terms, and it causes some mathematical confusion on other problems. Forming clear, clean mathematical writing habits will pay great dividends later for you.

Below are some of the ways you can write the solutions and still have a means to identify like units. These are based on some samples from student work.

Solution 1

$$2\,\textcircled{\sqrt{7}} + 3\,\textcircled{\sqrt[3]{5}} + 13\,\textcircled{\sqrt{7}} + 7\,\textcircled{\sqrt[3]{5}} = (2 + 13)\,\textcircled{\sqrt{7}} + (3 + 7)\,\textcircled{\sqrt[3]{5}} = 15\,\sqrt{7} + 10\,\sqrt[3]{5}$$

Solution 2

$$2\,\underline{\sqrt{7}} + 3\,\underline{\sqrt[3]{5}} + 13\,\underline{\sqrt{7}} + 7\,\underline{\sqrt[3]{5}} = (2 + 13)\,\underline{\sqrt{7}} + (3 + 7)\,\underline{\sqrt[3]{5}} = 15\,\sqrt{7} + 10\,\sqrt[3]{5}$$

Solution 3

$$2\sqrt{7} + 3\sqrt[3]{5} + 13\sqrt{7} + 7\sqrt[3]{5} = (2+13)\sqrt{7} + (3+7)\sqrt[3]{5} = 15\sqrt{7} + 10\sqrt[3]{5}$$

The above three writing samples are acceptable ways to write your answer. The one below is not.

Solution 4 (Not an acceptable way of writing)

$$2\sqrt{7} + 3\sqrt[3]{5} + 13\sqrt{7} + 7\sqrt[3]{5} = (2 + 13)\sqrt{7} + (3+7)\sqrt[3]{5} = 15\sqrt{7} + 10\sqrt[3]{5}$$

CROSS OUT TERMS

If your habit energy makes you really want to cross things out as shown above, you could make use of a scratch pad area "For my eyes only" column, however you want to write down the correct solution as follows:

Add	For My Eyes Only
$2\sqrt{7} + 3\sqrt[3]{5} + 13\sqrt{7} + 7\sqrt[3]{5}$	$2\sqrt{7} + 3\sqrt[3]{5} + 13\sqrt{7} + 7\sqrt[3]{5}$
Solution	$= 15\sqrt{7} + 10\sqrt[3]{5}$
$2\sqrt{7} + 3\sqrt[3]{5} + 13\sqrt{7} + 7\sqrt[3]{5}$	
$= 15\sqrt{7} + 10\sqrt[3]{5}$	

Practice Examples
Perform the following additions.

1. Of the complex numbers $(3 + 8i) + (5 + 2i)$

2. Of the radical expressions $3\sqrt{2} + 5\sqrt[3]{7} + 4\sqrt{2} + 6\sqrt[3]{7}$

3. Of the radical expressions $3\sqrt{x} + 5\sqrt{x+1} + 6\sqrt{x} + 7\sqrt{x+1}$

4. Of the polynomials $(4.3x^2 + 2.50x + 3) + (3x^2 + 11.34x + 2)$

5. Of the algebraic expressions with fractional exponents $3a^{2/3} + 7b^{4/5} + 5a^{2/3} + 3b^{4/5}$

Again please use your intuition and solve the problems before checking your answers below. Remember to identify like terms. You can circle the like terms, or underline them as shown above.

Solutions

1. $(3 + 8i) + (5 + 2i)$

    Remember $i = \sqrt{-1}$. (You saw complex numbers in Module 1.) Here we can see that the real parts add together and the imaginary parts add together

    $(3 + 8i) + (5 + 2i) = (3 + 5) + (8 + 2)i = 8 + 10i$

2. $3\sqrt{2} + 5\sqrt[3]{7} + 4\sqrt{2} + 6\sqrt[3]{7}$

    Adding like terms we get

    $3\sqrt{2} + 5\sqrt[3]{7} + 4\sqrt{2} + 6\sqrt[3]{7} = (3 + 4)\sqrt{2} + (5 + 6)\sqrt[3]{7} = 7\sqrt{2} + 11\sqrt[3]{7}$

3. $3\sqrt{x} + 5\sqrt{x+1} + 6\sqrt{x} + 7\sqrt{x+1}$

    Similar to the previous problem, remember when working with radicals that the units are the same only if the radicand and the index of the radical are the same. So here $\sqrt{x}$ and $\sqrt{x+1}$ are not the same units as the index is the same but the radicands are different.

    $3\sqrt{x} + 5\sqrt{x+1} + 6\sqrt{x} + 7\sqrt{x+1} = (3 + 6)\sqrt{x} + (5 + 7)\sqrt{x+1} = 9\sqrt{x} + 12\sqrt{x+1}$

For the next two problems the units are the same if the base and the exponents are the same.

4. $(4.3x^2 + 2.50x + 3) + (3x^2 + 11.34x + 2)$

    $= (4.3 + 3)x^2 + (2.50 + 11.34)x + (3 + 2)$

    $= 7.3x^2 + 13.84x + 5$

5. $3a^{2/3} + 7b^{4/5} + 5a^{2/3} + 3b^{4/5}$

    $3a^{2/3} + 7b^{4/5} + 5a^{2/3} + 3b^{4/5} = (3 + 5)a^{\frac{2}{3}} + (7 + 3)b^{\frac{4}{5}} = 8a^{2/3} + 10b^{4/5}$

Now consider what happens if we have a problem like $2in + 3/4\ in$. We all are familiar with writing the answer as $2\frac{3}{4}in = \left(2 + \frac{3}{4}\right)in$. In other words we can sometimes add and write the answer in such a way that the units are visible but the quantity $\left(2 + \frac{3}{4}\right)$ can stay as is and does not have to necessarily be combined together in one number or quantity.

In the quantity $2(x + 1)$, you can think of this $(x + 1)$ as a unit just the way $inches$, cms, or $apples$ are units. Therefore a problem like $2(x + 1) + 7(x + 1)$ could be thought of as two $(x + 1)$'s and seven $(x + 1)$'s added together to give us nine $(x + 1)$'s and we can write $2(x + 1) + 7(x + 1) = (2 + 7)(x + 1) = 9(x + 1)$. When we have $2(x + 1) + a(x + 1)$ as two $(x + 1)$'s and a more $(x + 1)$'s added together to give us $2 + a$ many of $(x + 1)$'s and we can write

$2(x + 1) + a(x + 1) = (2 + a)(x + 1)$.

Consider the same problem as above with different units, $2\sqrt{x+1} + a\sqrt{x+1} = (2 + a)\sqrt{x+1}$.

The key in addition is always looking for combining terms that have the same units.

Practice Examples

1. $2\pi r^2 + 4r^2$

2. $3(x + 1) + a(x + 1)$

3. $3x(2x - 3) + 5(2x - 3)$

4. $3\sqrt{2}x + 7x$

5. Let $f(x) = 4x^2 + 2x + 3$ and $g(x) = 3x^2 + 2 + 5\sqrt{x}$, find $f(x) + g(x)$.
   Another way to represent the new function that results from the addition of two known functions is with the notation $(f + g)(x)$ which you interpret as meaning $(f + g)(x) = f(x) + g(x)$. This is a notation just for functions and it is not the distributive property of multiplication over addition. The distributive property will be discussed soon.

6. $3(a + b) + u(a + b) + v(a + b)$

7. $4\ cm + 3\ cm^2 + 9\ cm + 5\ cm^2$

8. $3\ km + 7\ m + 200\ cm$

Solutions

1. $2\pi r^2 + 4r^2$
   $2\pi r^2 + 4r^2 = (2\pi + 4)r^2$

2. $3(x + 1) + a(x + 1)$
   $3(x + 1) + a(x + 1) = (3 + a)(x + 1)$ (since the two summands in $3 + a$ cannot be combined as they do not have the same units)

3. $3x(2x - 3) + 5(2x - 3)$
   $3x(2x - 3) + 5(2x - 3) = (3x + 5)(2x - 3)$

4. $3\sqrt{2}x + 7x$
   $3\sqrt{2}x + 7x = \left(3\sqrt{2} + 7\right)x$

5. Let $f(x) = 4x^2 + 2x + 3$ and $g(x) = 3x^2 + 2 + 5\sqrt{x}$, find $f(x) + g(x)$.
   $(f + g)(x) = f(x) + g(x)$ (This is the meaning of the notation of the $(f + g)$ function.)
   $(f + g)(x) = (4x^2 + 2x + 3) + \left(3x^2 + 2 + 5\sqrt{x}\right) = 7x^2 + 2x + 5 + 5\sqrt{x}$. This last expression states how the output of the function $(f + g)$ is computed for any given input x. An example where functions might be added like this is if $f(x)$ & $g(x)$ represent the electric and heat bill for month x, then the function $(f + g)$ would be the total utility bill function.

6. $3(a + b) + u(a + b) + v(a + b)$
   $3(a + b) + u(a + b) + v(a + b) = (3 + u + v)(a + b)$

7. $4\ cm + 3\ cm^2 + 9\ cm + 5\ cm^2$

$4\ cm + 3\ cm^2 + 9\ cm + 5\ cm^2 = (4+9)cm + (3+5)cm^2 = 13\ cm + 8\ cm^2$

8. $3\ km + 7\ m + 200\ cm$

We need to use the facts that $1\ km = 1000\ m$, so $3km = 1km + 1km + 1km = 3000m$, we also know that $1m = 100\ cm$, or $2m = 1m + 1m = 200cm$, therefore we have $3\ km + 7\ m + 200\ cm = 3000m + 7m + 2m = (3000 + 7 + 2)m = 3072m$

This is an example where quantities did not have the same units but, with easily performed unit conversion in the metric system, were able to rewrite them all in the common unit of meters.

Video log 2.1e

1. Perform the additions below without using a calculator. Explain what the similarities and dissimilarities are between all of the problems below.

    a. $2 + 15$

    b. $2apples + 15apples$

    c. $2cm + 15cm$

    d. $2a + 15a$

    e. $2x^2 + 15x^2$

    f. $2\sqrt{3} + 15\sqrt{3}$

    g. $2\sqrt{x} + 15\sqrt{x}$

    h. $2\sqrt[3]{x} + 15\sqrt[3]{x}$

    i. $2a^{\frac{2}{3}} + 15a^{\frac{2}{3}}$

    j. $2x^2 + 15x^2$

    k. $2(a + b) + 15(a + b)$

    l. $2x(a + b) + 15(a + b)$

    m. $2x\sqrt{3} + 15\sqrt{3}$

2. Explain what the difference is between $a + a$ and $a \times a$.

3. Perform the additions below without using a calculator, and show all your reasoning where necessary.

a. Apple + Apple

b. $\sqrt{x} + \sqrt{x}$

c. $sigma + sigma$

d. $3sigma + 5sigma$

e. $3a(a + b) + 5a(a + b)$

f. $7x + 5 + 8x + 9$

g. $(7 + 5i) + (8 + 9i)$

h. $7a + 5b + 8a + 9b$

i. $\sqrt{3a}(t + p) + \sqrt{3a}(t + p)$

j. $\sqrt{x}(x + y) + 3(x + y)$

k. $5\sqrt{ab} + 7\sqrt{ab} + 8\sqrt{ab}$

l. $a(u + v) + b(u + v)$

m. $12a\sqrt{b} + 7b\sqrt{a} + 8a\sqrt{b} + 3\sqrt{a}$

n. $7\sqrt{x} + 5 + 8\sqrt{x} + 9$

o. $7\sqrt[3]{x} + 5\sqrt{x} + 8\sqrt[3]{x} + 9\sqrt{x}$

p. $7a^{\frac{2}{3}} + 5\sqrt[5]{a} + 8a^{\frac{2}{3}} + 9\sqrt[5]{a}$

q. $7(a + b) + 5(a^2 + b^2) + 8(a + b) + 9(a^2 + b^2)$

r. $6(3x + 4) + 5x(3x + 4)$

s. $\sqrt{2}(x - 3) + a(x - 3)$

t. $a(u + v) + b(u + v)$

u. $a(a - b) + b(a - b)$

v. $\sqrt{2}(x - 3) + b(x - 3) + 3(x - 3) + a(x - 3)$

w. $a(u + v) + b(u + v) + c(u + v)$

x. $2\sqrt{6} + \sqrt[5]{3} + 3\sqrt{5} + 7\sqrt{2} + 6\sqrt[5]{3} + 4\sqrt{5}$

y. $(4x^3 + 6x^2 + 7x + 12) + (5x^6 + 3x^4 + 7x^3 + 10x + 21)$

z. $4\sqrt{x + 1} + 7x\sqrt{x + 1} + x\sqrt[3]{x} + 10x\sqrt[3]{x} + 11x\sqrt{x + 1}$

aa. $f(t) = 4 + \sqrt{t}, g(t) = 5t + 2$, simplify the expression for $(f + g)(t)$.

4. Perform the additions below without using a calculator. For the first couple problems, you can use the facts that $1km = 1000m, 1m = 100cm, 1ft = 12in$. For the other problems, remember to simplify when able before adding so you can see what the like terms are.

a. $4km + 7m + 100cm$

b. $10ft + 5in + 12ft + 9in$

c. $2\ weeks + 5days + 4hours + 6weeks + 6days + 23hours$

d. $30\ dollars + 8\ dollars + 28\ cents + 2\ dollars + 100dollars + 92cents$

e. $4\sqrt{x^2} + 7x\sqrt{x} + 5\sqrt[3]{x} + 10x + 11x\sqrt{x}$

f. $15\sqrt{2x - 1} + 8\sqrt[3]{2a^4b} + 5\sqrt{2x + 1} + 5\ a\sqrt[3]{2ab} + 3\sqrt{2x + 1}$

g. $9\sqrt{a^2b^3} + 7\sqrt{ab} + 19ab + 21ab\sqrt{b} + 8\sqrt{ab} + 11ab$

h. $9x(x + y) + 2y(x - y) + 10(x - y) + 5(x + y)$

i. $(3a + 2\sqrt{a}) + (4\sqrt{a^2} + 5) + (6\sqrt{a} + 9) + (12a + 15\sqrt{a} + 3)$

j. $12\sqrt{b^2} + 7\sqrt{a^4} + 8\sqrt{b^2} + 3\sqrt{a^4}$

k. $\sqrt{4x^2} + 5x\sqrt{9y^2} + 7xy + 5x\sqrt{y}$

l. $\sqrt{4x^2y} + 5x\sqrt{9xy^2} + 7xy + 5x\sqrt{y}$

m. $5a\sqrt[5]{b^6} + 11a\sqrt[3]{b^5} + \sqrt{3a} + 2b\sqrt[3]{a^3b^2} + 6ab\sqrt[5]{ab} + \sqrt{3a}$

n. $5\sqrt{a^2b^3} + 10ab\sqrt{b} + 5b\sqrt{a^6b}$

o. $5ab\sqrt{a^6b^3} + 7\sqrt[3]{a^9b^6} + 3a^3b^2 + 4b^2\sqrt{a^8} + 6b^2\sqrt[3]{a^9}$

p. $5\sqrt[3]{2a^5y^7} + 7ab^2\sqrt[5]{a^3b^2} + 8ay^2\sqrt[3]{54a^2y} + \sqrt[5]{32a^8b^{12}}$

5. Write an expression using addition of at least two mathematical objects whose sum is given below.

    e.   58.65   g. $17x + 23$

    f.   7089   h. $4x^4 + 12x^3 + 5x^2 + 7x + 10$

Addition of Fractions

Lecture

🖥 Introduction to Addition of Fractions and Rational Expressions

http://www.youtube.com/watch?v=y_LvHKSC10E (9 min)

Consider the fraction addition problem $\frac{3}{5} + \frac{2}{3}$. We know the fraction $\frac{3}{5}$ is made up of three $\frac{1}{5}$ units, and $\frac{2}{3}$ is two $\frac{1}{3}$ units as shown below. As before, we can only add if we have the same sized pieces. However, $\frac{1}{5}$ units and $\frac{1}{3}$ units are not the same size, but can be converted to like units by changing each fraction into an equivalent fraction as we saw in Module 1. Remember that to make equivalent fractions we can multiply the numerator and denominator of a fraction by the same nonzero quantity. So $\frac{3}{5} = \frac{3 \times 3}{5 \times 3} = \frac{9}{15}$, and $\frac{2}{3} = \frac{2 \times 5}{3 \times 5} = \frac{10}{15}$. This makes both fractions now have the same sized pieces of $\frac{1}{15}$ unit. That is, $\frac{9}{15}$ is made up of nine $\frac{1}{15}$ units and $\frac{10}{15}$ is made up of ten $\frac{1}{15}$ units. This means we can look at this problem as follows: $\frac{3}{5} + \frac{2}{3} = \frac{3 \times 3}{5 \times 3} + \frac{2 \times 5}{3 \times 5} = \frac{9}{15} + \frac{10}{15}$ as having nine $\frac{1}{15}$ units plus ten $\frac{1}{15}$ units which is a total of nineteen $\frac{1}{15}$ units or one whole unit with an additional four $\frac{1}{15}$ units. We write this mathematically as shown below and also visualize as shown below.

$$\frac{3}{5} + \frac{2}{3} = \frac{3 \times 3}{5 \times 3} + \frac{2 \times 5}{3 \times 5} = \frac{9}{15} + \frac{10}{15} = \frac{19}{15} = 1\frac{4}{15}$$

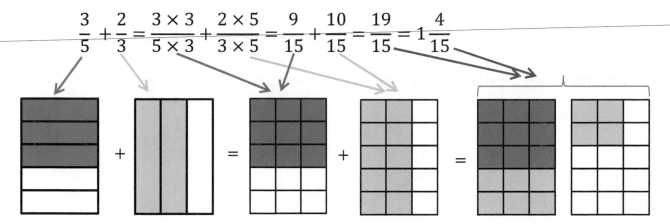

The diagrams above are referred to as strip diagrams or area diagrams to represent fractions. The visual representation helps in understanding how the units play a role. You may have seen this kind of representation in elementary school. Make sure you can draw these kind of diagrams as they will play a crucial role later.

Let us take a look at a different example and apply the same process as above and see what happens. Consider the example $\frac{3}{4} + \frac{5}{6}$. Then we can make the common unit as $\frac{1}{24}$ and we get

$$\frac{3}{4} + \frac{5}{6} = \frac{3 \times 6}{4 \times 6} + \frac{5 \times 4}{6 \times 4} = \frac{18}{24} + \frac{20}{24} = \frac{38}{24} = 1\frac{14}{24} = 1\frac{14 \div 2}{24 \div 2} = 1\frac{7}{12}$$

Or we could have also done the problem by making the common piece size as $\frac{1}{12}$ unit.

$$\frac{3}{4} + \frac{5}{6} = \frac{3 \times 3}{4 \times 3} + \frac{5 \times 2}{6 \times 2} = \frac{9}{12} + \frac{10}{12} = \frac{19}{12} = 1\frac{7}{12}$$

Both methods are valid, but having the common size as $\frac{1}{12}$ unit gives us smaller numbers to work with and seems to be more efficient. We will later discuss strategies on how to find the most efficient common denominator for addition of rational expressions.

We can also add mixed numbers by combining the whole number parts and the fractional parts and then bringing these together as in

$$3\frac{2}{3} + 5\frac{1}{4} = 3 + 5 + \frac{2}{3} + \frac{1}{4}$$

$$= 8 + \frac{2 \times 4}{3 \times 4} + \frac{1 \times 3}{4 \times 3}$$

$$= 8\frac{11}{12}$$

Playing

Assumption just for playing purposes: *Assume that for the example below, our variable x is any real number more than 3. This assumption is necessary to give you a visual sense. In general, the mathematical process shown below is valid for the addition of any rational expressions as long as the denominators are nonzero.*

We can extend our addition of rational expressions as in $\frac{3}{x} + \frac{2}{5}$. As before to have the same sized pieces and we use $\frac{1}{5x}$. The steps below show how this leads to $15 + 2x$ copies of $\frac{1}{5x}$ units.

$$\frac{3}{x} + \frac{2}{5} = \frac{3 \times 5}{x \times 5} + \frac{2 \times x}{5 \times x} = \frac{15}{5x} + \frac{2x}{5x} = \frac{15 + 2x}{5x}$$

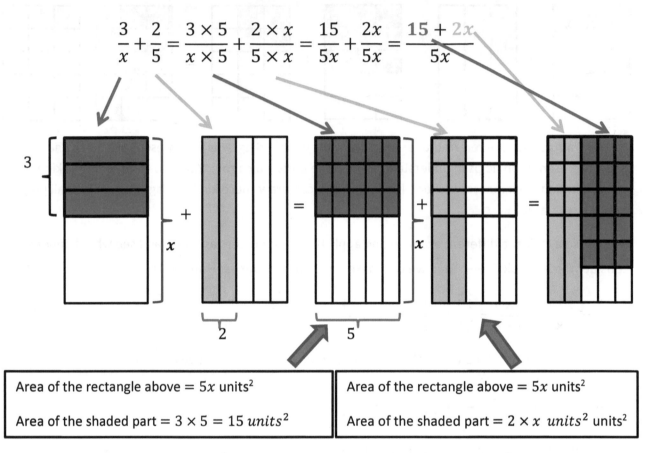

Area of the rectangle above $= 5x$ units^2	Area of the rectangle above $= 5x$ units^2
Area of the shaded part $= 3 \times 5 = 15 \ units^2$	Area of the shaded part $= 2 \times x \ units^2$ units^2

To understand the pictures drawn above, think of all the overall outer rectangles as having area of $5x$ units^2. The first rectangle's orange shaded area represents $\frac{3}{x}$ of the whole rectangle, and the second rectangle's blue shaded area as $\frac{2}{5}$ of the whole rectangle. In their addition, if we make equal sized pieces, we can compare what we have a total of. The blue area represents $\frac{2}{5} = \frac{2 \times x}{5 \times x}$ fraction of the rectangle and the orange area represents $\frac{3}{x} = \frac{3 \times 5}{x \times 5} = \frac{15}{5x}$ fraction of the rectangle for a total of $\frac{2x + 15}{5x}$ fraction of the total rectangle area as shaded.

1. Draw a strip diagram or rectangles to represent the addition process for the following examples. Use the above examples to help you.

   a. $\frac{2}{7} + \frac{3}{7}$

   b. $\frac{1}{4} + \frac{1}{3}$

   c. $\frac{2}{5} + \frac{2}{3}$

   d. $4\frac{1}{5} + 1\frac{3}{5}$

   e. $4\frac{2}{5} + 1\frac{4}{5}$

   f. $\frac{1}{x} + \frac{3}{x}$

2. Perform the following addition and explain why your method works.

   a. $\frac{3}{4} + \frac{1}{3}$

   b. $\frac{3}{2} + \frac{4}{3}$

   c. $4\frac{2}{3} + 3\frac{1}{2}$

   d. $2\frac{1}{2}gal + 1\frac{1}{4}qts$

   (use: $4qts = 1gal$, and also $1qt = 4cups$)

   e. $\frac{5}{x} + \frac{3}{7}$

   f. $\frac{5}{x} + \frac{3}{4}$

   g. $\frac{3}{x+1} + \frac{5}{x+1}$

   h. $\frac{4}{x} + \frac{3}{y}$

3. Write an expression using addition of two fractions whose sum is given below.

   a. $\frac{5}{12}$

   b. $4\frac{5}{7}$

   c. $\frac{14}{x+1}$

   d. $\frac{5x+3}{7x}$

2.2 Multiplication

Lecture

🖥 Properties of Multiplication
http://www.youtube.com/watch?v=5tt0WWHEJm4 (10 min)

As you saw when adding rational expressions we need to know how to multiply integers, polynomials and other objects when obtaining a common denominator. Before we go into the definition of what multiplication is or what the meaning of multiplication is, we would like you to think in your own words what multiplication is.

> **Definition: Multiplication** is a <u>**binary operation**</u> denoted by $\times$ *or* $\cdot$, which means it acts on <u>two</u> objects with specific rules. If we are working with at least one positive quantity you can think of it as a repeated addition. The objects themselves are called factors or multiplicative factors and the result is the product of two factors. We define $a \times b$ or $a \cdot b$ or ab to be the number of objects in a groups where each group has b objects in it.

Each of the numbers a and b are called factors and the result of the multiplication is called the product of the two numbers. Some examples are: The number of eggs in three one-dozen cartons is $3 \times 12 = 36 \; eggs$, i.e., three groups of twelve.

The number of golf balls in 12 boxes with three balls in each box is given by $12 \cdot 3 = 36 \; balls$, i.e., twelve groups of three. The number of feet in 2.5 miles is given by $2.5 \times 5{,}280 \; ft = 13{,}200 \; ft$, i.e., two and a half groups of 5280 feet.

Another useful model for multiplication is when we multiply length times width to compute the area of a rectangle. Consider a rectangle which is 3 cm wide by 8 cm long as depicted below. Here each of the squares in the first picture is one unit of area called a "square centimeter" denoted by $1 \; cm^2$.

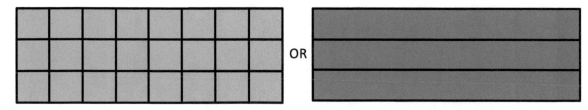

3 groups of 8 square centimeters   3 groups of 8 square centimeters

We can think of this as 3 groups of $8cm^2$ in that for each cm in the vertical direction on the rectangle there are $8cm^2$ of area, thus in this case 3 groups of $8cm^2$ or $8cm^2 + 8cm^2 + 8cm^2 = 3 \times 8cm^2 = $

$24cm^2$. The square centimeter (cm^2) is an area-unit and is consistent with multiplying two lengths in (cm) to get an area with cm^2-units. Thus area=$w \cdot l = (w\ cm) \times (l\ cm) = (w \cdot l)cm^2$. When dealing variables like x, our exponential notation is consistent with the square units concept and we will get $x \times x = x^2$, and $x^2 + x^2 + x^2 = 3 \times x^2 = 3x^2$.

Note: *There is a difference between $x + x = 2x$ and $x \times x = x^2$. So remember the difference between an exponent and a coefficient. A coefficient of 2 on x makes x a summand twice, where as an exponent of 2 on x makes x a multiplicative factor twice.*

Properties of Multiplication

Commutative Property of Multiplication: If we let a and b be any two of the mathematical objects studied so far, then it is always true that $a \times b = b \times a$ or $ab = ba$ (a and b are referred to as factors).

In other words: Changing the order of two factors in a product doesn't change the result.

Terminology: Multiplication is commutative.

What this property is saying is that if you put items in rows and columns, then if we interchange the rows to columns and columns to rows, the number of items remains the same. Or that the area-of-rectangle remains unchanged whether the long side is horizontal or vertical.

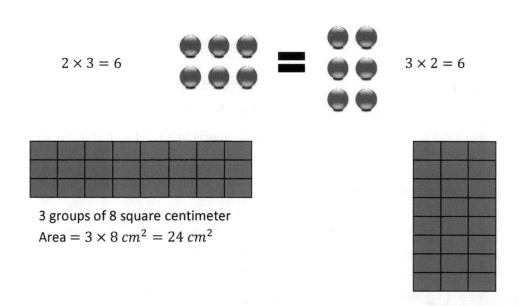

$2 \times 3 = 6$ $3 \times 2 = 6$

3 groups of 8 square centimeter
Area $= 3 \times 8\ cm^2 = 24\ cm^2$

8 groups of 3 square centimeter
Area $= 8 \times 3\ cm^2 = 24\ cm^2$

Playing

Now that we know how to work with multiplication of two objects, a natural question is how does this extend to multiplying more than two factors.

The example below illustrates through a volume calculation of a rectangular box that the product of three or more factors is independent of which multiplication is done first. If we start with a rectangular box say 3 inches wide by 7 inches long and 5 inches tall, the area of the base is $3 \times 7 \ in^2 = 21in^2$. Then for each one inch in height, there would be 21 one inch squares that were one inch high for a total of 21 cubic inches of volume. With the height of 5in, the volume is $5 \times (3 \times 7) = 5 \times 21 = 105 \ in^3$. The volume remains the same if we turn the box on its side so the base is 5 in by 3 in and height is 7 inches: the base area is $15 \ in^2$ and seven layers makes the total volume $(15in^2) \times 7in = 105in^3$. Note that in the second case, we multiplied 5×3 first and then multiplied by 7. Thus $5 \times (3 \times 7) = (5 \times 3) \times 7$.

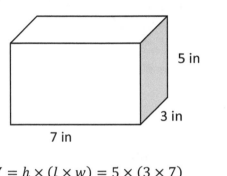

$$V = h \times (l \times w) = 5 \times (3 \times 7)$$
$$= 5 \times 21 = 105 \ in^3$$

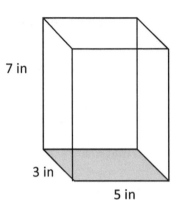

$$V = (l \times w) \times h = (5 \times 3) \times 7$$
$$= 15 \times 7 = 105 \ in^3$$

Associative Property of Multiplication: If a, b, and c represent any three mathematical objects studied so far, then $(a \times b) \times c = a \times (b \times c)$ or $(ab)c = a(bc)$

In other words: Changing the grouping of three mathematical objects in a product doesn't change the result.

Terminology: Multiplication is associative.

Note: There are more advanced mathematical objects that fail to have the commutative and associative properties. For example, multiplication of matrices (if you know what they are) usually produce a different result when the order of multiplication is reversed.

Multiplicative identity is "One": If we let a represent any mathematical object that we have studied, then $1 \times a = a \times 1 = a$.

In other words: Multiplying by 1 leaves that mathematical object unchanged.

Terminology: The number 1 is a multiplicative identity.

Thus $a \times 1$ is a groups with 1 object in each group for a total of a objects and equivalently $1 \times a$ is 1 group of a objects also resulting in a total of a objects. The number 1 is called the multiplicative identity.

Sometimes we do multiplication and addition together. When we write these operations, we must be careful as to which is done first. Consider the problem of finding the area of the polygon to the right.

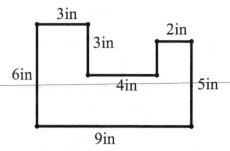

The polygon can be sliced into three rectangles as shown to the right and their areas can be computed and then added.

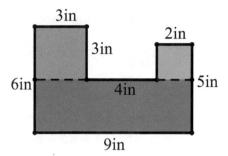

The total area $A = (3 \times 3) + (2 \times 2) + (9 \times 3) = 9 + 4 + 27 = 40 in^2$. The parentheses indicate that the multiplications are done first and then the additions. We could also write this as $A = 3 \times 3 + 2 \times 2 + 9 \times 3$ where the standard convention is that multiplications are done before the additions.

Consider the following example and diagrams where we are applying multiplication by 4 to the sum $(3 + 2)$.

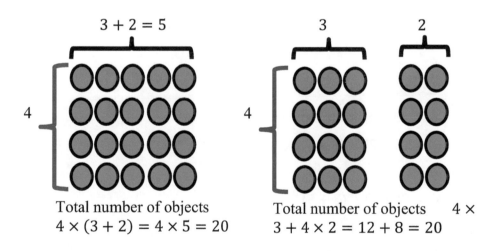

Total number of objects
$4 \times (3 + 2) = 4 \times 5 = 20$

Total number of objects $4 \times$
$3 + 4 \times 2 = 12 + 8 = 20$

The commutative property also gives us $(3 + 2) \times 4 = 3 \times 4 + 2 \times 4 = 12 + 8 = 20$

In the picture on the left, in each row we put down $3 + 2$ items at a time for a total of four times. In the picture on the right we put down 3 items down at a time for a total of four times and then we put down 2 items in a similar pattern for a total of four times. The number of items we put down is the same and the arrangement looks the same after the process is complete in both pictures. This process is called the distributive property of multiplication over addition. We are applying the multiplication by four to the three and then to the two, and the resulting sum is the same as if we were to add the 2 and 3 first to get 5, and take the product of 4 and 5.

We can extend this property to all mathematical objects we have seen so far.

Distributive property of multiplication over addition: If a, b, and c represent any three mathematical objects we have studied so far, then
$$a \times (b + c) = a \times b + a \times c, \text{ or } a(b + c) = ab + ac$$
$$(b + c) \times a = b \times a + c \times a, \text{ or } (b + c)a = ba + ca = ab + ac$$

Also recall the convention that the products in $ab + ac$ are done first, and then the sum.

In other words: We can distribute multiplication over the addition of two or more summands.

Terminology: Multiplication distributes over addition.

Examples

- $a(b + c + d + e) = ab + ac + ad + ae$ or
- $(b + c + d + e)a = ba + ca + da + ea = ab + ac + ad + ae$

A simple example of this is when $a = 2$ and b is the number of boys in a school and c is the number of girls in the same school, then $2 \times (b + c)$ says first add the number of girls plus the number of boys and then double to obtain, say, the total number of legs on the kids in the school. The expression $(2 \times b + 2 \times c)$ arrives at the same total number of legs by counting the number of boys' legs and then the number of girls' legs and then adding them. Either way, you arrive at the total number of legs on the children in the school.

It is very important to realize the difference between addition and multiplication operations.

Video Log 2.2a

1. Answer true of false and justify your answer.

   a. Is $3 \times (2 \times 5) = (3 \times 2) \times (3 \times 5)$?

   b. Is $3 + (2 + 5) = (3 + 2) \times (3 + 5)$?

   c. Is $3 + (2 + 5) = (3 + 2) + (3 + 5)$?

   d. Is $3 \times (xy) = (3x)(3y)$?

2. Convert each statement into a multiplication of two numbers.

   a. $8 + 8 + 8 + 8 + 8 =$

   b. How many pays total are there in a group of 7 dogs?

   c. What is the value in dollars of 7 pounds of strawberries that cost $2.40 a pound?

   d. How many miles does a car travel in three hours if in each hour it travels 65 mi?

3. John bought 4 tires at $65 each and spent another $53 on gasoline. Write the total spent as an

arithmetic problem and compute this amount.

4. Please include appropriate units for the area and volume when answering questions below.

a. Find the volume of the box that is $7ft$ by $4ft$ by $3ft$ as shown to the right.

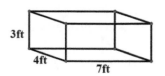

b. Find the total surface area of the box from part a (that means add the area of all six faces of the box).

c. If just the length of the box were to be made three times longer, this would clearly be like having three boxes stacked end-to-end. Find the volume of this new long box shown on the right.

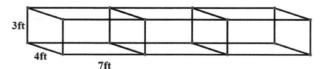

d. What happens to the volume if just the height or just the width of the original box from part a is made three times as large?

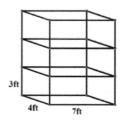 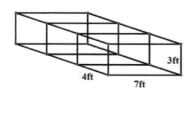

e. Use your answer from part c. and d. to explain why

$$3 \cdot (l \cdot w \cdot h) = 3l \cdot w \cdot h = l \cdot 3w \cdot h = l \cdot w \cdot 3h.$$

f. Use answers from part e to determine if multiplication distributes over multiplication?

g. Find the volume of the box in which all the dimensions of the box from part a are 3 times longer.

5. Identify the property of real numbers that justifies each equation a.-h. Please enter the property number i.-vii in the box provided below. Properties to select from are listed below.

i.	Commutative property of addition	v.	Additive identity property
ii.	Commutative property of multiplication	vi.	Multiplicative identity property
iii.	Associative property of addition	vii.	Distributive property of multiplication over
iv.	Associative property of multiplication		addition

	Equation	Property		Equation	Property
a.	$5 \cdot x = x \cdot 5$		b.	$50 \cdot (4 \cdot 3) = (50 \cdot 4) \cdot 3$	
c.	$50\left(\frac{1}{2} + 2\right) = 50 \cdot \frac{1}{2} + 50 \cdot 2$		d.	$26\left(5 \cdot \frac{1}{2}\right) = 26\left(\frac{1}{2} \cdot 5\right)$	
e.	$(5 + 0) \cdot x = 5 \cdot x$		f.	$3 + x = x + 3$	
g.	$3 \times (5 \times 6) = (3 \times 5) \times 6$		h.	$6 \times 1 = 6$	
i.	$a(x + y) = ax + ay$		j.	$0 + 5 = 5$	

🖥 Visualizing Multiplication http://www.youtube.com/watch?v=0ofeTiqGSFs (13 min)

The representation of multiplication for computing areas of rectangles provides another visualization that is useful to support the standard routine for decimal multiplication.

Consider the product 23×37 as being $23 \times (30 + 7)$ represented below as the area of a 23 by 37 rectangle. It is clear that the total area is equal to the area of all the four smaller rectangles added together.

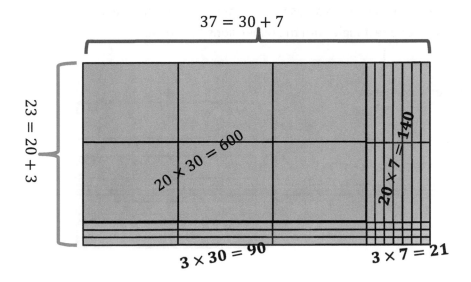

The figure above can be represented algebraically by the methods shown below.

$$23 \times 37 = 23 \times (30 + 7)$$
$$= 23 \times 30 + 23 \times 7$$

$$= (20 + 3) \times 30 + (20 + 3) \times 7$$
$$= 20 \times 30 + 3 \times 30 + 20 \times 7 + 3 \times 7$$
$$= 600 + 90 + 140 + 21$$
$$= 690 + 140 + 21$$
$$= 690 + 161$$
$$= 851$$

```
      23
    × 37
    ─────
      2 1
  +  140
  +   90
  +  600
  ─────
     851
```

```
          2
      2  3
    × 3  7
  ─────────
    1
    1  6  1
  + 6  9  0
  ─────────
    8  5  1
```

You can use the processes shown above to multiply decimal numbers and other mathematical objects as shown below.

To multiply decimals the only additional information you have to keep track of is figuring out the correct decimal position. For example, to multiply 2.3×0.037, if we write the decimals as fractions like $\dfrac{23}{10} \times \dfrac{37}{10^3}$, we see that we still multiply 23×37 and then simply divide by 10 four times. Dividing by ten four times amounts to moving the decimal point a total of four places to the left of the decimal point in $(23 \times 37) = 851$.

In this example $2.3 \times 0.037 = \dfrac{851}{10^4} = 0.0851 = 0.0851$

This algorithm for decimal multiplication is readily extended to multiplying polynomials. In the two examples below, if we assume that the variable x is a positive real number, we can visualize the polynomial multiplication as an area of a rectangle with the dimensions as shown.

1. Multiply $4(x + 2)$.

    Using our distributive property we have

    $4\,(x + 2) = 4 \times x + 4 \times 2 = 4x + 8$

    Total area of the rectangle of the dimension 4 by $x + 2$ equals the area of the smaller rectangles of the size 4 by x and 4 by 2 added together.

    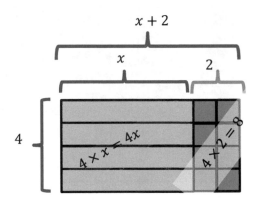

2. Multiply $x(x + 2)$

    Using our distributive property we have

    $x\,(x + 2) = x \times x + x \times 2 = x^2 + 2x$

    Total area of the rectangle of the dimension x by $x + 2$ equals the area of the smaller rectangles of the size x by x and x by 2 added together.

    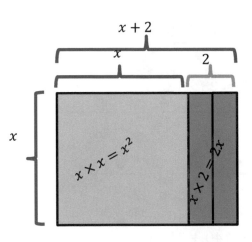

3. Multiply $(2x + 3) \times (3x + 7)$.

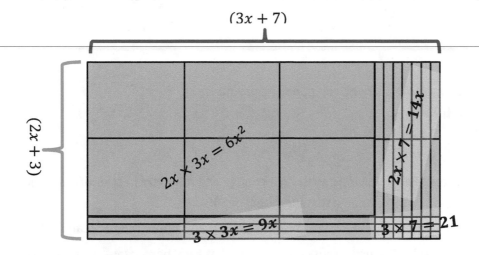

We have used the commutative and associative property of multiplication to write $2x \times 3x = 6x^2$. You can see that the two ways shown below are valid no matter how many terms are in each factor. You can also extend this method for more than two factors, we just have to do two at a time and be persistent and aware of what we are doing.

4.

$(2x + 3) \times (3x + 7)$

$= \mathbf{2x} \times \mathbf{3x} + \mathbf{2x} \times \mathbf{7} + 3 \times 3x + 3 \times 7$
$= 6x^2 + 14x + 9x + 21$
$= 6x^2 + 23x + 21$

$(2x + 3) \times (3x + 7)$

$= (2x + 3) \times 3x + (2x + 3) \times 7$
$= \mathbf{2x} \times \mathbf{3x} + \mathbf{3} \times \mathbf{3x} + 2x \times 7 + 3 \times 7$
$= 6x^2 + 9x + 14x + 21$
$= 6x^2 + 23x + 21$

5. Multiply $(2x^2 + 3x + 6)(3x^3 + 4x + 7)$

$(2x^2 + 3x + 6)(3x^3 + 4x + 7)$

$= 2x^2 \cdot 3x^3 + 2x^2 \cdot 4x + 2x^2 \cdot 7 + 3x \cdot 3x^3 + 3x \cdot 4x + 3x \cdot 7 + 6 \cdot 3x^3 + 6 \cdot 4x + 6 \cdot 7$

$= 6x^5 + 8x^3 + 14x^2 + 9x^4 + 12x^2 + 21x + 18x^3 + 24x + 42$

$= 6x^5 + 9x^4 + 26x^3 + 26x^2 + 45x + 42.$

The act of multiplying out expressions like this is referred to as expanding the product. It is important that you become proficient at multiplying binomials as it will be used often in later work. The algebraic processes shown above, work for all polynomial multiplications. Remember to use the correct properties of multiplication. Each term in the first factor gets distributed to all of the terms in the second factor.

Practice Examples

1. Multiply each of the polynomials below (Expand the products).

   a. $(3x + 4)(4x + 1)$ c. $(2x^3 + 3x^2 + 5x + 7)(2x^2 + 4)$

   b. $(2x + 5)(4x + 3)$ d. $(2x + 3)^2$

2. Compute the products below involving percentage change and numbers in scientific notation.

   a. Find the amount of a 15% tip on a restaurant bill of $45.

   b. Simple interest rate of $r\frac{\%}{yr}$ on a constant principal P is computed over n years by the formula $I = n \cdot r \cdot P$. The first product $n \cdot r$ tells what total percentage is earned over n years. Compute the simple interest earned on a principal of $4000 over 4 years with interest rate 8%.

   c. Find the dollar value decrease in the value of a home that declined by 12% from $150,000.

   d. Evaluate in scientific notation the square of the radius of the earth (r^2) where $r = 6.4 \times 10^6 m$

Solutions

1.

   a. $(3x + 4)(4x + 1) = 12x^2 + 3x + 16x + 4 = 12x^2 + 19x + 4$

   b. $(2x + 5)(4x + 3) = 8x^2 + 6x + 20x + 15 = 8x^2 + 26x + 15$

   c. $\left(2x^3 + 3x^2 + 5x + 7\right)(2x^2 + 4)$

   $= 4x^5 + 8x^3 + 6x^4 + 12x^2 + 10x^3 + 20x + 14x^2 + 28$

   $= 4x^5 + 18x^3 + 26x^2 + 20x + 28$

   d. $(2x + 3)^2 = (2x + 3)(2x + 3) = 4x^2 + 6x + 6x + 9 = 4x^2 + 12x + 9$

2.

a. We need to compute 15% of $45. This means $15\% \times \$45 = 0.15 \times \$45$.

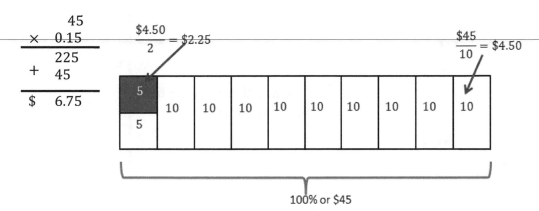

$$\begin{array}{r} 45 \\ \times \quad 0.15 \\ \hline 225 \\ + \quad 45 \\ \hline \$ \quad 6.75 \end{array}$$

$$\frac{\$4.50}{2} = \$2.25$$

$$\frac{\$45}{10} = \$4.50$$

100% or $45

The whole (100%) is worth $45. So 10% is worth a tenth of the whole or $\frac{\$45}{10} = \$4.50$, and 5% is half of 10% or $\frac{\$4.50}{2} = \$2.25$.

So combining the two we get that 15%=(10+5)% will be $\$4.50 + \$2.25 = \$6.75$.

b. $I = n \cdot r \cdot P$, where $P = \$4000$, $n = 4$ years, and $r = 0.08$. So interest earned is $I = 4 \times 4000 \times 0.04 = 640$ dollars.

c. We need to compute 12% of $150,000 This means $12\% \times \$150,000 = 0.12 \times \$150,000$.

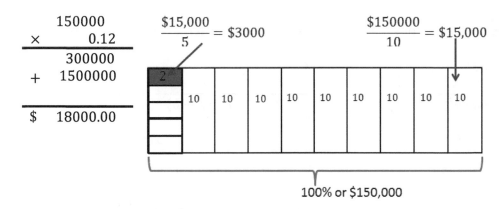

$$\begin{array}{r} 150000 \\ \times \quad 0.12 \\ \hline 300000 \\ + \quad 1500000 \\ \hline \$ \quad 18000.00 \end{array}$$

$$\frac{\$15,000}{5} = \$3000$$

$$\frac{\$150000}{10} = \$15,000$$

100% or $150,000

The whole (100%) is worth $150,000. So 10% is worth a tenth of the whole or $\frac{\$150,000}{10} = \$15,000$, and 2% is a 5th of 10% or $\frac{\$15,000}{5} = \$3000$. So combining the two we get that 12%=(10+2)% will be $\$15000 + \$3000 = \$18,000$.

d. We need to evaluate $(6.4 \times 10^6)^2 = (6.4 \times 10^6)(6.4 \times 10^6)$. We can multiply the powers of 10 and the 6.4×6.4 separately to get:

$(6.4 \times 10^6)^2$

$= (6.4 \times 10^6) \times (6.4 \times 10^6)$

$= (6.4 \times 6.4) \times (10^6 \times 10^6)$ (Associative, and Commutative Property of Multiplication)

$= 40.96 \times 10^{12}$

$= 4.096 \times 10 \times 10^{12}$

$= 4.096 \times 10^{13}$

$10^6 \times 10^6 = 10^{12}$

$$
\begin{array}{r}
6.4 \\
\times\ 6.4 \\
\hline
256 \\
+\ 384 \\
\hline
40.96
\end{array}
$$

Video Log 2.2b

1. Multiply the following and combine like terms.

a. 3×24	e. $3(2x + 4)$
b. 324×2	f. $(3x^2 + 2x + 4)(2)$
c. 23×65	g. $(2x + 3)(6x + 5)$
d. 4.01×0.0023	h. $(4x^2 + 1)(2x + 3)$
What are the differences or similarities between a & e, between b & f, between c & g, and between d & h?	
i. 23^2 (*no calculators*)	n. $(a + b)^2$
j. 3.45×5.3	o. $(2a + 3b)^2$
k. 34.5×0.0053	p. $(a + b)^3$
l. 600×9	q. $(7x + 3)(8x^2 + 3x + 4)$
m. 400×67	r. $(5x^2 + 7x + 3)(8x^2 + 3x + 4)$

2. Use a strip diagram to compute the percentages below and how you would use multiplication to represent the solution.

   a. 15% of 1200\$ b. 40% of 1020

   c. 71% of 1500\$ d. \$25% of 630

3. Use the distributive property to compute 12×306 by viewing $306 = 300 + 6$ and filling in the blanks $12 \times (300 + 6) =$ (_____) + (_____) = (_____).
4. If a coat that is $80 has a 35% markdown, determine the sale price of the coat.
5. Compute the simple interest earned over 3 years on a principal of $4000 with interest rate of 3.5%.
6. Compute the product of the number $G = 6.7 \times 10^{-11}$ and $M = 6 \times 10^{24}$. $M \cdot G =$? Give the final result in scientific notation.
7. If $f(x) = 3$, and $g(x) = 2x + 4$, then find $y = f(x) \cdot g(x)$. This function is referred to as the product of functions f and g and is denoted as $(f \cdot g)(x)$.

Using Multiplication To Add Rational Expressions
Playing

Lecture

Adding Rational Expressions Using Multiplication

https://www.youtube.com/watch?v=J9qz5xSlIOA **(6 min)**

With our ability to multiply polynomials we can now play with adding rational expressions that have more complicated denominators. Remember that in adding rational expressions the key is to make them have the same size pieces which means making their denominators the same. Thus the first task is changing each rational expression into another equivalent rational expression so that all the addends have the same denominator. The examples below show how to use multiplication of polynomials to obtain common denominators to solve more complicated addition problems.

Practice examples

Combine each sum of rational expressions into a single rational expression.

1. $\dfrac{2}{3 + 4x} + \dfrac{4}{x}$

Like Terms

$$\frac{2}{3+4x} + \frac{4}{x} = \frac{2(x)}{(3+4x)(x)} + \frac{4(3+4x)}{x(3+4x)} = \frac{2x + 12 + 16x}{x(3+4x)} = \frac{18x + 12}{x(3+4x)}$$

2. $\dfrac{1}{3+a}+\dfrac{2}{1+a}$

$$\frac{1}{3+a}+\frac{2}{1+a}=\frac{1(1+a)}{(3+a)(1+a)}+\frac{2(3+a)}{(1+a)(3+a)}$$

Like Terms   Like Terms

$$=\frac{1+a+6+2a}{(1+a)(3+a)}$$

$$=\frac{7+3a}{(1+a)(3+a)}$$

3. $\dfrac{5x}{2+x}+\dfrac{x}{2x+3}$

$$\frac{5x}{2+x}+\frac{x}{2x+3}=\frac{5x(2x+3)}{(2+x)(2x+3)}+\frac{4(2+x)}{(2x+3)(2+x)}$$

Like Terms

$$=\frac{10x^2+15x+8+4x}{(2+x)(2x+3)}=\frac{10x^2+19x+8}{(2+x)(2x+3)}$$

4. $\dfrac{3x}{3+4x}+\dfrac{2x+1}{x+2}$

$$\frac{3x}{3+4x}+\frac{2x+1}{x+2}=\frac{3x(x+2)}{(3+4x)(x+2)}+\frac{(2x+1)(3+4x)}{(x+2)(3+4x)}$$

Like Terms   Like Terms

$$=\frac{(3x^2+6x)+(6x+8x^2+3+4x)}{(3+4x)(x+2)}=\frac{11x^2+16x+3}{(3+4x)(x+2)}$$

5. $\dfrac{3x + 1}{x + 3} + \dfrac{5x + 12}{2x + 1}$

$$\dfrac{3x + 1}{x + 3} + \dfrac{5x + 12}{2x + 1} = \dfrac{(3x + 1)(2x + 1)}{(x + 3)(2x + 1)} + \dfrac{(5x + 12)(x + 3)}{(2x + 1)(x + 3)}$$

Like Terms   Like Terms   Like Terms

$$= \dfrac{(6x^2 + 5x + 1) + (5x^2 + 27x + 36)}{(x+3)(2x+1)} = \dfrac{11x^2 + 32x + 37}{(x+3)(2x+1)}$$

We want to write our final answers to all these problems with least amount of effort. We could multiply the denominator out, but it is most often more useful to leave the bottom as a product of factors. This will be useful when the final result can be reduced by dividing out factors common to the top and bottom.

Video Log 2.2c

1. Perform the following additions.

   a. $\dfrac{2}{5} + \dfrac{3}{4}$

   b. $\dfrac{3}{x} + \dfrac{4}{5}$

   c. $\dfrac{1}{x+1} + \dfrac{3}{2}$

   d. $\dfrac{1}{a+1} + \dfrac{a}{a+2}$

   e. $\dfrac{x}{2x+1} + \dfrac{5x}{x+3}$

   f. $\dfrac{(3x+2)}{x+1} + \dfrac{5x}{x+4}$

   g. $\dfrac{(x+3)}{x+4} + \dfrac{(5x+2)}{2x+1}$

Additive and Multiplicative Inverses

Lecture

💻 Properties of Subtraction http://www.youtube.com/watch?v=W9PEgpFyAYg (15 min)

Subtraction is also a binary operation and is denoted by "−". Subtraction is the inverse or reverse process of addition. That means we can think of subtraction as undoing addition. When we introduced addition of two quantities or groups of objects, we visualized this by starting with the count of one of the groups and counting upwards through the second group to get the total number of objects in both groups. Subtraction which is the inverse of this process can be thought of as starting with a given number of objects and counting down from it by the amount of the second group or you can think of it as removing or taking some number of objects away from a group. Thus $7apples - 4apples$ means we start with a group of seven apples and count 4 down from 7, which would look like 6,5,4,3. So our answer would be 3 apples. Or you can think of it as take 4 apples away and the number remaining is $(7 - 4)apples$. When we are dealing with whole number subtraction, we can simply count backwards.

Terminology

If a is any mathematical object we studied so far then, $-a$ is called the **additive inverse** of a and when added to a, gives the sum of zero.

In other words: $a + (-a) = 0$ and also a is the additive inverse of $-a$. The sum of an object and its additive inverse is always equal to zero. On a number line, the additive inverse of a number lies the same distance from zero, but on the opposite side from zero as the original number.

Examples

Find the additive inverse of

1. 2
2. $\frac{1}{4}$
3. -3

4. $\sqrt{x + 1}$
5. x^2
6. $f(x)$

Solutions

1. The additive inverse of 2 is -2.
2. The additive inverse of $\frac{1}{4}$ is $-\frac{1}{4}$.

---

3. The additive inverse of -3 is $-(-3) = 3$

4. The additive inverse of $\sqrt{x+1}$ is $-\sqrt{x+1}$.

5. The additive inverse of x^2 is $-x^2$.

6. The additive inverse of $f(x)$ is $-f(x)$.

Remember how we said that multiplication is repeated addition? This means $2(-1)$ is adding two copies of (-1) giving us $2(-1) = (-1) + (-1) = -2$. Also, since multiplication is commutative, $(2)(-1) = (-1)(2) = -2$. In a similar way multiplying any algebraic object by (-1) on the left or the right gives the additive inverse of that object.

Observation: Multiplying any mathematical object a we have studied so far by -1 gives us its additive inverse $-a$.

This fact would give us $-1(-a) = -a(-1) = a$ since a is the additive inverse of $-a$. Thus a negative times a negative is positive.

Observation: Any mathematical object $-a$ we have studied so far can be thought of as $-1(a)$.

Note that it is true that $a - a = 0$ by our our definition of subtraction as taking a objects away from a objects and also $a + (-a) = 0$. Therefore, adding the negative of an object can be thought of as subtracting that object: $a + (-b) = a - b$. Also note that subtraction is clearly not commutative since, e.g. $2 - 5 = -3$ and $5 - 2 = 3$. In the expression $a - b - c$, the convention is to perform the subtractions in order from left to right when no grouping symbols are present. This can also be rewritten as $a + (-b) + (-c) = a + (-c) + (-b) = a - c - b$, due to the commutative and associative property of addition. Thus thinking of subtraction as adding the additive inverse allows us to use the commutative property of addition to move subtracted terms as long as we move the minus with the terms being subtracted. Thus $a - b - c = -b + a - c$. This property will allows us to use an algorithm for subtraction similar to the addition algorithm by focusing on like units. The only difference being that instead of the carry over process, we will use an unbundling process as will be seen a little later.

Note that since $a(-b) = a\big(b(-1)\big) = (ab)(-1) = (-1)(ab)$ (we have used the commutative and associative property of multiplication here), and the fact that $(-1)(ab)$ represents additive inverse of ab which is $-ab$ we have the observation below.

Observation: For any two mathematical objects a, b we have studied so far, $a(-b) = -ab$.

Notice that $(-a)(-b) = -1(a)(-b) = -1(-ab)$ or that $(-a)(-b)$ is the additive inverse of $-ab$ which is ab.

Observation For any two mathematical objects a, b we have studied so far, $(-a)(-b) = ab$,

Notice too that $a(1 - 1) = a \cdot 0$ but also, $a(1 + (-1)) = a + (-a) = 0$.

Observation $a \cdot 0 = 0$ for any mathematical object a we have studied so far. This is called the zero product property of real numbers.

Playing

Since the multiplicative process is based on the concept of repeated addition, a natural question to ask would be: Is there a multiplicative inverse for a mathematical object like we talked about additive inverse? The answer is yes. Remember we defined that an additive inverse of a mathematical object a is an object that when added to a gives the additive identity which is 0, i.e. $a + (-a) = 0$. So to get a multiplicative inverse of a mathematical object a, we require the product of the object and its multiplicative inverse to be the multiplicative identity which is 1. Thus for all the objects $a \neq 0$ that we have studied so far, $a \cdot (multiplicative\ inverse\ of\ a) = 1$.

Terminology: If we let a represent any non-zero mathematical object that we have studied, then b is called the **multiplicative inverse** of a, or the **reciprocal** of a *if and only if*

$$a \times b = b \times a = 1.$$

Note: *For all $a \neq 0$ mathematical objects, $a \times \frac{1}{a} = \frac{1}{a} \times a = 1$. Thus $\frac{1}{a}$ is the multiplicative inverse of a, (as long as $a \neq 0$.)*

In other words: Multiplying a nonzero mathematical object by its multiplicative inverse or reciprocal, results in the multiplicative identity or 1.

Note: *Some facts you may want to note so as to avoid confusion between the two mathematical objects a^{-1}, and $-a$. Recall that $a^{-1} = \frac{1}{a}$. So a^{-1} is the multiplicative inverse of a, and $-a = -1(a)$ is the additive inverse of a. Additive inverses have opposite signs (or are symmetrically on opposite sides of zero on the real number line e.g., $2 + (-2) = 0$), but multiplicative inverses have the same sign (or are on the same side of zero on the real number line e.g., $3 \cdot \frac{1}{3} = 1$, and $(-4) \cdot \left(-\frac{1}{4}\right) = 1$).*

Example

Find the multiplicative inverse of the following.

1. 3

2. −4

3. x (assume x is a real number not equal to zero)

4. $\sqrt{x+1}$ (assume x is a real number greater than -1)

Solutions

1. The multiplicative inverse of 3 is $\frac{1}{3}$.

2. The multiplicative inverse of -4 is $\frac{1}{-4}$, or since we know how to create equivalent fractions, we have $\frac{1}{-4} = \frac{1 \times -1}{-4 \times -1} = \frac{-1}{4} = -\frac{1}{4}$.

3. The multiplicative inverse of x is $\frac{1}{x}$.

4. The multiplicative inverse of $\sqrt{x+1}$ is $\frac{1}{\sqrt{x+1}}$.

Note: *The multiplicative inverse of a mathematical object has the same sign as the original object. This supports the fact that a negative multiplied by a negative is a positive number.*

Playing

Multiplication distributes over addition as we saw earlier, e.g., $3(x+2) = 3 \times x + 3 \times 2 = 3x + 6$. This fact and the knowledge that we can write a subtraction problem as an addition problem using additive inverse (which means $a - b = a + (-b)$) allows us to extend that **multiplication distributes over subtraction.**

Distributive property of multiplication over subtraction: If a, b, and c represent any three mathematical objects we have studied so far, then

$a \times (b - c) = a \times b - a \times c$, or $a(b - c) = ab - ac$

$(b - c) \times a = b \times a - c \times a$, or $(b - c)a = ba - ca = ab - ac$

In other words: We can distribute multiplication over subtraction of two or more mathematical objects.

Terminology: Multiplication distributes over subtraction.
For example, $a(b - c - d - e) = ab - ac - ad - ae$, or

$(b - c - d - e)a = ba - ca - da - ea = ab - ac - ad - ae$

Examples

1. Multiply $2(-4x)$.

Remember that multiplication can be thought of as repeated addition so we have

$$2(-4x) = -4x + (-4x) = -8x$$

Do you think the statement below is true since we have the distributive property of multiplication?

$$-2(-4x) = -2(-4)(-2(-x))$$

The answer to this questions is NO. Remember the full words of the property "Distributive property of multiplication **over addition or subtraction**". So it is not the same as just saying distributive property of multiplication. Pay careful attention to the words as that is how your brain is going to remember it. You can also think of $-2(-4x)$ as the additive inverse of $2(-4x) = -4x + (-4x) = -8x$. We know that additive inverse of $-8x$ is $8x$ therefore $-2(-4x) = 8x$ and in contrast to $-2(-4)(-2(-x))$ which simplifies to $8(2x) = 16x$. So remember -"Multiplication does not distribute over multiplication!"

Another way to stress the point that multiplication does not distribute over multiplication is to think about the expression $3(wl)$, where w represents width of a rectangle and l represents the length of the rectangle, and let $A = wl$ represent the area of the rectangle. Draw a picture of a rectangle of length l and width w and also draw a picture of three of these i.e., $3(wl)$. Next consider the quantity $3w \times 3l$ and draw a rectangle with width $3w$ and length $3l$ and convince yourself that this is not the same as $3(wl)$ and that indeed $3(wl) = 3wl$ and not $(3w) \times (3l) = 9wl$.

2. Multiply $3(x^2 - 5)$

We know that $3(x^2 - 5) = 3(x^2 + (-5)) = 3x^2 + (-15) = 3x^2 - 15$, or that

$3(x^2 - 5) = 3 \times x^2 - 3 \times 5 = 3x^2 - 15$. Note that we used the distributive property of multiplication over addition (or over subtraction depending on how one writes the terms in the parentheses).

Remember that $-(3x^2 - 4x)$ can also be thought of as $-1(3x^2 - 4x) = (-1)3x^2 - (-1)(4x) = -3x^2 + 4x$. We know that multiplying by a -1 gives the additive inverse of the object. Therefore $(-1)3x^2 = -3x^2$ and subtracting an additive inverse is the same as adding the original object so $-(-1)4x = 4x$.

Note: We have seen that addition is commutative, but a single example shows that subtraction is not commutative e.g. $3 - 5 = -2$, but $5 - 3 = 2$. Since we have seen that subtracting a quantity is the same as adding its additive inverse, we can move terms around in a combination of addition and subtraction of terms, but the subtracted terms must move with their subtraction sign. For example $3x^2 - 5x - 3 + 3x - 6x^2$ can be rearranged as $3x^2 -$

> $6x^2 - 5x + 3x - 3$. *This follows from the commutative property of addition as:* $3x^2 + (-5x) + (-3) + 3x + (-6x^2)$ *which rearranged becomes* $3x^2 + (-6x^2) + (-5x) + 3x + (-3)$ *which simplifies to* $-3x^2 - 2x - 3$.

Note: *Subtraction is also not associative as you can see from the example* $2 - (4 - 3) \neq (2 - 4) - 3$ *since* $2 - (4 - 3) = 2 - 1 = 1$ *and* $(2 - 4) - 3 = -2 - 3 = -5$.

Just like we focused on like units and bundling while working with addition, we now focus on like units and unbundling when necessary while working with subtraction.

Lecture

💻 Subtraction Algorithm <u>http://www.youtube.com/watch?v=azaR-4ySSwQ</u> (9 min)

Practice Examples

Perform following subtractions.

1. $5ft\ 3in - 1ft\ 10in$

2. $(5\ weeks + 3\ days + 5\ hours + 23\ minutes)$

   $-(4\ weeks + 6\ days + 19\ hours + 53\ minutes)$

3. Identify the property of real numbers that justifies each equation. Select from: Commutative property of addition; Commutative property of multiplication; Associative property of addition; Associative property of multiplication; Additive identity property; Additive inverse property; Distributive property of multiplication over addition; Multiplicative identity property; Multiplicative inverse property; And zero product property.

   a. $x \cdot 0 = 0$

   b. $\frac{1}{2} \times 2 = 1$

   c. $-4\sqrt{2} + 4\sqrt{2} = 0$

   d. $26 - 0 = 26$

   e. $(5 + y) \cdot x = 5x + yx$

Attempt these problems yourself before looking at the answers below.

Solutions

To solve these problems you can write them one under the other so that the units are lined up. This helps you understand how you can only subtract like units and that some units can unbundle into smaller units.

1. $5\,ft\,3\,in - 1\,ft\,10\,in$
   To solve this problem remember that to unbundle a ft. we can use, $1ft = 12in$, and that we can only take way from like units.

   $$1ft\,3in = 12in + 3in = 15in$$

   Unbundle $1ft$ from the $5ft$ leaving us with $4ft$.

ft	in
4	15
$\cancel{5}$	$\cancel{3}$
$-$ 1	10
3	5

   Final Answer:
   $5ft\,3in - 1ft\,10in$
   $= 4ft\,15in$
   $- 1ft\,10in = 3ft\,5in$

2. $(5\,weeks + 3\,days + 5\,hours + 23\,minutes)$
   $-(4\,weeks + 6\,days + 19\,hours + 53\,minutes)$
   Remember that $7days = 1week$, $24hours = 1day$, $1hour = 60minutes$
   Let the variables stand for $w = weeks, d = days, h = hours, m = minutes$.
   So our problem now looks as $(5w + 3d + 5h + 23m) - (4w + 6d + 19h + 53m)$
   In order to subtract like units, we may have to unbundle using the facts above if necessary. So for example, the weeks go together, the days go together, and so on.

   $(5w + 3d + 5h + 23m) - (4w + 6d + 19h + 53m)$

   $= (4w + 7d + 2d + 24h + 4h + 60m + 23m) - (4w + 6d + 19h + 53m)$

   $= (4w + 9d + 28h + 83m) - (4w + 6d + 19h + 53m)$

   $= (4w - 4w) + (9d - 6d) + (28h - 19h) + (83m - 53m)$

   $= (4 - 4)w + (9 - 6)d + (28 - 19)h + (83 - 53)m$

   $= 0w + 3d + 9h + 30m$

   $= 3d + 9h + 30m$

   (The work below shows another way to show your steps using the unbundling principle.)

$w = Weeks$	$d = Days$	$h = Hours$	$m = Minutes$
4	$7 + 2 = 9$	$24 + 4 = 28$	$60 + 23 = 83$
$\cancel{5}$	$\cancel{3}$	$\cancel{5}$	$\cancel{23}$
$-$ 4	6	19	53
0	3	9	30

   ($1w = 7d$, $1d = 24h$, $1h = 60m$)

   Final Answer: $3days\ 9\ hour\ 30\ minutes$

3.   a. $x \cdot 0 = 0$ Zero product property of real numbers

        b. $\frac{1}{2} \times 2 = 1$ Multiplicative inverse property of real numbers

        c. $-4\sqrt{2} + 4\sqrt{2} = 0$ Additive inverse property of real numbers

        d. $26 - 0 = 26$ Additive identity property of real numbers

        e. $(5 + y) \cdot x = 5x + yx$ Distributive property of multiplication over addition.

In examples 1. and 2. above, we subtracted the same kind of objects, i.e., distance with distance, and time with time, but they consisted of different units of each. We used unbundling of larger units into smaller groups much like in the standard algorithm for subtracting decimal numbers except the rate of bundling varies for minutes, hours, days and weeks. We start with the smallest units and unbundle a neighboring larger unit if necessary to combine with the smaller unit so we can subtract. This means you move right to left and borrow (unbundle) from the left digit as necessary when working with decimal number subtraction similar to the problems above.

Subtraction Algorithm

The standard method for subtracting decimal numbers follows the above examples. The only difference while subtracting decimal numbers is that the unbundling occurs always at a rate of one to ten. Recall that in a decimal number, each digit has its own unit based on its place (as we saw in chapter one). For example, in the number 123.58, the digit 8 is in the hundredths place, the 5 is in the tenths place, the 3 is in the ones place, and so on. Also remember that one group of tenths make ten one hundredths, one group of ones makes ten tenths, one group of tens makes ten ones, and so on. So to subtract decimal numbers, we subtract only like terms (That would mean you subtract the digits in the hundredths places together, the digits in the tenths places together, and so on.). Do keep in mind that if the digit you are subtracting from is smaller than the number you are subtracting, unbundle a group of the next larger place value to the left to yield ten of the smaller units. For example, if we wanted to subtract $523.27 - 294.48$, then we first subtract the 8 hundredths from the 7 hundredths, but since that is not possible, we unbundle one tenth to ten hundredths to obtain 17 hundredths. Now we can subtract 8 hundredths from it leaving us with 9 hundredths. A similar unbundling is used when subtracting $52,327 - 29,448$.

See below

$$
\begin{array}{r}
\ 4 \quad 11 \quad 12 \quad 11 \\
\ \cancel{5}\ \cancel{2}\ \cancel{3}.\ \cancel{2}\ \ 17 \\
-\ 2\ \ 9\ \ \ 4.\ \ 4\ \ \ \ 8 \\
\hline
\ 2\ \ 2\ \ \ 8.\ \ 7\ \ \ \ 9
\end{array}
\qquad
\begin{array}{r}
\ 4 \quad 11 \quad 12 \quad 11 \\
\ \cancel{5}\ \cancel{2}\ \cancel{3}\ \cancel{2}\ \ 17 \\
-\ 2\ \ 9\ \ \ 4\ \ \ 4\ \ \ \ 8 \\
\hline
\ 2\ \ 2,\ \ 8\ \ \ 7\ \ \ \ 9
\end{array}
$$

Video Log 2.3a
1. Evaluate the following.
   a. $456 - 315$
   b. $514.21 - 40.89$
   c. On August 16, 1991 at 5:25pm Vandana got married. Can you tell Vandana how long she has been married to the minute on June 27th, 2016 at 11:00am?
   d. Suzy took medicine at 1:17pm today, and the previous dose was 5 hours, 10 mins, and 38 seconds ago. At what time did Suzy take her previous dose?
   e. $1550 - 404 - 378$
2. What do you do when there is a zero in the next place value to the left as occurs in the problem '505 − 179' ?
3. What happens if there is no digit on the left to borrow from as in $17 - 56$?
   Explain what to do then.
4. Answer the following questions.
   a. Is subtraction commutative? In other words if a and b are any two mathematical objects we have studied so far, is $a - b = b - a$?
   b. Explain if $a - b$ is the additive inverse of $b - a$.
   c. Explain if $-1(a - b) = b - a$.
5. Multiply the following and explain the similarities and differences between the problems.
   a. $3(40 - 2)$ c. $3(4x - 2)$

   b. $(31)(40 - 2)$ d. $(3x + 1)(4x - 2)$

Practice Examples

Subtract the following decimal numbers by hand! No calculators allowed on these problems.

1. $505 - 179$
2. $0.0056 - 0.003589$
3. $56987.45 - 8795.579$

Solutions

1. $505 - 179 = 326$

$$
\begin{array}{r}
9 \;\; 15 \\
4 \;\; \cancel{10} \\
\cancel{5} \;\; \cancel{0} \;\; \cancel{5} \\
- \; 1 \;\; 7 \;\; 9 \\
\hline
3 \;\; 2 \;\; 6
\end{array}
$$

2. $0.0056 - 0.003589$

    $= 0.005600 - 0.003589$

    $= 0.002011$

$$
\begin{array}{cccccccc}
 & & & & & & 9 & \nearrow 10 \\
 & & & & 5 & \nearrow \cancel{10} & & \\
0. & 0 & 0 & 5 & \cancel{6} & \cancel{0} & \cancel{0} & \\
-\;\; 0. & 0 & 0 & 3 & 5 & 8 & 9 & \\
\hline
0. & 0 & 0 & 2 & 0 & 1 & 1 & \\
\end{array}
$$

3. $56987.45 - 8795.579$

    $= 56987.450 - 8795.579$

    $= 48191.871$

$$
\begin{array}{cccccccc}
 & & & & & & 13 & 14 \\
4 & 16\,_8 & _8 & 18 & 6\,\nearrow3 & \nearrow\cancel{4} & \nearrow 10 \\
5 & \cancel{6} & \cancel{9} & 8 & 7. & \cancel{4} & \cancel{5} & \cancel{0} \\
-\;0 & 8 & 7 & 9 & 5. & 5 & 7 & 9 \\
\hline
4 & 8 & 1 & 9 & 1. & 8 & 7 & 1 \\
\end{array}
$$

Number Line Visualization of Adding And Subtracting Real Numbers

Lecture

🖥 Visualizing Subtraction

http://www.youtube.com/watch?v=PwQGc_1p0jQ (8 min)

You already know how to plot numbers on a number line. Visualizing negative numbers on the number line is very helpful in doing subtraction of real numbers. On a number-line you can think of adding as going in the direction of the number that you are adding. Whereas subtraction corresponds to moving in the direction opposite to the number you are subtracting. For example, think of $200 - 300 = -100$ as you had $200 and you bought a TV for $300, which means you now have a $100 debt. So you can think of negative numbers like -3 as being debt of 3 dollars and $-(-3)$ as taking away a debt of $3. We will work more with negative numbers and subtraction of negative numbers shortly.

Addition and subtraction can be viewed geometrically as movements on a number line. Each real number x can be associated with a movement from the origin to the place on the number line corresponding to the value of the number x. Thus positive numbers correspond to moving to the right and negative numbers movement to the left. Adding two numbers corresponds to the net overall movement that results from doing the two movements one after another. Thus for $a + b$, we start at the origin, move "a" to the number a and from there move "b" to end at $(a + b)$. Adding b moves you in the direction of the sign of b number that many units. Subtracting b moves you in the opposite direction of the sign of b that many units. Thus for $2 + 1.5$ you start at zero, move 2 units right and then a further 1.5 units to the right to end up at 3.5. In the problem $2 - 1.5$ you start at zero, move 2 units to the right and then move 1.5 units left to end at 0.5. In the problem $2 - (-1.5)$, start at zero, move two units right and then move the opposite of (-1.5) or 1.5 units to end at 3.5. See the examples below to visualize the addition and subtraction of real numbers on a number line.

Examples:

1. $2 + 1.5$

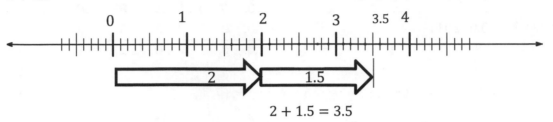

$$2 + 1.5 = 3.5$$

2. $-2 + 3.5$

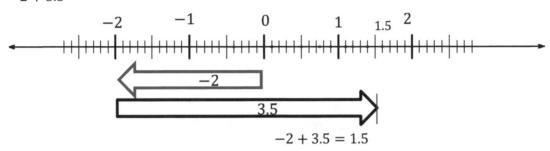

$$-2 + 3.5 = 1.5$$

3. $2 - 2$ or $2 + (-2)$

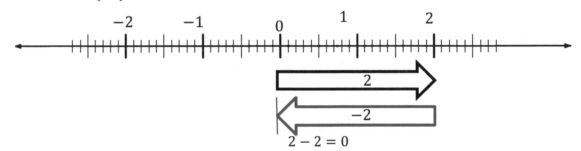

$$2 - 2 = 0$$

4. $2 - 3$

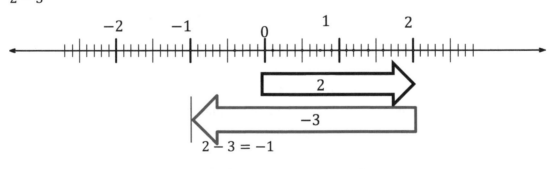

$$2 - 3 = -1$$

$$2 - 3 = 2 + (-3) = -1$$

5. $-2 - (-3)$

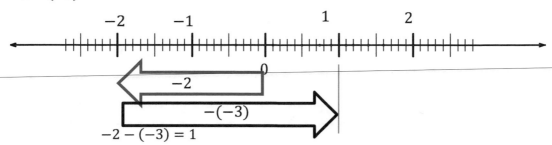

$$-2 - (-3) = 1$$

Remember that subtracting a negative number is like taking away debt.

6. $-23.5 + 31.3 - 45.6$
   Here we see that the result will be negative, so we determine how far left of zero(negative numbers) we will end up at. Adding $23.5 + 45.6 = 69.1$, then move 69.1 units left of zero or imagine being at -69.1. Then move 31.3 units right from -69.1. We end $69.1 - 31.3 = 37.8$ units left of zero, or imagine being at -37.8. Thus the answer is -37.8.

Note: *What you see so far is that while showing $a + b$ on a number line we first move a units from zero and then move the distance indicated by b in the direction indicated by the sign of b. While showing $a - b$ means we first move a units from zero and then move the distance indicated by b except in the opposite direction as b.*

Video Log 2.3b

1. For all problems below show how to visualize the addition or subtraction on a number line.
   a. $-4.5 + 2$ f. $2.3 - 4$
   b. $-3 - 2$ g. $-23 - 35$
   c. $-1.1 - (-5)$ h. $-54 + 22$
   d. $-5 + 3$ i. $-11.3 - 8.5 + 4.2$
   e. $5 - (-3)$

2. Use subtraction and/or addition to express what is shown in each of the problems below.
   a.

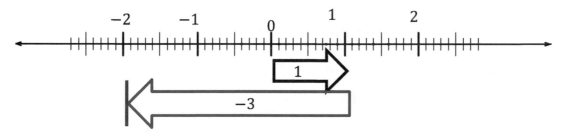

b.

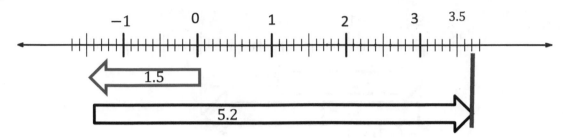

c.

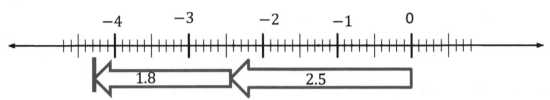

3. Create an addition-subtraction problem by filling in two numbers in the blanks
    $-4.5 + (\quad) - (\quad) = -3$.
    Also insert two arrows corresponding to your numbers so that you end up at -3 in the diagram below.

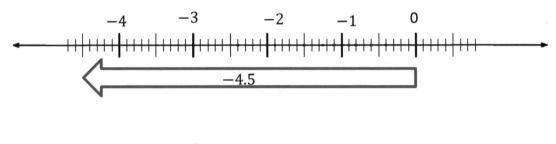

4. Describe scenarios which lead to each of the subtraction problems below.
    a. $45.27 - 6.85$
    b. $-200 - 40 + 530$

Absolute Value of Real and Complex Numbers

Terminology: The **absolute value** of a real number x is defined to be the distance one travels on a number line to go from zero to the number x, and is denoted by $|x|$. For all nonzero real numbers x, this distance is always considered to be a positive number.

Examples:

$|3| = 3, |{-3}| = 3$, and $|0| = 0$. Also if $|x| = 5$ then there are only two places on a number line where x could be, i.e., 5 units from zero would require that x either be 5 or -5.

From the geometric view of addition it should be clear we can always get back to zero on a number line by starting with any movement from zero (any number x) and then going the same distance but in the opposite direction. Algebraically we'd write this as $x + (-x) = 0$.

Complex Plane Visualization of Adding And Subtracting Complex Numbers

You can visualize adding and subtracting complex numbers in a similar manner. In Module 1 you saw how to visualize plotting complex numbers in the plane. Recall that when adding and subtracting complex numbers we add or subtract real parts together and imaginary parts together.

Practice examples

1. $(2 + i) + (1 + 3i)$
    $= (2 + 1) + (1 + 3)i$
    $= 3 + 4i$
    The two summands $2 + i$, and $1 + 3i$ are represented by the movement arrows as shown on the right and the resulting sum is represented by the purple arrow. You will notice that the result of the addition is the diagonal of the parallelogram formed by the two complex number summands. You can arrive at the sum by first moving from zero to the tip of the green arrow and from there, move in the direction and amount indicated by the red arrow.

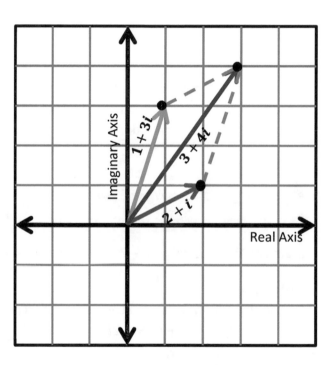

2. $(1 + 3i) - (-2 + 2i)$
    $= (1 - (-2)) + (3 - 2)i$
    $= 3 + 1i = 3 + i$

> **Note** *that the additive inverse of* $-2 + 2i$ *is given by* $-(-2 + 2i) = 2 - 2i$. *You can see that the additive inverse is the arrow shown in orange going in the opposite direction from 0. Again the result of the subtraction is also the diagonal of the parallelogram formed by the two arrows consistent with vector addition.*

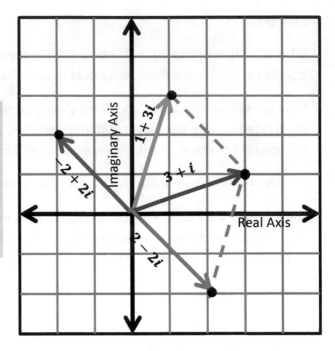

When a complex number is viewed as a point in the complex plane we can consider its distance from the origin. When a complex number is viewed as a vector in the complex plane the concept of distance is referred to as its magnitude.

Terminology

Absolute value (also known as magnitude) of a complex number $a + bi$ denoted as $|a + bi| = \sqrt{a^2 + b^2}$ is the distance from the origin to the point at $a + bi$.

Example: Absolute value of $-2 + 3i$ would be $|-2 + 3i| = \sqrt{(-2)^2 + (3)^2} = \sqrt{4 + 9} = \sqrt{13}$

Video Log 2.3c

1. Plot the following addition and subtraction problems of complex numbers in the complex plane.

    a. $(3 - 4i) + (-5 + 2i)$

    b. $(2 - 4i) - (3 - 2i)$

2. Find the value of

    a. $|-51|$

    f. $|-8 - 5|$

    b. $|51|$

    g. $|-3i|$

    c. $-|6|$

    h. $|2 + 5i|$

    d. $8 - |-5|$

    i. $|3 - 4i|$

    e. $|-5 - 8|$

3. Draw the complex number $z = 2 + 5i$ and then draw another number such that $(2 + 5i) +$
   (   ) $= 7 + 2i$.

Subtraction of Other Mathematical Objects

Playing

Lecture

🖥 Subtraction   http://www.youtube.com/watch?v=E7Cj8QnEmNo (12 min)

We can extend the method of subtracting decimal numbers to subtracting polynomials and other mathematical objects studied so far; e.g., $(9x^4 + 2x^3 + 3x^2 + 5x + 6) - (5x^4 + 9x^3 + 4x^2 + x + 7)$, where the like units are identified with common exponent on x. The only difference in subtracting polynomials compared to decimal number system is that we do not unbundle as there is no equivalency between a certain number of "x" making a group of "x^2". Where we would have had to unbundle we may end up with negative coefficients instead.

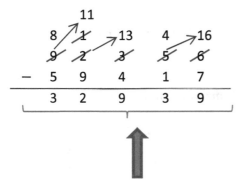

Borrowing or Unbundling

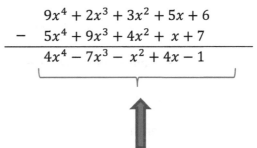

No borrowing or unbundling

Practice Examples

Perform the subtractions.

1. $3(a + b) - u(a + b) - v(a + b)$

2. $9\ cm + 6\ cm^2 - 4\ cm - 2\ cm^2$

3. $3km - 7m - 200cm$

4. $6.3m - 4.7cm$

5. $(3 + 4i) - (5 + 2i)$

6. $3(x + 1) - 5(x + 1)$

7. $-3(x + 1) - a(x + 1)$

8. $\qquad -3(2x+1) - 7(2x+1)$

9. $\qquad -3\sqrt{2x+1} - 7\sqrt{2x+1}$

10. $\qquad 3\sqrt{2}x - 5x$

11. $\qquad 5\sqrt{2x+1} - 3\sqrt{2x+1}$

12. $\qquad 3x^4\sqrt[3]{x^2 y} - 5x^4\sqrt[3]{x^2 y}$

13. $\qquad 2x\sqrt{3y} - 3\sqrt{3y}$

14. $\qquad 9\sqrt{x} + 15\sqrt[3]{x} - 3\sqrt{x} - 7\sqrt[3]{x}$

15. $\qquad -3a^{\frac{2}{3}} + 7b^{\frac{4}{5}} - 5a^{\frac{2}{3}} - 13b^{\frac{4}{5}}$

Solutions

1. $3(a+b) - u(a+b) - v(a+b) = (3 - u - v)(a+b)$ Just like we did with addition of like unit terms, now we are subtracting like unit terms.

2. $9\,cm + 6\,cm^2 - 4\,cm - 2\,cm^2 = (9-4)cm + (6-2)cm^2 = 5\,cm + 4\,cm^2$

3. $3km - 7m - 200cm = 3000m - 7m - 2m = (3000 - 7 - 2)m = 2991m$

   Here we remember that $1m = 100cm, 1km = 1000m$ or that $200cm = 2m$, and $3km = 3000m$

4. $6.3m - 4.7cm = 630cm - 4.7cm = 625.3cm$

5. $(3+4i) - (5+2i) = (3-5) + (4-2)i = -2 + 2i$ Again we are subtracting like terms and so the real parts go together which is the $3-5$ and the imaginary parts go together which is the $(4-2)$ copies of i.

6. $3(x+1) - 5(x+1) = (3-5)(x+1) = -2(x+1)$, $(x+1)$ is the common unit here.

7. $-3(x+1) - a(x+1) = (-3-a)(x+1)$, $(x+1)$ is the common unit here.

8. $-3(2x+1) - 7(2x+1) = (-3-7)(2x+1) = -10(2x+1)$,

   $(2x+1)$ is the common unit here.

9. $-3\sqrt{2x+1} - 7\sqrt{2x+1} = (-3-7)\sqrt{2x+1} = -10\sqrt{2x+1}$,

   $\sqrt{2x+1}$ is the common unit here.

10. $3\sqrt{2}x - 5x = (3\sqrt{2} - 5)x$, x is the common unit here.

11.

$5\sqrt{2x+1} - 3\sqrt{2x+1} = 2\sqrt{2x+1}$, $\sqrt{2x+1}$ is the common unit here.

12.

$3x^4\sqrt[3]{x^2y} - 5x^4\sqrt[3]{x^2y} = -2x^4\sqrt[3]{x^2y}$, $x^4\sqrt[3]{x^2y}$ is the common unit here.

13.

$2x\sqrt{3y} - 3\sqrt{3y} = (2x-3)\sqrt{3y}$, $\sqrt{3y}$ is the common unit here.

14.

$9\sqrt{x} + 15\sqrt[3]{x} - 3\sqrt{x} - 7\sqrt[3]{x} = (9-3)\sqrt{x} + (15-7)\sqrt[3]{x} = 6\sqrt{x} + 8\sqrt[3]{x}$.

There are two different units involved here $\sqrt{x}$, and $\sqrt[3]{x}$.

15.

$-3a^{\frac{2}{3}} + 7b^{\frac{4}{5}} - 5a^{\frac{2}{3}} - 13b^{\frac{4}{5}} = (-3-5)a^{\frac{2}{3}} + (7-13)b^{\frac{4}{5}} = -8a^{\frac{2}{3}} - 6b^{\frac{4}{5}}$,

There are two different units involved here, $a^{\frac{2}{3}}$ and $b^{\frac{4}{5}}$. Note that we are not adding the exponents here since it is not multiplication and the bases of the units are different.

Video Log 2.3d

1. Perform the subtractions below without using a calculator. Pay attention to the bundling at each place value where it is required.

a. $46 - 21$	e. $(4x + 6) - (2x + 1)$
b. $736 - 122$	f. $(7x^2 + 3x + 6) - (x^2 + 2x + 2)$
c. $303 - 474$	g. $(2x^2 + 9) - (4x^2 + 7x + 4)$
d. $3489 - 896$	h. $(3x^3 + 4x^2 + 8x + 9) - (8x^2 + 9x + 6)$
What are the differences or similarities between a & e, between b & f, between c & g, and between d & h?	
i. $4507.89 - 103.54$	m. $(4507x + 0.89) - (103x + 0.54)$
j. $2482 - 55 - 797$	n. $(2x^4 + 4x^3 + 8x + 2) - (5x + 5) - (7x^2 + 9x + 7)$
k. $32.9 - 24.7 - 29.8$	o. $(3x + 2.9) - (2x + 4.7) - (2x + 9.8)$
l. $73,407 - 8200$	p. $(7x^4 + 3x^3 + 4x^2 + 7) - (8x^3 + 2x^2)$
What are the differences or similarities between i & m, between j & n, between k & o, and between l & p?	

2. Perform the following subtractions and explain the similarities and differences in the basic process you used.

a. $(4 - 2i) - (-7 - 6i)$	i. $(4 - 2x) - (-7 - 6x)$

b. $6(3x-4)-5x(3x-4)$	j. $6a(3x-4)-5x(3x-4)$
c. $\sqrt{2}(x-3)-a(x-3)$	k. $\sqrt{2}(x-\sqrt{3})-a(x-\sqrt{3})$
d. $6(u+v)-2(u+v)$	l. $a(u+v)-b(u+v)$
e. $3(a-b)-5(a-b)$	m. $3a(a-b)-5b(a-b)$
f. $3a(a+b)-2a(a+b)$	n. $3a(a+b)-2b(a+b)$
g. $\sqrt{3a}(t+p)-\sqrt{3a}(t+p)$	o. $\sqrt{3a}(\sqrt{t+p})-\sqrt{3a}(\sqrt{t+p})$
h. $4km-7m-500kg$	p. $4\sqrt{27}-7\sqrt{3}+5$

3. Perform the following subtractions and combine like terms.

a. $8x-4x$	f. $3x^2-4x+6\sqrt[3]{x}-5x-8x^2-10\sqrt[3]{x}$
b. $8\sqrt{x}-4\sqrt{x}$	g. $12a\sqrt{b}-7b\sqrt{a}+8a\sqrt{b}-3\sqrt{a}$
c. $x-x$	h. $12\sqrt{b^2}-7\sqrt{a^4}-8\sqrt{b^2}+3\sqrt{a^4}$
d. $\sqrt{x}-\sqrt{x}$	i. $-5\sqrt{4x^2}-5x\sqrt{9y^2}-7xy-5x\sqrt{y}$
e. $5\sqrt{ab}+7\sqrt{ab}-8\sqrt{ab}$	j. $-3\sqrt{4x^2y}-5x\sqrt{9xy^2}+7xy-5x\sqrt{y}$

k. $15a\sqrt[5]{b^6}-11a\sqrt[3]{b^5}-\sqrt{3a}+2b\sqrt[3]{a^3b^2}-6ab\sqrt[5]{ab}+\sqrt{3a}$

l. $\sqrt{a^2b^3}-10ab\sqrt{b}-5b\sqrt{a^6b}$

m. $-5ab\sqrt{a^6b^3}-7\sqrt[3]{a^9b^6}+3a^3b^2+4b^2\sqrt{a^8}-6b^2\sqrt[3]{a^9}$

n. $5\sqrt[3]{2a^5y^7}-7ab^2\sqrt[5]{a^3b^2}-8ay^2\sqrt[3]{54a^2y}-\sqrt[5]{32a^8b^{12}}$

o. $(4x^3-6x^2-7x+12)-(5x^6+3x^4-7x^3+10x-21)$

p. $-2\sqrt{6}-\sqrt[5]{3}-3\sqrt{5}-7\sqrt{2}+6\sqrt[5]{3}-4\sqrt{5}$

q. $f(t)=4-\sqrt{t}, g(t)=5t-2$, find $(f-g)(t)$

4. First round each number to the nearest hundreds place and then subtract to approximate $1378-652$.

5. Adam skied 1245 km in 2013 and 1057 km in 2012. How many more km did he ski in 2013 than in 2012?

6. Write an expression using subtraction of at least two mathematical objects whose difference is given below.

    a. 58.65

    b. 7089

    c. $17x + 23$

    d. $4x^4 - 12x^3 - 5x^2 - 7x + 10$

7. Use subtraction with a 24-hour clock time to compute the number of days, hours and minutes that passed between Monday May 4th at 3:45PM and later that week on Saturday at 8:47 AM. Express this vertically and show the undbundling that is required at three unit levels.

Subtraction of Rational Expressions

Lecture

🖥 Subtraction of Rational Expressions
http://www.youtube.com/watch?v=Vuvmrq54b4w (8 min)

Across the examples above we subtract like units. When dealing with fractions, remember we have to make like units by converting to equivalent fractions with the same denominator so we can then add or subtract the numerators.

Practice Examples

1.
$$\frac{3}{7} - \frac{5}{7}$$
$$= \frac{3-5}{7}$$
$$= \frac{-2}{7}$$
$$= -\frac{2}{7}$$

    $\frac{1}{7}$ is the common unit here

2.
$$\frac{3}{7} - \frac{5}{2}$$
$$= \frac{3 \times 2}{7 \times 2} - \frac{5 \times 7}{2 \times 7}$$
$$= \frac{6}{14} - \frac{35}{14}$$
$$= -\frac{29}{14}$$

    $\frac{1}{14}$ is the common unit here

3.

$$\frac{3}{x} - \frac{5}{2}$$

$$= \frac{3 \times 2}{x \times 2} - \frac{5 \times x}{2 \times x}$$

$$= \frac{6}{2x} - \frac{5x}{2x}$$

$$= \frac{6 - 5x}{2x}$$

$\frac{1}{2x}$ is the common unit here

4.

$$4\frac{3}{5} - 2\frac{1}{4}$$

$$= \left(4 + \frac{12}{20}\right) - \left(2 + \frac{5}{20}\right)$$

$$= 4 - 2 + \frac{12 - 5}{20}$$

$$= 2\frac{7}{20}$$

We can subtract the wholes and the fractional parts separately with a common denominator of 20:

5.

$$7\frac{2}{3} - 3\frac{4}{5}$$

$$= \left(7 + \frac{10}{15}\right) - \left(3 + \frac{12}{15}\right)$$

$$= \left(6 + \frac{25}{15}\right) - \left(3 + \frac{12}{15}\right)$$

$$= 3\frac{13}{15}$$

We can subtract the wholes and the fractional parts separately with a common denominator of 15.

Since we have only $\frac{10}{15}$ and have to subtract $\frac{12}{15}$ from it, we need to unbundle a unit from 7 giving us $7 + \frac{10}{15} = 6 + \frac{15}{15} + \frac{10}{15} = 6 + \frac{25}{15}$.

6.

$$\frac{2 + x}{x + 4} - \frac{5x - 2}{x + 4}$$

$$= \frac{(2 + x) - (5x - 2)}{x + 4}$$

$$= \frac{(2 - (-2)) + (x - 5x)}{x + 4}$$

$$= \frac{(2 + 2) + (-4x)}{x + 4}$$

$$= \frac{4 - 4x}{x + 4}$$

$\frac{1}{x+4}$ is the common unit here

Note that we can't reduce this rational expression because there is no common factor between the top and bottom.

More examples:

Find the value of the problems below where

$f(x) = \sqrt{x} + 4x$	$g(x) = 5\sqrt{x} + 2x$	$h(t) = 2t + 4$
$r(t) = t^2 + 3t$	$s(t) = 5t^2 + 4t + 12$	

1. $(f - g)(x)$
2. $(r - s)(t)$
3. $(h - f)(a)$

Solutions

1. $(f - g)(x) = f(x) - g(x)$

$$= \sqrt{x} + 4x - (5\sqrt{x} + 2x)$$
$$= (1 - 5)\sqrt{x} + (4 - 2)x$$
$$= -4\sqrt{x} + 2x$$

2. $(r - s)(t) = r(t) - s(t) = t^2 + 3t - (5t^2 + 4t + 12)$

$$= (1 - 5)t^2 + (3 - 4)t + (0 - 12)$$
$$= -4t^2 - t - 12$$

3. $(h - f)(a) = h(a) - f(a) = 2a + 4 - \left(\sqrt{a} + 4a\right)$

$$= (2 - 4)a + 4 - \sqrt{a}$$
$$= -2a + 4 - \sqrt{a}$$

Now that we know how to subtract, let's work with the distributive property of multiplication over subtraction (keep in mind you already know how to use the distributive property of multiplication over addition).

Practice Examples

1. Multiply $-4(x - 2)$.

   Using our distributive property we have

   $$-4\,(x - 2) = -4 \times x - 4 \times (-2) = -4x + 8$$

2. Multiply $-x(x - 2)$

   Using our distributive property we have

   $$-x\,(x - 2) = -x \times x - x \times (-2) = -x^2 + 2x$$

3. Multiply $(2x - 3) \times (3x - 7)$.

We have used the distributive property of multiplication over addition and the commutative and associative property of multiplication to write $2x \times 3x = 6x^2$. You can see that the two ways shown below are valid no matter how many terms are in each factor. You can also extend this method for more than two factors, you just have to multiply two of the factors at a time and then multiply that product by the third factor etc. and have patience.

$(2x - 3) \times (3x - 7)$

$$= 2x \times 3x + 2x \times (-7) - 3 \times 3x - 3 \times (-7)$$
$$= 6x^2 - 14x - 9x + 21$$
$$= 6x^2 - 23x + 21$$

Or

$(2x - 3) \times (3x - 7)$

$$= (2x - 3) \times 3x + (2x - 3) \times (-7)$$
$$= 2x \times 3x - 3 \times 3x + 2x \times (-7) - 3 \times (-7)$$
$$= 6x^2 - 9x - 14x + 21$$
$$= 6x^2 - 23x + 21$$

4. Multiply $(2x^2 - 3x - 6)(3x^3 - 4x + 7)$

$(2x^2 - 3x - 6)(3x^3 - 4x + 7)$

$$= 2x^2 \cdot 3x^3 + 2x^2 \cdot (-4x) + 2x^2 \cdot 7 - 3x \cdot 3x^3 - 3x \cdot (-4x) - 3x \cdot 7 - 6 \cdot 3x^3 - 6\,(-4x) - 6(7)$$

$$= 6x^5 - 8x^3 + 14x^2 - 9x^4 + 12x^2 - 21x - 18x^3 + 24x - 42$$

$$= 6x^5 - 9x^4 - 26x^3 + 26x^2 + 3x - 42$$

5. Multiply $(2x - 5)^2$

$$(2x - 5)^2 = (2x - 5)(2x - 5) = 2x(2x) + 2x(-5) - 5(2x) - 5(-5)$$

$$= 4x^2 - 10x - 10x + 25 = 4x^2 - 20x + 25$$

6. Multiply $-1(a - b)$

$$-1(a - b) = -1(a) - 1(-b) = -a + b$$

Since addition is commutative we have $-a + b = b + (-a) = b - a$

Notice that $-1(a - b) = b - a$.

Playing

Now that we have worked with subtraction a little and the distributive property of multiplication over addition and subtraction we can revisit addition and subtraction of rational expressions and rational numbers.

Practice Examples

Perform the addition and subtraction of the rational expressions below.

1. $\dfrac{2}{2+3x} - \dfrac{3}{2x}$

2. $\dfrac{1}{3-a} - \dfrac{2}{1-a}$

3. $\dfrac{5x}{2-x} - \dfrac{x}{2x+3}$

4. $\dfrac{2+x}{3x+1} - \dfrac{5x-2}{x+4}$

Solutions

1. $\dfrac{2}{2+3x} - \dfrac{3}{2x}$

As you know when adding or subtracting fractions we need to have the same units. When the denominators are not the same, we must first convert each rational expression (as needed) to equivalent expressions so as to obtain a common denominator, i.e., like units. When the denominators are different, one fast way to get the fractions to have like units is to multiply the first fraction top and bottom by the denominator of the second fraction, and multiply the second fraction's top and bottom by the denominator of the first fraction.

$$\frac{2}{2+3x} - \frac{3}{2x} = \frac{2(2x)}{(2+3x)(2x)} - \frac{3(2+3x)}{2x(2+3x)}$$

$$= \frac{4x}{2x(2+3x)} - \frac{6+9x}{2x(2+3x)}$$

$$= \frac{4x - (6+9x)}{2x(2+3x)}$$

$$= \frac{4x - 1(6+9x)}{2x(2+3x)}$$

$$= \frac{4x - 6 - 9x}{2x(2+3x)}$$

$$= \frac{(4-9)x - 6}{2x(2+3x)}$$

$$= \frac{-5x - 6}{2x(2+3x)}$$

Caution!
Make sure you remember to subtract both terms in the numerator as shown. You can think of the negative sign on the outside as being multiplied by -1. So remember to use the distributive property of multiplication over subtraction.

2.
$$\frac{1}{3-a} - \frac{2}{1-a}$$

Following the same principles as the first example we get:

$$\frac{1}{3-a} - \frac{2}{1-a} = \frac{1(1-a)}{(3-a)(1-a)} - \frac{2(3-a)}{(1-a)(3-a)}$$

$$= \frac{1-a}{(3-a)(1-a)} - \frac{6-2a}{(1-a)(3-a)} \quad \text{Caution!}$$

$$= \frac{(1-a) - 1(6-2a)}{(3-a)(1-a)}$$

$$= \frac{(1-a) - 6 + 2a}{(3-a)(1-a)}$$

$$= \frac{1-6-a+2a}{(3-a)(1-a)}$$

$$= \frac{-5+a}{(1-a)(3-a)}$$

Make sure you remember to subtract both terms in the numerator as shown. You can think of the negative sign on the outside as being multiplied by −1 (which is the same as adding additive inverse). So remember to use the distributive property of multiplication over addition/subtraction.

A similar discussion as in the above problems will allow you to solve the rest of the problems. Try them on your own first before checking the solutions.

3.
$$\frac{5x}{2-x} - \frac{x}{2x+3} = \frac{5x(2x+3)}{(2-x)(2x+3)} - \frac{x(2-x)}{(2x+3)(2-x)}$$

$$= \frac{(5x)(2x) + (5x)(3)}{(2-x)(2x+3)} - \frac{x(2) + x(-x)}{(2x+3)(2-x)}$$

$$= \frac{10x^2 + 15x}{(2-x)(2x+3)} - \frac{2x - x^2}{(2-x)(2x+3)}$$

$$= \frac{10x^2 + 15x - (2x - x^2)}{(2-x)(2x+3)}$$

$$= \frac{10x^2 + 15x - 2x + x^2}{(2-x)(2x+3)}$$

$$= \frac{11x^2 + 13x}{(2 - x)(2x + 3)}$$

4. $\dfrac{2 + x}{3x + 1} - \dfrac{5x - 2}{x + 4}$

$$\frac{2 + x}{3x + 1} - \frac{5x - 2}{x + 4} = \frac{(2 + x)(x + 4)}{(3x + 1)(x + 4)} - \frac{(5x - 2)(3x + 1)}{(x + 4)(3x + 1)}$$

$$= \frac{x^2 + 6x + 8}{(3x + 1)(x + 4)} - \frac{15x^2 - x - 2}{(x + 4)(3x + 1)}$$

$$= \frac{x^2 + 6x + 8 - (15x^2 - x - 2)}{(3x + 1)(x + 4)}$$

$$= \frac{x^2 + 6x + 8 - 15x^2 + x + 2)}{(3x + 1)(x + 4)}$$

$$= \frac{(1 - 15)x^2 + (6 + 1)x + (8 + 2)}{(3x + 1)(x + 4)}$$

$$= \frac{-14x^2 + 7x + 10}{(x + 4)(3x + 1)}$$

<u>Caution</u>: In general be careful to multiply the numerators using the distributive property of multiplication over addition or subtraction as necessary, and then carry out the subtraction.

1. Multiply the following and simplify by combining like terms.

    a. $-15(3x - 4)$

    e. $(x + 5)(3x - 4)$

    b. $x(3 - x)$

    f. $(2x - 3)(3x - 7)$

    c. $(x - 1)(x + 1)$

    g. $x(7x - 2) - 3x(5x - 4)$

    d. $a(2 - a) - 3(a - 5)$

    h. $(a + 2)(3a - 1) - (a - 2)(2a - 5)$

2. Perform the following subtractions and simplify your answer.

    a. $\dfrac{7}{9} - \dfrac{2}{9}$

    g. $\dfrac{2}{3} - \dfrac{1}{2}$

    l. $\dfrac{4}{a-1} + \dfrac{a}{a-2}$

    b. $\dfrac{7}{x} - \dfrac{2}{x}$

    h. $-\dfrac{2}{3} - \dfrac{1}{2}$

    m. $\dfrac{x}{2x-1} - \dfrac{5x}{3-x}$

    c. $\dfrac{5}{x+2} - \dfrac{3}{x+2}$

    i. $2\dfrac{1}{3} - 4\dfrac{3}{4}$

    n. $\dfrac{(3x-2)}{x-1} - \dfrac{5x}{x-4}$

    d. $\dfrac{5x}{x+2} - \dfrac{3x}{x+2}$

    j. $\dfrac{2}{x} - \dfrac{1}{2}$

    o. $\dfrac{(x+3)}{x-4} + \dfrac{(2-5x)}{2x-1}$

    e. $\dfrac{5x}{x+2} - \dfrac{3}{x+2}$

    k. $\dfrac{1}{x-1} + \dfrac{3}{2x-1}$

    p. $\dfrac{(x+3)}{x-4} - \dfrac{(2-5x)}{2x-1}$

    f. $\dfrac{2}{3} + \dfrac{1}{2}$

3. Answer true or false and justify your answers using correct mathematical terminology.

    a. $(-3x^3 - 4x^2) - (5x^3 - 9x^2) = -8x^3 - 13x^2$

    b. $x^2(x^3)(x^4) = (x^2 x^3)(x^2 x^4)$

    c. $2(3 \times 5) = (2 \times 3) \times (2 \times 5)$

    d. $4 - (3 + 2) = (4 - 3) + (4 - 2)$

    e. $(3 + 2) - 4 = (3 - 4) + (2 - 4)$

    f. $-2(-4 - 5) = 8 - 10$

    g. $\dfrac{\cancel{3}}{5} + \dfrac{2}{\cancel{3}} = \dfrac{2}{5}$

4. Below you see problems that are solved by some students. Please read them to determine if the solutions are correct or incorrect. If you notice a solution that is incorrect, carefully explain where the mistake is. Explain what mathematical property or process was misapplied.

a. $(2x^2 - 11x - 10) - (5x^3 - 9x^2 + 7x - 1)$

$$= 2x^2 - 11x - 10 - 5x^3 - 9x^2 + 7x - 1$$

$$= -5x^3 - 7x^2 - 4x - 11 \text{ (Final Answer)}$$

b. $(2x^2 - 11x - 10) - (5x - 1)$

$$= 10x^3 - 2x^2 - 55x^2 + 11x - 50x + 10$$

$$= 10x^3 - 57x^2 - 39x + 10 \text{ (Final Answer)}$$

c. $5\frac{3}{7} - 3\frac{1}{2} = (5 - 3)\left(\frac{3}{7} - \frac{1}{2}\right)$

$$= 2\left(\frac{6}{14} - \frac{7}{14}\right)$$

$$= 2\frac{-1}{14} \text{ (Final Answer)}$$

d. $\dfrac{(2x-3)}{x-2} - \dfrac{(7-2x)}{2x-3}$

$$= \frac{(2x - 3)(2x - 3)}{(x - 2)(2x - 3)} - \frac{(7 - 2x)(x - 2)}{(2x - 3)(x - 2)}$$

$$= \frac{4x^2 - 6x - 6x + 9 - 7x - 14 - 2x^2 + 4x}{(x - 2)(2x - 3)}$$

$$= \frac{2x^2 - 15x - 5}{(x - 2)(2x - 3)} \text{ (Final Answer)}$$

2.4 Factoring

Lecture

🖥 **Prime factors and multiples of expressions**
http://www.youtube.com/watch?v=wy7pm8wjm_8 (8 min)

Playing

Now that we know how to add and subtract some rational expressions, let's look at the problems below where the denominators are more complicated. We start by using our previous strategies look what happens:

Examples
Perform the arithmetic operations below.

1. $\dfrac{61}{810} + \dfrac{53}{150}$

2. $\dfrac{x+5}{x^2 - 3x + 2} - \dfrac{x-3}{x^2 - 4}$

Solutions

1. $\dfrac{61}{810} + \dfrac{53}{150} = \dfrac{61 \times 150}{810 \times 150} + \dfrac{53 \times 810}{150 \times 810} = \cdots$

   You would then multiply the numerators and finish adding them over the denominator. In this and many problems a much simpler common denominator can be found, e.g., $81 \times 10 \times 15$ would be simpler.

2. $\dfrac{x+5}{x^2 - 3x + 2} - \dfrac{x-3}{x^2 - 4} = \dfrac{(x+5) \times (x^2 - 4)}{(x^2 - 3x + 2) \times (x^2 - 4)} - \dfrac{(x-3) \times (x^2 - 3x + 2)}{(x^2 - 4) \times (x^2 - 3x + 2)}$

   Similar to the first problem there is a simpler denominator that will work.

Mathematicians are not always satisfied with solving problems in one way. They strive to do things as efficiently as possible. We will now look at how to find the simplest common denominators for problems above.

Let us look at the above two above problems a bit more carefully. If we look at each denominator, they already have some similarity to each other.

1. $\dfrac{61}{810} + \dfrac{53}{150} = \dfrac{61}{2 \times 3^4 \times 5} + \dfrac{53}{2 \times 3 \times 5^2}$.
   We can make the denominators the same here by multiplying the numerator and denominator by much smaller numbers than 150 and 810. In fact we can use 5 for the first and $3^3 = 27$ for the second denominator. Then both denominators become $2 \times 3^4 \times 5^2$.

$$\frac{61}{810} + \frac{53}{150} = \frac{61}{2 \times 3^4 \times 5} + \frac{53}{2 \times 3 \times 5^2}$$

$$= \frac{61 \times 5}{2 \times 3^4 \times 5 \times 5} + \frac{53 \times 3^3}{2 \times 3 \times 5^2 \times 3^3}$$

$$= \frac{61 \times 5}{2 \times 3^4 \times 5 \times 5} + \frac{53 \times 3^3}{2 \times 3 \times 5^2 \times 3^3}$$

$$= \frac{305}{2 \times 3^4 \times 5^2} + \frac{1431}{2 \times 3^4 \times 5^2}$$

$$= \frac{1736}{2 \times 3^4 \times 5^2} = \frac{868}{3^4 \times 5^2}$$

2. The two denominators can be written in factored form as $x^2 - 3x + 2 = (x - 2)(x - 1)$ and $x^2 - 4 = (x - 2)(x + 2)$ Thus:

$$\frac{x + 5}{x^2 - 3x + 2} - \frac{x - 3}{x^2 - 4} = \frac{(x + 5)}{(x - 2) \times (x - 1)} - \frac{(x - 3)}{(x + 2)(x - 2)}$$

$$= \frac{(x + 5) \times (x + 2)}{(x - 2) \times (x - 1)(x + 2)} - \frac{(x - 3) \times (x - 1)}{(x + 2)(x - 2)(x - 1)}$$

$$= \frac{(x^2 + 2x + 5x + 10) - (x^2 - x - 3x + 3)}{(x - 2)(x + 2)(x - 1)}$$

$$= \frac{x^2 + 2x + 5x + 10 - x^2 + x + 3x - 3}{(x - 2)(x + 2)(x - 1)}$$

$$= \frac{(x^2 - x^2) + (7x + 4x) + (10 - 3)}{(x - 2)(x + 2)(x - 1)}$$

$$= \frac{11x + 7}{(x - 2)(x + 2)(x - 1)}$$

Even though the original problems seemed much more complicated, once we knew the factors of the denominators, making like size pieces or a common denominator was much easier. To understand this concept we first develop some terminology and get comfortable with it, and then we will come back to these kinds of problems.

Multiples
Lecture

🖥 **Multiples** http://www.youtube.com/watch?v=f3ZdozzChjQ (9 min)

Terminology: In a product ab, where a, and b, are any two mathematical objects we have studied so far, the individual objects a and b are referred to as **factors**, and the quantity ab can be referred to also as a **multiple** of a, and also as a **multiple** of b.

Examples

1. $a = 1(a), 2a, a^2, ab, a(x+1), a\sqrt{x+1}, a\sqrt[3]{b}, a^2b^2c$, are all multiples of a. A multiple of a is $a \cdot (something)$.

2. $1, 5, 7, and\ 25$ are all factors of 175 as $175 = 1 \times 25 \times 7$

3. If a is a mathematical object we have studied so far, then are there finitely or infinitely many multiples of a?

4. List two multiples of 6, and two factors of 6.

Note: *In general many mathematical objects can be written as a product of other objects called factors.*

Terminology: A mathematical object that can only be written as a product of the multiplicative identity 1 and the object itself is called a **prime** object. Objects that are not prime objects are referred to as **composite** objects.

Examples:

1. The whole numbers 6, 9, 24 and 39 are all composite numbers since $6 = 2 \times 3$, $9 = 3 \times 3$, $24 = 4 \times 6$, $39 = 3 \times 13$.

2. The whole numbers 13, 41, 43, and 97 are all prime numbers since they cannot be written as the product of two whole numbers larger than one.

3. The polynomial $x^2 + 3x + 2 = (x+2)(x+1)$ is called a composite polynomial and $x + 2$ and $x + 1$ are its factors.

4. The polynomials like x, and $(x+1)$, are called **irreducible** or **prime polynomials**.

The number $650 = 2 \cdot 5^2 \cdot 13$ is a multiple of both $26 = 2 \cdot 13$ and of $325 = 5^2 \cdot 13$ since 650 is obtained by multiplying 26 by 5^2 and also 650 is obtained by multiplying 325 by 2. We say 650 is a common multiple of both 26 and 325. In fact since no other smaller whole number can be a multiple of both 26 and 325, 650 is called the **least common multiple** of 26 and 325. We will now develop this concept more fully. All integers and polynomials can be written as a product of prime numbers or prime (irreducible) polynomials respectively. This is known as the fundamental theorem of arithmetic or algebra respectively.

Factoring an expression into a product of prime (or irreducible) factors turns out to be useful in many situations in addition to the motivating examples with fraction addition above.

Observation: An integer or a polynomial a is a multiple of b if and only if all factors of b are also factors of a.

Examples:

Answer the following questions and justify your answers.

1. Is 72 a multiple of 24?

2. Is $2^4 \times 3^{10} \times 5^4 \times 7^3$ a multiple of $2^2 \times 3^4 \times 5^3$?

3. Is $2^4 \times 3^{10} \times 5^2 \times 7^3$ a multiple of $2^2 \times 3^5 \times 5^6 \times 7^{12}$?

4. Is $(x-1)^4 \times (2x+5)^{10} \times (x+\sqrt{3})^{19} \times x^3$ a multiple of $(x-1)^2 \times (x+\sqrt{3})^5 \times x^3$?

5. Is $(x-1)^2 \times (2x+5)^6 \times (x+\sqrt{3})^2$ a multiple of $(x-1)^4 \times (x+\sqrt{3})^2 \times x^3$?

Do think about the answers before reading any further the solutions to these problems.

Remember that for object A to be a multiple of object B, object A must consists of all the factors of object B and possibly more. One way to determine whether or not you have a multiple of an object is to check factor by factor.

Solutions

1. We need to see if all factors of 24 are also factors of 72. We check this by looking at the prime factorization of both numbers. Thus $24 = 8 \cdot 3 = 2^3 \cdot 3$ and $72 = 8 \cdot 9 = 2^3 \cdot 3^2$. Now since 72 has all the prime factors of 24 (and one extra 3) it will have as factors every factor that 24 does and hence 72 is a multiple of 24.

2. Let us look at all the factors one by one to determine if $2^4 \times 3^{10} \times 5^4 \times 7^3$ is a multiple of $2^2 \times 3^4 \times 5^3$.

    The number $2^4 \times 3^{10} \times 5^4 \times 7^3$ must contain all the factors with exponent or power at least as large as in the second number $2^2 \times 3^4 \times 5^3$

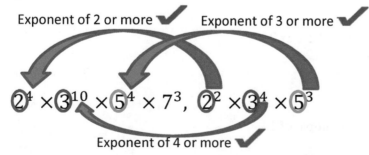

As you can see all the factors match up and their exponents in the first number are greater than or equal to the exponents of the factors in the second number making the first number a multiple of the second number. Therefore, $2^4 \times 3^{10} \times 5^4 \times 7^3$ is a multiple of $2^2 \times 3^4 \times 5^3$.

---

3. Is $2^4 \times 3^{10} \times 5^2 \times 7^3$ a multiple of $2^2 \times 3^5 \times 5^6 \times 7^{12}$?

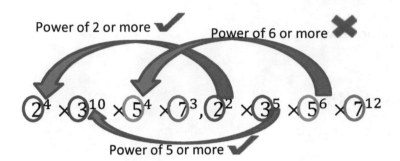

As you can see all factors match up but not all exponents in the first number are greater than or equal to the exponents of the second number. For example the exponent of the base 5 in the first number is 4 which less than the exponent of the same base in the second number which is 6. Note also that the exponent on the base 7 is too small for the first number to be a multiple of the second.

So $2^4 \times 3^{10} \times 5^2 \times 7^3$ is not a multiple of $2^2 \times 3^5 \times 5^6 \times 7^{12}$

4. Is $(x-1)^4 \times (2x+5)^{10} \times \left(x+\sqrt{3}\right)^{19} \times x^3$ a multiple of $(x-1)^2 \times \left(x+\sqrt{3}\right)^5 \times x^3$

You can see that all factors of the second algebraic expression appears in the first expression, further the exponents of each of the bases in the second expression are lower than or equal to the corresponding exponents of the first expression so

$(x-1)^4 \times (2x+5)^{10} \times \left(x+\sqrt{3}\right)^{19} \times x^3$ is a multiple of $(x-1)^2 \times \left(x+\sqrt{3}\right)^5 \times x^3$.

5. Is $(x-1)^2 \times (2x+5)^6 \times \left(x+\sqrt{3}\right)^2$ a multiple of $(x-1)^4 \times \left(x+\sqrt{3}\right)^2 \times x^3$

You can see that the factor of x in the second expression does not appear in the first expression and therefore $(x-1)^2 \times (2x+5)^6 \times \left(x+\sqrt{3}\right)^2$ is not a multiple of $(x-1)^4 \times \left(x+\sqrt{3}\right)^2 \times x^3$.

Video Log 2.4a

1. Which of the following, if any, is a multiple of 24:

    a. 4   b. 24   c. 12   d. 72

2. Which of the following, if any, is a multiple of 14:

    a. 2   b. 28   c. 1400   d. 21

3. Which of the following, if any, is a multiple of $11^4 \times 5^5 \times 13^8$:

   A. $11^4 \times 5^{14} \times 13^{10} \times 7^8$ B. $11^3 \times 5^2 \times 13^2$

4. Which of the following, if any, is a multiple of $(x-1)(2x-3)$:

   A. $x-1$ D. $(x-1)(2x-3)(3-x)$

   B. $x(x-1)$ E. $x(x-1)(2x-3)(4+x)$

   C. $(x-1)^2(2x-3)^2$ F. $(x+\sqrt{2})^5(x-1)^4(3-5x)^6(x^2+1)^8$

5. Which of the following, if any, is a multiple of $(x+1)$:

   A. $x(x-1)$ D. $5(x+1)^4$

   B. $x+1$ E. $x^2(x+1)$

   C. x F. $(x+\sqrt{2})^5(x+1)^4(3-5x)^6(x^2+1)^8$

6. Which of the following, if any, is a multiple of $(x-1)^2 \cdot x^6 \cdot (3x+1)^8$:

   A. $(x-1)^{12} \cdot x^2 \cdot (3x-1)^3$ B. $(x-1)^2 \cdot x^6$

7. Which of the following, if any, is a multiple of $2^4 \times \left(3^2\right)^5 \times 5^3$:

   A. $2^2 \times 3^7$
   B. $2^3 \times 3 \times 5^0$

8. List at least one multiple of the mathematical objects below.
   a. 5
   b. $5x$
   c. $x-4$
   d. $x(3x+2)(x-1)$

9. The number 13 is considered to be prime. However a student noticed that $13 = \frac{1}{2} \cdot 26$ and claimed that this means 13 is not prime. Is the student correct, or is there more to being prime than that a number cannot be written as a product of two other numbers?

Lecture

> 🖥 Least Common Multiples http://www.youtube.com/watch?v=wJCWNcytyXE (15 min)

As we have seen, any integer or polynomial has infinitely many multiples, since we can simply multiply the integer or polynomial by any factor as often as we want to get a multiple. So given two or more integers or polynomials, a common multiple is a quantity that is a multiple of all the given objects and must contain all the factors of the given integers or polynomials.

Examples

1. The number 24 is a multiple of 2,3,4,6, and 12.

2. The polynomial $x^{31}(3x+1)^5(x+\sqrt{3})^{24}$ is a multiple of $x^3(3x+1)^5(x+\sqrt{3})^{12}$, $x^2(3x+1)^4$ and $(x+\sqrt{3})^2$.

You can see that just by changing the exponents we can generate infinitely many common multiples of two or more given integers or polynomials.

Terminology: The smallest common multiple of two or more algebraic objects is called their **Least Common Multiple.**

Examples

3. The number 12 is the least common multiple of 2, 3, 4 and 6, however 12, 24, 36,… and so on are also common multiples of 2, 3, 4, and 6.

4. The polynomial $x^3(3x+1)^5(x+\sqrt{3})^{12}$ is the least common multiple of
   $x^2(3x+1)^5(x+\sqrt{3})^{12}$, $x^3(3x+1)^4$ and $(x+\sqrt{3})^2$.

To find the least common multiple of two or more objects, we need to know all the prime factors of each object. Thus we start by writing each object in the list as a product of prime factors. Then the least common multiple is the product of all the distinct prime factors that appear in all of the objects, with each prime factor raised to the maximum exponent it appears to in any of the objects. It is also true that any common multiple of two or more objects can be obtained as a multiple of the least common multiple.

Examples

Find the least common multiple of the numbers or polynomials below.

1. 24 and 42

2. Find the LCM of 9, 12 and 18 and also all the common multiples of the three numbers that

are between 40 and 110.

3. $2^4 \times 3^{10} \times 7^3$, and $2^{12} \times 3^4 \times 5^2$

4. $(x+1)^4(3x-1)^{10}(x+\sqrt{3})^3$, and $(x+1)^{12}(3x-1)^4(1-x)^2$

5. $a^2b^{10}c^3$, and $b^3c^{12}d^5$

6. $3^2(x-1)^2(5x+1)^2(x+\sqrt{3})^7$, and $x^3(x+1)^9(5x+1)^{12}(x+\sqrt{3})$

7. $(x-1)(x+1)$, $(x+1)(2x-3)$, and $(2x-3)(x-1)$

8. $2^3(x-1)^3(x+5)^3$, and $3^2(x+1)^3(x-5)^3$

9. $(x+1)(x-1)$, and $(x-1)(2x+1)$

Solutions

1. We write $24 = 2^3 \cdot 3$ and $42 = 2 \cdot 3 \cdot 7$. The least common multiple has the factors 2, 3, and 7 raised to the exponents 3, 1 and 1 respectively, i.e. LCM$= 2^3 \cdot 3 \cdot 7$. Note that the LCM of a group or objects always has at least as many factors as any individual object.

2. The prime factorizations of 9, 12, and 18 are $9 = 3^2$, $12 = 3 \cdot 2^2$, $18 = 2 \cdot 3^2$. Thus the LCM of these three numbers is $LCM = 2^23^2 = 36$. All the other common multiples are multiples of 36. The only common multiples that are between 40 and 110 are $36 \cdot 2 = 72$ and $36 \cdot 3 = 108$

3. $2^4 \times 3^{10} \times 7^3$, and $2^{12} \times 3^4 \times 5^2$ is $2^{12} \times 3^{10} \times 5^2 \times 7^3$

   To find the least common multiple of the two numbers above we look at the prime factors involved and then choose appropriate exponents as shown below.

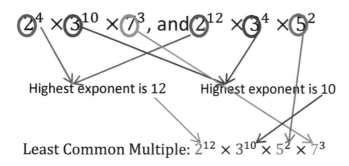

4. $(x + 1)^4 \times (3x - 1)^{10} \times (x + \sqrt{3})^3$, and $(x + 1)^{12} \times (3x - 1)^4 \times (1 - x)^2$

Again the least common multiple we can see must have the factors of $(x + 1), (3x - 1), (x + \sqrt{3})$, and $(1 - x)$. We use the highest exponent on each factor in the least common multiple. Therefore we choose the exponent of 12 on the factor $(x + 1)$, the exponent of 10 on the factor $(3x - 1)$, the exponent of 3 on the factor $(x + \sqrt{3})$, and 2 on the factor $(1 - x)$, giving us the least common multiple as $(x + 1)^{12} \times (3x - 1)^{10} \times (x + \sqrt{3})^3 \times (1 - x)^2$.

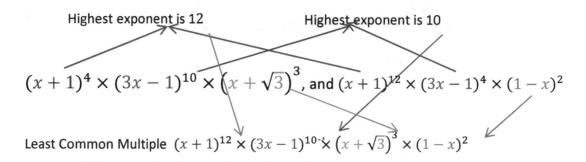

5. $a^2 b^{10} c^3$, and $b^3 c^{12} d^5$

The least common multiple is $a^2 b^{10} c^{12} d^5$. We took all the prime factors and raised them to the exponent that is highest amongst the two terms.

6. $3^2 (x - 1)^2 (5x + 1)^2 (x + \sqrt{3})^7$, and $x^3 (x + 1)^9 (5x + 1)^{12} (x + \sqrt{3})$

The least common multiple is $3^2 x^3 (x - 1)^2 (x + 1)^9 (5x + 1)^{12} (x + \sqrt{3})^7$.

7. $(x - 1)(x + 1)$, $(x + 1)(2x - 3)$, and $(2x - 3)(x - 1)$.

The least common multiple is $(x - 1)(x + 1)(2x - 3)$.

8. $2^3 (x - 1)^3 (x + 5)^3$, and $3^2 (x + 1)^3 (x - 5)^3$

Since the two terms do not share any common factors, the product of the two polynomials is the least common multiple.

The least common multiple is $2^3 \times 3^2 (x - 1)^3 (x + 5)^3 (x + 1)^3 (x - 5)^3$.

9. $(x + 1)(x - 1)$, and $(x - 1)(2x + 1)$

Since the two polynomials have no exponents higher than one we just have to make sure we account for all the prime factors, and therefore the least common multiple is

$(x + 1)(x - 1)(2x + 1)$.

Video Log 2.4b
1. Find the least common multiple. of
   a. 28 and 24

   b. 12, 6, and 8

   c. 4, 7, and 15

   d. $2^4 \times 3^5 \times 3^8$, $2^9 \times 3^{24}$, and $11^3 \times 5^2 \times 2^9 \times 3^{24}$

   e. $2^4 \times (3^2)^5 \times 5^3\ 2^2 \times 3^7$, and $2^3 \times 3 \times 5^0$

   f. $x(x+1)$, and $(x+1)(x-2)$

   g. $(2x-1)(3-x)$, and $(2x+1)(3+x)$

   h. $x^2(3x+1)$, and $x(3x+1)$

   i. $(x^2+1)(x-1)$, and $(x+1)(x-1)(x^2+1)$

   j. $(1+5x)(x-7)$, and $(5x+1)(1-x)(x-7)$

   k. $(2x+1)(1-x)$, and $(1+x)(2x+1), (3-x)(1-x)$

   l. $(x+1)^2\ x^6\ (x^2+x+1)^8,\ x(x^2+x+1)^2$, and

   $\left(x-\sqrt{3}\right)^5(x-1)^2\ (x+1)^3\ x^2\ (x^2+x+1)^4$

2. Answer true or false and justify your answer.

   a. The least common multiple of 2, and $(2+1)$ is 2.

   b. The least common multiple of 2, and $(2+1)$ is $2+1$.

   c. The least common multiple of x and $(x+1)$ is x.

   d. The least common multiple of x and $(x+1)$ is $x+1$.

   e. The least common multiple of x and $(x+1)$ is $x(x+1)$.

   f. The least common multiple of (x^2+1), and $(x+1)$, is x^2+1

3. If two numbers a both divisible by 18, does this mean their least common multiple is also divisible

   by 18?   Must any common multiple be divisible by 18?

Lecture

> 🖥 Adding Rational Expressions Using LCM
> http://www.youtube.com/watch?v=OOV6hbTE-2s (**12 min**)

Now that we have learned the concept of least common multiples, let's use it to find the least common multiples of two or more denominators (Least common denominators or LCD) to efficiently add and subtract rational expressions. Below are some practice problems and we would like you to try them using the logic above before you look at the solutions presented.

Practice Problems

Perform the following operations and simplify your answers.

1. $\dfrac{5}{12} - \dfrac{7}{18}$

2. $\dfrac{1}{2^2 \times 3^2 \times 5} + \dfrac{1}{2^3 \times 3^2 \times 7}$

3. $\dfrac{c^3}{a^5 b^2} - \dfrac{a^2}{7b^3 c^2}$

4. $\dfrac{(5x-1)}{(x+1)(x-2)} - \dfrac{3x}{(x-2)(x-1)}$

5. $\dfrac{(2x+1)}{(x-1)(3x+2)} - \dfrac{(5x-2)}{(3x-2)(x-1)}$

Solutions:

1. $\dfrac{5}{12} - \dfrac{7}{18}$ We first factor 12 and 18 to find the LCD. $12 = 2^2 \cdot 3$, and $18 = 2 \cdot 3^2$ thus the LCD $= 2^2 \cdot 3^2 = 36$. Converting to this LCD we have: $\dfrac{5 \cdot 3}{12 \cdot 3} - \dfrac{7 \cdot 2}{18 \cdot 2} = \dfrac{15-14}{36} = \dfrac{1}{36}$.

2. $\dfrac{1}{2^2 \times 3^2 \times 5} + \dfrac{1}{2^3 \times 3^2 \times 7}$

Remember that when adding or subtracting rational expressions, we need to convert to a common denominator. Using the least common multiple of the denominators can be much simpler than our previous method where we just multiplied the denominators together. Thus, the least common multiple of $(2^2 \times 3^2 \times 5)$ and $(2^3 \times 3^2 \times 7)$ is $(2^3 \times 3^2 \times 5 \times 7)$. In order to make both denominators the same we need to convert each fraction to equivalent fractions. We multiply the numerator and the denominator of each fraction by the factors missing from their denominators to get both fractions to the least common denominator. In the first fraction, the denominator $2^2 \times 3^2 \times 5$ is missing a factor of

2 and a factor of 7, the second denominator $2^3 \times 3^2 \times 7$ is missing the factor of 5. Converting each to the same denominator:

$$\frac{1}{2^2 \times 3^2 \times 5} + \frac{1}{2^3 \times 3^2 \times 7} = \frac{1 \times 2 \times 7}{2^2 \times 3^2 \times 5 \times 2 \times 7} + \frac{1 \times 5}{2^3 \times 3^2 \times 7 \times 5}$$

$$= \frac{14 + 5}{2^3 \times 3^2 \times 5 \times 7}$$

$$= \frac{19}{2^3 \times 3^2 \times 5 \times 7}$$

3. $\dfrac{c^3}{a^5 b^2} - \dfrac{a^2}{7b^3 c^2}$

Just like the previous example let us use the least common multiple of the two denominators. The least common multiple of $a^5 b^2$ and $7b^3 c^2$ is $7a^5 b^3 c^2$. The first denominator, which is $a^5 b^2$, is missing a factor $7bc^2$, so we will multiply the first fraction by that factor in the numerator and the denominator; the second denominator is $7b^3 c^2$ and is missing the factors of a^5 therefore the second term will get multiplied by a^5 in the numerator and the denominator. So we have

$$\frac{c^3}{a^5 b^2} - \frac{a^2}{7b^3 c^2} = \frac{c^3(7bc^2)}{a^5 b^2(7bc^2)} - \frac{a^2(a^5)}{7b^3 c^2(a^5)}$$

$$= \frac{7bc^5 - a^7}{7a^5 b^3 c^2}$$

You can see that we needed to remember how to combine the exponents of quantities that are multiplied and have the same base that you learned in Module 1. This is an example of how mathematics builds upon itself. It is critical that a full working understanding is learned at each stage to allow one to proceed with confidence and ease. We recommend that if you are having trouble with these problems from just reading the material you may want to watch the video lectures.

4. $\dfrac{(5x - 1)}{(x + 1)(x - 2)} - \dfrac{3x}{(x - 2)(x - 1)}$

The least common multiple of the two denominators $(x + 1)(x - 2)$ and $(x - 2)(x - 1)$ is $(x + 1)(x - 2)(x - 1)$. So you multiply each numerator and denominator with the appropriate missing factor so they both have a common denominator. Just to see if you remember – why do you think we need to make a common denominator?

$$\frac{(5x - 1)}{(x + 1)(x - 2)} - \frac{3x}{(x - 2)(x - 1)} = \frac{(5x - 1)(x - 1)}{(x + 1)(x - 2)(x - 1)} - \frac{3x(x + 1)}{(x - 2)(x - 1)(x + 1)}$$

$$= \frac{(5x^2 - 5x - x + 1) - (3x^2 + 3x)}{(x+1)(x-2)(x-1)}$$

$$= \frac{5x^2 - 5x - x + 1 - 3x^2 - 3x}{(x+1)(x-2)(x-1)}$$

$$= \frac{(5-3)x^2 + (-6-3)x + 1}{(x+1)(x-2)(x-1)}$$

$$= \frac{2x^2 - 9x + 1}{(x+1)(x-2)(x-1)}$$

5.

$$\frac{(2x+1)}{(x-1)(3x+2)} - \frac{(5x-2)}{(3x-2)(x-1)} = \frac{(2x+1)(3x-2)}{(x-1)(3x+2)(3x-2)} - \frac{(5x-2)(3x+2)}{(3x-2)(x-1)(3x+2)}$$

$$= \frac{(6x^2 - 4x + 3x - 2) - (15x^2 + 10x - 6x - 4)}{(x-1)(3x+2)(3x-2)}$$

$$= \frac{6x^2 - x - 2 - (15x^2 + 4x - 4)}{(x-1)(3x+2)(3x-2)}$$

$$= \frac{6x^2 - x - 2 - 15x^2 - 4x + 4}{(x-1)(3x+2)(3x-2)}$$

$$= \frac{-9x^2 - 5x + 2}{(x-1)(3x+2)(3x-2)}$$

1. Perform the additions below without using a calculator. Pay attention to the bundling at each place value where it is required.

a. $\dfrac{3}{5} - \dfrac{5}{6}$	d. $\dfrac{3}{a} - \dfrac{5}{a+1}$
b. $\dfrac{2}{15} - \dfrac{5}{6}$	e. $\dfrac{x}{15} - \dfrac{5}{6}$
c. $\dfrac{10}{21} - \dfrac{4}{20}$	f. $\dfrac{10}{x+1} - \dfrac{4}{x-1}$

What are the differences or similarities between a & d, between b & e, and between c & f?

2. Perform the following operations and simplify your answers.

a. $4\dfrac{2}{15} - 2\dfrac{5}{6}$

b. $-3\dfrac{5}{12} - 7\dfrac{1}{2}$

c. $\dfrac{3a}{b^2c^3} - \dfrac{4bk}{a^7b^{12}c}$

d. $\dfrac{29}{2^{13}3^{22}5^2} - \dfrac{11}{2^73^{12}5^{12}}$

e. $\dfrac{2}{a^{13}b^{22}c^2} - \dfrac{3}{a^7b^{12}d^{12}}$

f. $\dfrac{3d^3}{b^{10}c^2} - \dfrac{b^3}{c^7d^6}$

g. $\dfrac{3a^2}{5b^{10}c^{10}} - \dfrac{6b^3}{2^2a^{10}c^7}$

h. $-\dfrac{2a}{b^2cd^3} - \dfrac{3b^5}{a^2b^{12}d^{12}}$

i. $\dfrac{(5x+1)}{(x+1)(x-2)} - \dfrac{(3+x)}{(x-2)(x-1)}$

j. $\dfrac{x}{(x+1)(x-1)} + \dfrac{(x+5)}{(x-2)(x-1)}$

k. $\dfrac{(x-2)}{(x-1)(3x-2)} - \dfrac{(x-1)}{(x-2)(3x-2)}$

l. $\dfrac{4}{2(x+5)} - \dfrac{5}{6(x+5)(x-5)}$

m. $-\dfrac{3}{(x-4)(x-1)} + \dfrac{(3+x)}{(x-1)}$

n. $\dfrac{(1-5x)}{(x+2)(x-2)} - \dfrac{(2+x)}{(x-2)(x-1)}$

o. $\dfrac{3}{(x+1)^3(x-2)^2} - \dfrac{5x}{(x-2)^3(x+1)^2}$

p. $\dfrac{2}{6\sqrt{3}} - \dfrac{5}{3\sqrt{2}}$

Next, we investigate what to do when adding or subtracting rational expressions when the denominators are not given in factored form. For example, how do we get started in the problem $\frac{x^2-4x+3}{x^2-4} + \frac{2x+5}{2\,x^2-x-10}$? We need to be able to find a way to factor the denominators or decompose them into products of prime factors. This is what we will concentrate on next.

Decomposition of Whole Numbers

Lecture

    🖥 Factoring Whole Numbers http://www.youtube.com/watch?v=snMzQARfX_M
    (8 min)

Terminology: Multiplicative decomposition is a process of breaking a bigger or complex mathematical object into a product of simpler or smaller mathematical objects. When this process is applied to integers or polynomials, it is referred to as **factoring**.

For example $12 = 2^2 \times 3$, $14568 = 2^3 \times 3 \times 607$, $6x^2 + x - 1 = (2x + 1)(3x - 1)$

Why would we want to decompose a complex mathematical object into a product of simpler smaller mathematical objects of the same type?

The motivation to factor comes from examples at the beginning of this lecture where you had to add/subtract rational expressions. Knowing the factors of each denominator made it much easier to convert the expressions to the **least** common denominator. Using **least** common denominators also made for less work to simplify the combined rational expression.

You can also think of how it is easier to understand smaller objects, and then we can use these smaller objects as building blocks of the mathematical world where these objects reside. You can think of it as trying to understand the individual components of an object that the whole object is made up of. You will see this phenomenon in many other subjects. For example in Physics or Chemistry you may try to understand the components (electrons, protons, quarks,..) that make up an atom. A biologist may want to understand the organs and the skeletal system to understand an organism. A businessman has to account for the different costs like the storage cost, insurance cost, cost to hire, and all the other factors that make up the business, to be successful. To get an object to be written as a product of its irreducible factors is not always a straightforward process and at times we may have to manipulate the objects using the properties studied before.

Remember that a mathematical object 'a' is called a factor of another mathematical object 'b', if and only if 'b' can be written as a product of 'a' and another object.

You may recall how to factor whole numbers from your previous education, but we briefly review it here. We start by creating a number tree to factor 180 into its prime factors. You keep breaking the number down until you have it written as a product of prime factors.

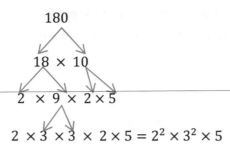

$$18 \times 10$$
$$2 \times 9 \times 2 \times 5$$
$$2 \times 3 \times 3 \times 2 \times 5 = 2^2 \times 3^2 \times 5$$

Sometimes this way of representing the factors of 180 is called a tree diagram. In order to factor whole numbers, you may want to review some divisibility tests.

Review of divisibility tests

1. A whole number is divisible by 2 if and only if its last digit is divisible by 2. For example 756 is divisible by 2, since the last digit is 6 which is divisible by 2.

    Even number: Any whole number that is divisible by 2 is called an even number.
    Odd number: Any whole number that is not divisible by 2 is called an odd number

2. A whole number is divisible by $4 = 2^2$ if and only if the number formed by the last two digits is divisible by 4. For example 756 is divisible by 4, since the number formed by the last two digits, 56, is divisible by 4.

3. A whole number is divisible by 2^n if and only if the number formed by the last n digits is divisible by 2^n.

4. A whole number is divisible by 3 if and only if the number formed by the sum of all its digits is divisible by 3. For example 756 is divisible by 3, since the number formed by the sum of all its digits is $7 + 5 + 6 = 18$ which is divisible by 3.

5. A whole number is divisible by $3^2 = 9$ if and only if the number formed by the sum of all its digits is divisible by 9. For example 756 is divisible by $9 = 3^2$, since the number formed by the sum of all its digits is $7 + 5 + 6 = 18$ which is divisible by 9.

6. A whole number is divisible by 5 if and only if its last digit is divisible by 5, or the last digit is either a zero or a 5. For example 765 is divisible by 5, since the last digit is 5 which is divisible by 5.

7. A whole number is divisible by $25 = 5^2$ if and only if the number formed by the last two digits is divisible by 25. For example 750 is divisible by 25, since the number formed by the last two digits, 50, is divisible by 25.

8. A whole number is divisible by 5^n if and only if the number formed by its last n digits is divisible by 5^n.

9. A whole number is divisible by 11 if and only if the difference of the sums of all alternate digits is divisible by 11. For example, 4510 is divisible by 11 since the difference $(4 + 1) - (5 + 0) = 0$ is divisible by 11.

Practice examples

Write the following numbers as a product of prime factors

1. 48

2. 504

3. 1024

Solution

1. $48 = 2^4 \times 3$

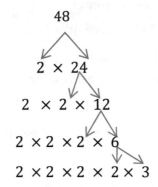

Make tree diagrams as shown above to verify the factors of the numbers below.

2. $504 = 2^3 \times 3^2 \times 7$

3. $1024 = 2^{10}$

🖥 Introduction to Factoring Polynomials
http://www.youtube.com/watch?v=JR4rMAd0Mhg (13 min)

Terminology: A **common factor** of two or more algebraic objects is an object that is a factor of each of the individual algebraic objects. The largest (factor with the most prime factors in it) of all such common factors is called the **greatest common factor**. That means no object with more prime factors than the greatest common factor can be a common factor of the given objects.

For example, consider the two algebraic objects $4x^2$ and 12. We can see that $4x^2 = 2 \times 2 \times x \times x$, $12 = 2 \times 2 \times 3$ and so 1,2, and 4, are all common factors of $4x^2$ and 12. But 4 is the greatest common factor of the algebraic objects $4x^2$ and 12. Let us work with the concept of common factors, and the greatest common factor like we did with common multiples, and least common multiple.

Note: 1 is always a common factor amongst any two or more polynomials.

Practice examples

Find all the common factors of the algebraic expressions given below.

1. $5a, 35$
2. $5a^3b, -10ab^2$
3. $-4t, -2p$

Solutions

1. $5a, 35$

   $5a = (-5)(-a)$, $35 = 5 \times 7 = (-5) \times (-7)$, therefore the common factors are $1, 5, -1$, and -5

2. $5a^3b, -10ab^2$

   $5a^3b = -5(a^3)(-b) = \cdots$ *and so on*,

   where as $-10ab^2 = -2 \times 5ab^2 = 2(-5)ab^2 = ..$ *and so on*, therefore the common factors are $1, 5, a, b, 5a, 5b, ab, 5ab, -1$, and $-5, -a, -b, -5a, -5b, -ab, -5ab$

3. $-4t, -2p$

   $-4t, -2p$, the common factors here are $1, 2, -1$, and -2

Now that you have some practice with finding common factors, let's work on finding the greatest common factor.

Practice examples

Find the greatest common factors of the algebraic expressions given below.

1. 360, 2100

2. $2^4 \times 3^{10} \times 7^3$, $2^{12} \times 3^5 \times 5^2$

3. $(x + 1) \times (2x - 3)^{10} \times x^3$, $x^{12} \times (x + 1)^4 \times (x - 3)^2$

4. $(x + 1) \times (2x - 3)^{10} \times x^3$, $(x - 1)^4 \times (x - 3)^2$

Solutions

1. $360 = 2^3 \cdot 3^2 \cdot 5$ and $2100 = 2^2 \cdot 3 \cdot 5^2 \cdot 7$ The greatest common factor consists of only the prime factors that reside in both of the prime factorizations and each raised to its minimum exponent in each of the prime factorizations. Thus the greatest common factor of 360 and 2100 is GCF = $2^2 \cdot 3 \cdot 5 = 60$.

2. $2^4 \times 3^{10} \times 7^3$, $2^{12} \times 3^5 \times 5^2$
   You can see that the prime numbers 2 and 3 are the only prime factors that are common to both numbers. So the greatest common factor will contain only powers of 2 and 3. The exponent on each base is the lowest exponent on that base amongst the two numbers so that it still remains a factor of both the numbers.

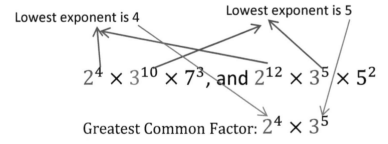

Lowest exponent is 4

Lowest exponent is 5

$2^4 \times 3^{10} \times 7^3$, and $2^{12} \times 3^5 \times 5^2$

Greatest Common Factor: $2^4 \times 3^5$

3. $(x + 1) \times (2x - 3)^{10} \times x^3, x^{12} \times (x + 1)^4 \times (x - 3)^2$

Again look for common factors first and then choose the lowest exponent for each factor between the two polynomials. Also remember that $(x + 1) = (x + 1)^1$

Lowest exponent is 1   Lowest exponent is 3

$$(x + 1) \times (2x - 3)^{10} \times x^3, \quad x^{12} \times (x + 1)^4 \times (x - 3)^2$$

Greatest common Factor: $(x + 1)x^3$

4. $(x + 1) \times (2x - 3)^{10} \times x^3, (x - 1)^4 \times (x - 3)^2$

Notice that these two polynomials do not share any factors that are written, and since 1 is the multiplicative identity, any mathematical object a can be written as $a = a \times 1$.

Greatest common Factor: 1

Video Log 2.4d

1. Determine which of the numbers below are divisible by 2, 3, 5, or 9 by putting a check in the appropriate box.

Number	Divisible by			
	2	3	5	9
285	☐	☐	☐	☐
432	☐	☐	☐	☐
666	☐	☐	☐	☐
2430	☐	☐	☐	☐

2. Determine all factors of the following

Object	Factors
a. 24	
b. $18x^2$	
c. $(x + 1)(x - 2)$	
d. $(3x + 5)^2(x + 6)^3$	

3. Create numbers or algebraic expressions that have the quantities below as one of their factors.

Factor	Answer
a. 12	
b. $(x+2)^2(3x-5)$	
c. $6x^3(4+x)$	

4. The numbers or algebraic expressions that are your answers for problem 3 would also be called as _____.

5. For each problem below find the greatest common factor.

   a. 24, 30

   b. 324, 360

   c. $a^4b^{10}c^3,\ a^{12}c^4d^2$

   d. $-16p^4q,\ 54pq^4$

   e. $-4p,\ -18q$

   f. $(2x-1)(x+3),\ (2x-1)(x-3)$

   g. $2u(u+v),\ -6v(u+v)$

   h. $(x+1)(x-1),\ x^2(x+3)$

   i. $2(x+1)x^3,\ 6x^4(x+1)^4$

   j. $(2x+1)(2x-1)^{10},\ (2x-1)^4(x-1)^2$

6. Consider the GCF of two numbers N and M. Thinking of the GCF as being equal to all the prime factors appearing in both M and N:

   a. Explain why the number $\frac{MN}{GCF}$ is a multiple of both M and N. (Think about all the prime factors in the product MN and then eliminating the factors GCF.)

   b. Try to show that $\frac{MN}{GCF}$ is the least common multiple of M and N. (You might think of $M = p_1p_2 \dots p_i \cdot GCF$ and $N = GCF \cdot q_1q_2 \dots q_j$ where none of the primes p are the same as any

Factoring (or dividing) the greatest common factor

How to find the least common multiple and greatest common factor

	Least Common Multiple	Greatest Common Factor
Prime Factors	Use all prime factors that appear across all the objects.	Use common prime factors that appear across all the objects. If there is no common factor across the objects then 1 is the greatest common factor.
Exponents	Highest exponent on each prime factor that appears across all the objects.	Lowest exponent of each prime factor that is common across all the objects.

In finding the least common multiple we took all the prime factors involved in each of the algebraic expressions raised to the highest power of that prime factor across all the expressions. To find the greatest common factor we must take the prime factors that are common across all the algebraic expressions raised to a power equal to its lowest power across all the expressions. So the least common multiples are at least as large as the original objects, while greatest common factors are not larger than the original objects.

Practice Examples

Rewrite the polynomials below as a product of factors, one of which must be the greatest common factor of all the terms in the polynomial.

1. $4a^2 + 12a$

Below is one way you can write the solutions if you cannot see right away what the greatest common factors are of the two terms involved. Notice that if you were to distribute the greatest common factor across the addition, you should end up with what you started with.

$4a^2 + 12a = 4a(a + 3)$

For my eyes only:

$4a^2 = 2^2 \times a^2$, and $12a = 2^2 \times 3 \times$

Lowest exponents is 2   Lowest expo

Greatest common factor of $4a^2$, and $12a$ is 2

2. $-3a^3b + 12a^2b$

$-3a^3b + 12a^2b$

$= -3a^3b + 2^2 \times 3a^2b$

$= 3a^2b(-a) + 3a^2b(2^2)$

$= 3a^2b(-a + 2^2)$

$= 3a^2b(-a + 4)$

OR

$-3a^3b + 12a^2b$

$= -3a^3b - 2^2 \times (-3a^2b)$

$= -3a^2b(a) + (-3a^2b)(-2^2)$

$= -3a^2b(a - 2^2)$

$= -3a^2b(a - 4)$

Notice that you can pull out (factor out or divide out) the positive greatest common factor or a negative of the greatest common factor. Depending on the sign you choose, adjust the signs inside the parentheses accordingly. Notice that if you were to distribute the greatest common factor across the subtraction, you should end up with what you started with.

3. $24a^6b^3 - 15a^2b^5$

$24a^6b^3 - 15a^2b^5 = 2^3(3)a^6b^3 - 3(5)a^2b^5$

$= 3a^2b^3(2^3a^4 - 5b^2)$

$= 3a^2b^3(8a^4 - 5b^2)$

You can see that the greatest common factor is $3a^2b^3$.

Multiply to give a^6. Multiply to give b

$= 3a^2b^3(2^3a^4) - 3a^2b^3(5b^2)$

4. $4x(x + y) - 5y(x + y)$

$4x(x + y) - 5y(x + y) = (x + y)(4x - 5y)$

5. $p(q - p) + q^2(p - q)$

At first glance, as the problem is written you might say the greatest common factor is 1. However, if you look carefully you can rewrite $q - p = -1(-q + p) = -1(p - q)$ (since addition is commutative, we can switch the order of $-q + p$). So rewriting our original problem in this manner we get

$$p(q-p)+q^2(p-q) = p(-1)(p-q)+q^2(p-q)$$
$$= (p-q)(p(-1)+q^2)$$
$$= (p-q)(-p+q^2)$$

Or

$$= (p-q)(q^2-p)$$

6. $(2x-3)^4(5x+7)+(3x-1)(2x-3)^3$

You can see that the greatest common factor is $(2x-3)^3$.
Notice that $(2x-3)^4 = (2x-3)^3(2x-3)^1$

$$(2x-3)^4(5x+7)+(3x-1)(2x-3)^3 = (2x-3)^3((2x-3)(5x+7)+(3x-1))$$

$$= (2x-3)^3(10x^2+14x-15x-21+3x-1)$$
$$= (2x-3)^3(10x^2+2x-22)$$

Video Log 2.4e

1. Factor the greatest common factor out in the polynomial expressions below.

  a. $-42a^3b^{10}-30a^5b^{15}$

  b. $a^2bc+ab^2c+abc^2$

  c. $8x^3-12x^2+10x$

  d. $16x^3y-18xy^3$

  e. $-75x^{23}y^{12}-30a^{15}b^{25}$

  f. $pq-p^2q^2$

  g. $xu+yu$

  h. $x(u+v)-y(u+v)$

  i. $3x(x-y)-5y(x-y)$

  j. $3x(x-y)+5y(x-y)$

  k. $3x(x-y)-5y(y-x)$

  l. $(x+1)(y+2)-(x+2)(y+2)$

  m. $(x+1)^2(4x-1)+(x+1)(4x-1)^2$

  n. $xy(2x+1)-xy(4-x)+xy(y+x)$

Now that you know how to factor out the greatest common factor from two-term expressions lets revisit our addition and subtraction problems with rational expressions.

Adding and Subtracting Rational Expression

Lecture

🖥 Adding and Subtracting Rational Expressions using Basic Factoring
http://www.youtube.com/watch?v=p8tMoTPFyPl (5 min)

Practice examples

Perform the operations and simplify as much as you can.

1. $\dfrac{1}{x^2 + 4x} - \dfrac{x}{x + 4}$

As before, we need a common denominator. To find the least common multiple of the given denominators we need to write both in the factored form. For the denominator $x^2 + 4x$ we factor the greatest common factor of x out of both terms. You should factor the denominators on the side under the "For my eyes only" column so your original problem work stays clean and clear.

$$\frac{1}{x^2 + 4x} - \frac{x}{x + 4} = \frac{1}{x(x + 4)} - \frac{x}{(x + 4)}$$

$$= \frac{1}{x(x + 4)} - \frac{x \times x}{(x + 4) \times x}$$

$$= \frac{1 - x^2}{x(x + 4)}$$

For my eyes only:
The greatest common factor of x^2, and $4x$ is x. So we have $x^2 + 4x = x(x + 4)$

2. $$\frac{(2-4x)}{x(x-1)+5(x-1)} - \frac{(x+1)}{2(x+5)-x(x+5)}$$

As before, to make a common denominator let us write the two denominators in their factored form. We will factor them in the "For my eyes" column so our work can stay clean and clear.

$$\frac{(2-4x)}{x(x-1)+5(x-1)} - \frac{(x+1)}{2(x+5)-x(x+5)}$$

$$= \frac{(2-4x)}{(x-1)(x+5)} - \frac{(x+1)}{(x+5)(2-x)}$$

$$= \frac{(2-4x)(2-x)}{(x-1)(x+5)(2-x)} - \frac{(x+1)(x-1)}{(x+5)(2-x)(x-1)}$$

$$= \frac{(4-2x-8x+4x^2)-(x^2-x+x-1)}{(x-1)(x+5)(2-x)}$$

$$= \frac{4-10x+4x^2-x^2+1}{(x-1)(x+5)(2-x)}$$

$$= \frac{5-10x+3x^2}{(x-1)(x+5)(2-x)}$$

For my eyes only:

1. The greatest common factor of $x(x-1)$ and $5(x-1)$ is $(x-1)$.
   So $x(x-1)+5(x-1)$
   $= (x-1)(x+5)$.

2. The greatest common factor of $2(x+5)$ and $x(x+5)$ is $(x+5)$.

   So $2(x+5)-x(x+5)$
   $= (x+5)(2-x)$.

3. The least common multiple of
   $(x-1)(x+5)$ and $(x+5)(2-x)$ is
   $(x-1)(x+5)(2-x)$.

Video Log 2.4f

1. *Perform the following operations. Use the previous two examples as a template on how to write your answers. Show all your work clearly.*

   a. $\dfrac{1}{12x-6} + \dfrac{x}{5x^2+10x}$

   b. $\dfrac{(3+2x)}{x(x+1)-3(x+1)} - \dfrac{(2x-1)}{1(x+5)+x(x+5)}$

   c. $\dfrac{q}{p^2+pq} - \dfrac{p}{-pq-q^2}$

   d. $\dfrac{2a}{a^2-3ax} - \dfrac{4}{a^2+3ax}$

   e. $\dfrac{1}{3x^2+x} + \dfrac{3x}{5x^2+15x}$

   f. $\dfrac{2ac^3}{5b^2k^3} - \dfrac{3bk}{10a^3bc}$

Connections to Factoring

Recall that when you did the addition or subtraction problems like the ones below, you worked on keeping track of units.

1. $3(x + 1) + a(x + 1) = (3 + a)(x + 1)$ here $(x + 1)$ was treated like a unit. Notice the two terms $3(x + 1)$ and $a(x + 1)$ have the greatest common factor (GCF) of $(x + 1)$, and we can rewrite the polynomial as a product of the greatest common factor and the sum of the remaining terms with the GCF removed as $3(x + 1) + a(x + 1) = (x + 1)(3 + a)$. Given the commutative property of multiplication we also have $3(x + 1) + a(x + 1) = (3 + a)(x + 1)$.

Note: When we are working with actual measurements, then $5cm^2 + 3cm$ is not the same as $(5cm + 3)cm$. That is because cm^2 is a unit by itself. Just be careful about which quantities are being added or subtracted.

Below are a few more examples we have seen earlier.

2. $4x\left(\dfrac{2x}{3} - 1\right) + 5\left(\dfrac{2x}{3} - 1\right) = (4x + 5)\left(\dfrac{2x}{3} - 1\right)$

3. $5\sqrt{2}\sqrt{x + 1} + 6\sqrt{x + 1} = (5\sqrt{2} + 6)\sqrt{x + 1}$

4. $7(a + b) - u(a + b) + 3v(a + b) = (7 - u + 3v)(a + b)$

2.5 Factoring Trinomials and a geometric interpretation

We are now going to look at the factoring process above in a geometric sense.

Lecture

💻 Factoring by Grouping Geometrically as Rectangles

http://www.youtube.com/watch?v=JPWGp83_DUE (6 min)

For the next few examples just so you can visualize the polynomials, assume that all variables are real numbers greater than or equal to zero so that we can represent the polynomials as areas of rectangles.

To view the term $3x$, we can represent it as a rectangle of $3 \times x$ square units as shown below.

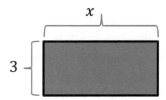

So if we wanted to view $3x + 3$, then we can view two rectangles, one as $3 \times x$ square units and the other as 3×1 square units. When we add the two terms, $3x$ and 3, we can view that as the two rectangles combined to form a new rectangle that is $3(x + 1)$ square units.

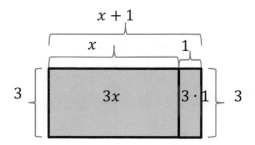
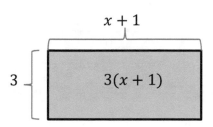

You can see that both the rectangles have the same area or that $3x + 3 = 3(x + 1)$.

The figures below show you geometrically what you are doing when you add and combine terms to form one product for the terms $3x + 3 + ax + a$.

Note that $a = a \times 1$. If you cannot visualize this, see the rectangle images below.

Figure 1 shows you each individual component of $3x + 3 + ax + a$.

Figure 2 shows you $3x + 3 + ax + a = 3(x + 1) + a(x + 1)$

Figure 3 shows you $3x + 3 + ax + a = 3(x + 1) + a(x + 1) = (3 + a)(x + 1)$

You can see from the visualization that we can take a sum of four algebraic terms and write them in factored form. This form of factoring is called **factoring by grouping** since we start by factoring two-term groups first.

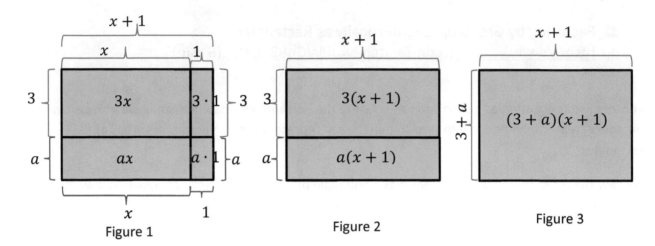

Figure 1

Figure 2

Figure 3

Below is another example showing how to visualize subtraction of polynomials.

For example, you can think of $3x - 3a$ as $3(x - a)$ and you can visualize it as shown below.

Terminology: The process of taking a polynomial (or any algebraic object) and writing it in factored form (a product of two or more factors) is called **factoring**.

Video Log 2.5a

1. Write an algebraic expression for each of the three stages of the rectangles below.

    a.

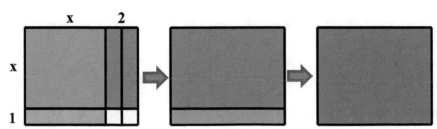

b.

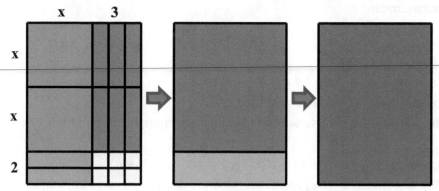

2. Using the previous example as your guide, draw rectangles showing all stages to show how the left hand side expression factors to become the right hand side. See above examples to help you solve these problems. **Hint**: start with the quantity furthest to the left.

a. $2x + 2 + bx + b = 2(x + 1) + b(x + 1) = (2 + b)(x + 1)$

b. $3x + 6 + ux + 2u = 3(x + 2) + u(x + 2) = (3 + u)(x + 2)$

c. $2ax + 3a + 2bx + 3b = a(2x + 3) + b(2x + 3) = (a + b)(2x + 3)$

d. $2x - 2 + bx - b = 2(x - 1) + b(x - 1) = (2 + b)(x - 1)$

Factor by Grouping

Sometimes in order to factor by grouping you may have to reorganize the terms to get the subgroups to have a common factor. Below are examples of such problems.

Lecture

💻 Factoring by Grouping http://www.youtube.com/watch?v=yyMzSSw8KLQ (5 min)

Practice examples

Factor the following

1. $3x + ay + ax + 3y$

Note that associative property of addition allows us to add $ay + ax$ first and using the commutative property of addition we can write $ay + ax = ax + ay$. Using associative property of addition once more we can now add $(3x + ax) + (ay + 3y)$. (Without this reorganizing, we would not be able to factor anything out of the first two terms $(3x + ay)$.

So now we can rewrite our terms as $3x + ax + ay + 3y = x(3 + a) + y(a + 3)$ we also know that $3 + a = a + 3$ (commutative property of addition) and so now we have
$3x + ax + ay + 3y = x(a + 3) + y(a + 3) = (x + y)(a + 3)$.
You can see that by manipulating the terms in this polynomial, what originally seemed to be a prime

polynomial was able to be factored. Even though we found success here, it is often the case that we won't be able to factor some polynomials.

2. $ab - cd + ac - bd$

Again we can rewrite the terms as $ab - cd + ac - bd = ab + (-cd) + ac + (-bd)$. Now use our commutative and associative property of addition and rewrite it again.
(By seeing subtraction as addition of additive inverse we can basically rearrange terms by moving the $(-)$ with the subtracted terms.)
$ab - cd + ac - bd = ab + ac - bd - cd = a(b + c) - d(b + c) = (a - d)(b + c)$
Recall that when you pull out the negative with the greatest common factor you need to adjust the signs in the parentheses so that after distributing the $-d$ over the terms in the parentheses, you will still have the same terms as you started with.

Video Log 2.5b
Factor each polynomial by grouping.

1. $au - bv - bu + av$
2. $ax^2 - bx + acx - bc$
3. $st^2 - r^2 - rt + rst$
4. $3ax + ay - 3bx - by + 3cx + cy$ (here you may want to try grouping in groups of two for a total of 3 groups and see what happens, like first two terms as one group, then the 3rd and 4th terms as one group and so on)
5. $7x^2 - 14x + 2x - 4$
6. $-3t^2 + 5t - 6t + 10$
7. $ax - ay + bz + az - by + bx$
8. $a(u + v) - c(u - v) - c(u + v) + a(u - v)$

Now let us look at trinomials in the second degree and see how we can use the factor by grouping method. Again we assume all variables take on values so as to make sense of the polynomial as area of rectangles. Remember we are only putting these restrictions so we can see the visual representations.

Factoring Trinomials Using Algebra Tiles

Lecture

🖥 Factoring Trinomials using Algebra Tiles http://www.youtube.com/watch?v=-XyOzEGIb54 (11 min)

Example

1. The trinomial $x^2 + 7x + 12$ can viewed as made up of a square of side length x units, the $7x$ can be viewed as seven rectangles of $x \times 1$ square units, and the 12 as twelve 1×1 square units as shown below in figure 1.

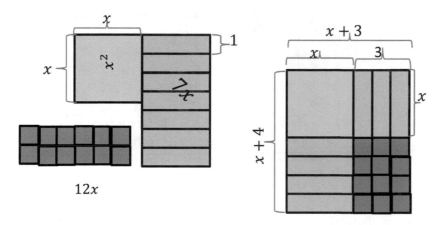

Total Area of both groups is the same and hence:

$$x^2 + 7x + 12$$
$$= (x + 4)(x + 3).$$

Figure 2

2. The trinomial $3x^2 + 8x + 4$ can viewed as made up of three squares of side length x units, the $8x$ can be viewed as eight rectangles of $x \times 1$ square units, and the 4 as four 1×1 square units as shown below in figure 1. Now think about rearranging these rectangles to form one rectangle with the same area. Algebraically this means that we write $3x^2 + 8x + 4$ as a product of two polynomials (*length x width*) as shown in figure 2. The yellow rectangles that are $x \times 1$ can fit horizontally under the three squares or vertically on the side of the three squares to make one large rectangle.

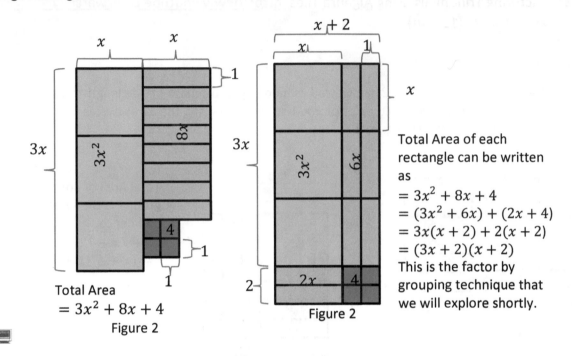

Total Area of each rectangle can be written as
$$= 3x^2 + 8x + 4$$
$$= (3x^2 + 6x) + (2x + 4)$$
$$= 3x(x + 2) + 2(x + 2)$$
$$= (3x + 2)(x + 2)$$
This is the factor by grouping technique that we will explore shortly.

You can play with this visual representation physically by moving these tiles around using something called Algebra Tiles. There are many websites that will allow you to play with these tiles. Here is one such site

http://nlvm.usu.edu/en/nav/frames_asid_189_g_4_t_2.html?open=activities&from=category_g_4_t_2.html.

1. For each polynomial below you are shown a possible arrangement of algebra tiles. Write the appropriate steps to show how the algebra tiles represent factor by grouping for the respective polynomials.

Polynomial	Algebra Tiles	Rearranged tiles
a. $3x^2 + 8x + 4$		
b. $4x^2 + 4x + 1$		
c. $2x^2 + 5x - 3$		

2. Use algebra tiles to factor the examples in the video log questions below. *Make sure you draw the rectangle representing your final answer..*

Polynomial	Algebra Tiles	Rearranged tiles
a. $x^2 + 3x + 2$		
b. $2x^2 + 8x + 6$		
c. $2x^2 + 5x + 3$		
d. $x^2 + 2x - 3$		
e. $x^2 - 9$		

Note: If you get stuck on the problems above, you can listen again to the Video Lectures.

Lecture

🖥 Factoring Trinomials Algebraically

http://www.youtube.com/watch?v=Ib9eeHyxwm4 (10 min)

For a single term expression, factoring really just involves breaking the coefficient into its prime factorization. For multi-term expressions, factoring is generally more complicated and sometimes not possible (prime expressions). Next we will use the factor by grouping techniques to factor trinomials.

Playing

If you did the previous examples using algebra tiles you may have noticed a pattern. We will explain that pattern and articulate a general process to rewrite trinomials into 4 terms so we can use factor by grouping. An alternative is to guess at the factors and check if it works. This can be efficient for trinomials $ax^2 + bx + c$ when $a = 1$ or a is a prime number. Most students however, report success in factoring trinomials using the grouping method.

Steps To Factor Trinomials $ax^2 + bx + c$ or $ax^2 + bxy + cy^2$ Using the Factoring By Grouping Method	
Step 1:	Factor out the greatest common factor. Then work with the remaining trinomial.
Step 2:	Arrange the trinomial's terms from highest to lowest powers. In case of trinomials with more than two variables, arrange the terms so that first and the last term are single variable terms of second degree.
Step 3:	Multiply the first and the last term in the remaining trinomial (this amounts to multiplying the highest degree term by the lowest degree term when working with trinomials in one variable). Now factor this product into two factors whose sum is the middle term. (If this can't be done, then the trinomial is prime and can't be factored.) Rewrite the middle term as this sum you should now have four terms.
Step 4:	Create two groups of two terms each. The first group should contain the highest degree term and one of the split terms. Factor out the greatest common factor (or its negative) from each group. Now each group should contain a binomial that is the same.
Step 5:	Now factor out the common binomial from step 4.

Note: You can always check your answer by multiplying all the factors. You should get your original polynomial back. In the case where the leading coefficient is 1, the process simplifies to factoring the constant term as the product, $c = f \cdot g$, so that the factors f and g add up to the coefficient of x. Then the trinomial factors as $(x + f)(x + g)$.

Factoring Trinomials By Grouping

Lecture

🖥 Factoring Trinomials by Grouping
http://www.youtube.com/watch?v=hvuH6eXbXWQ (14 min)

Practice examples

(The first three examples have leading coefficient 1, so the simplified method is used where we factor the constant term so the factors sum to the x-coefficient.)

1. $x^2 + 5x + 6$

The constant term 6 factors as $2 \cdot 3$ and $2 + 3 = 5$.

Therefore, $x^2 + 5x + 6 = (x + 2)(x + 3)$. It is always a good idea to check by multiplying.

$(x + 2)(x + 3) = x^2 + 3x + 2x + 6 = x^2 + 5x + 6$.

2. $x^2 - x - 6$

The constant term -6 factors as $2 \cdot (-3)$ and $2 + (-3) = -1$.

Therefore, $x^2 - x - 6 = (x + 2)(x - 3)$. It is always a good idea to check by multiplying. $(x + 2)(x - 3) = x^2 - 3x + 2x - 6 = x^2 - x - 6$.

3. $x^2 - 12x + 20$

The constant term 20 factors as $20 = (-2)(-10)$ and $-2 - 10 = -12$.

Therefore, $x^2 - 12x + 20 = (x - 2)(x - 10)$. Multiplying this out confirms our work.

4. $6x^2 + 11x + 4$

    Step 1   The greatest common factor for all three terms here is 1 so we can move on to Step 2.

    Step 2   Arrange the given polynomial's terms in decreasing order of exponents, which in this case they already are.

    Step 3.   Think of two factors of $24x^2$, whose sum is $11x$. Since the product is positive, both terms would have to either be positive or both negative. Since the sum is positive, we know both factors have to be positive.

$$\boxed{6x^2} + 11x + \boxed{4}$$

$$\text{Product} = 6x^2 \times 4 = 24x^2 = 2^3 \times 3 \times x^2$$

$$\text{Sum} = 11x = 8x + 3x$$

$$8x \times 3x = 24x^2$$

$$6x^2 + 11x + 4 = x^2 + 8x + 3x + 4$$

    Step 4. $6x^2 + 11x + 4 \qquad = 6x^2 + 8x + 3x + 4$

$$= 2x(3x + 4) + 1(3x + 4)$$

    Step 5. $= (2x + 1)(3x + 4)$

    So our final answer is $6x^2 + 11x + 4 = (2x + 1)(3x + 4)$. You can see that if you expand or multiply the two binomials you will get our initial trinomial. This is a way to check your work.

You do not have to write all 5 steps like shown above. We have done the first example in this manner so you can get familiar with these steps. You could write your work as shown below to keep your solution clean.

5. $6x^2 + 11x + 4$

$6x^2 + 11x + 4 \qquad = 6\text{x}^2 + 8\text{x} + 3x + 4$

$\qquad\qquad\qquad = 2x(3x + 4) + 1(3x + 4)$

$\qquad\qquad\qquad = (2x + 1)(3x + 4)$

Write the polynomial from highest power to lowest power which it is

$\boxed{6x^2} + 11x \boxed{+\ 4}$

$24x^2 = 2^3 \times 3 \times x^2$

$8x + 3x = 11x$

$6x^2 + 11x + 4 = 6x^2 + 8x + 3x + 4$

$\qquad = 2x(3x + 4) + 1(3x + 4)$

$\qquad = (2x + 1)(3x + 4)$

Very often students cannot find the two numbers in step 3 with the right product and sum. That is why we factor the product as shown above so you can play with different combinations. For example, you know that to multiply to get $24x^2$ the two numbers need to multiply to get 24 and so when the product is positive both numbers have to be positive or both have to be negative. If the product is negative then the two numbers should have opposite signs. Then since in the example above we wanted the numbers to add up to 11, we play with the factors of $24 = 2 \times 2 \times 2 \times 3$; we can work with any combinations of these as long as all the prime factors are used. So if we wanted the sum to be 25, we could use $24 = 2 \times 2 \times 2 \times 3$ and 1. If wanted the sum to be 14 we could use $12 = 2 \times 2 \times 3$ and 2. Some other examples of combinations of sums we could try to get could be $4 = 2 \times 2$ and $6 = 2 \times 3$ which would give us 10, $8 = 2 \times 2 \times 2$ and 3 would give us 11 and so on. One way to see all the possible products is to start from the smallest factor and work your way up, e.g. for 24 the possible products are: $1 \cdot 24,\ 2 \cdot 12,\ 3 \cdot 8,\ 4 \cdot 6, 6 \cdot 4$ ... Practicing these factoring problems will make you see these combinations faster eventually. When there isn't a way to get the factors to sum to the middle term, then the original trinomial is prime.

It is important for you to work hard to gain proficiency in factoring to a degree that if someone woke you up in the middle of your sleep cycle, you would still be able to factor trinomials. This efficiency of factoring will pay you great dividends not just in the intermediate algebra material but in more advanced math classes as well. Below are more examples.

6. $x^2t + 5xt + 6t$

$x^2t + 5xt + 6t = t(x^2 + 5x + 6)$

$\qquad\qquad = t(x+3)(x+2)$

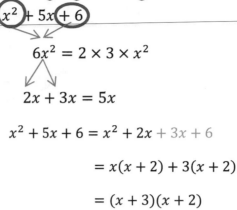

$6x^2 = 2 \times 3 \times x^2$

$2x + 3x = 5x$

$x^2 + 5x + 6 = x^2 + 2x + 3x + 6$

$\qquad\qquad = x(x+2) + 3(x+2)$

$\qquad\qquad = (x+3)(x+2)$

7. $24a^2b - 28ab^2 - 20b^3$

$24a^2b - 28ab^2 - 20b^3$

$= 2^3 3 a^2 b - 2^2 7 ab^2 - 2^2 5 b^3$

$= 2^2 b(2 \times 3a^2 - 7ab - 5b^2)$

$= 4b(6a^2 - 7ab - 5b^2)$

$= 4b(2a+b)(3a-5b)$

The greatest common factor of

$2^3 3 a^2 b,\ 2^2 7 ab^2, 2^2 5 b^3$ is $2^2 b$

$6a^2 - 7ab - 5b^2$

$-30a^2b^2 = -2 \times 3 \times 5 \times a^2 b^2$

$-10ab + 3ab = -7ab$

$6a^2 - 7ab - 5b^2$

$= 6a^2 - 10ab + 3ab - 5b^2$

$= 2a(3a-5b) + b(3a-5b)$

$= (2a+b)(3a-5b)$

8. $24x^2 - 22x - 10$

$$24x^2 - 22x - 10$$
$$= 2^3 3x^2 - 2 \times 11x - 2 \times 5$$
$$= 2(2^2 \times 3x^2 - 11x - 5)$$
$$= 2(12x^2 - 11x - 5)$$
$$= 2(3x + 1)(4x - 5)$$

For my eyes only:

The greatest common factor of

$2^3 \times 3x^2,\ 2 \times 7x, -2 \times 5$ is 2

$12x^2 - 11x - 5$

$-60x^2 = -2^2 \times 3 \times 5 \times x^2$

$-15x + 4x = -11x$

$$12x^2 - 11x - 5$$
$$= 12x^2 - 15x + 4x - 5$$
$$= 3x(4x - 5) + 1(4x - 5)$$
$$= (3x + 1)(4x - 5)$$

9. $-2x^2 + 5x - 3$

$$-2x^2 + 5x - 3$$
$$= -(2x^2 - 5x + 3)$$
$$= -(x - 1)(2x - 3)$$

For my eyes only:

We can first factor out the (−) to get $-(2x^2 - 5x + 3)$.

Now $2x^2 \cdot 3 = 6x^2 = (-3x)(-2x)$, so:

$$-(2x^2 - 3x - 2x + 3)$$
$$= -(x(2x - 3) - (2x - 3))$$
$$= -(x - 1)(2x - 3)$$

10. $8x^3 + 20x^2 + x$

$$8x^3 + 20x^2 + x \quad = 2^3 x^3 + 2^2 \times 5x^2 + x$$
$$= x(2^3 x^2 + 2^2 \times 5x$$
$$+ 1)$$
$$= x(8x^2 + 20x + 1)$$

This is the final answer since the trinomial in the parentheses is prime.

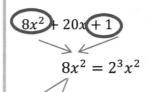
Using our newly learned factoring techniques let us revisit adding and subtracting rational expressions again.

Adding and Subtracting Rational Expressions
Lecture

📺 Factoring Trinomials and Application to Adding and Subtracting Rational Expressions http://www.youtube.com/watch?v=Ja2ul4TGuH0 (7 min)

Practice example

1. $\dfrac{x+1}{2x^2-5x+3} - \dfrac{x-1}{2x^2+x-6}$

Solution:

$$\dfrac{x+1}{2x^2-5x+3} - \dfrac{x-1}{2x^2+x-6}$$

$$= \dfrac{x+1}{(2x-3)(x-1)} - \dfrac{x-1}{(2x-3)(x+2)}$$

$$= \dfrac{(x+1)(x+2)}{(2x-3)(x-1)(x+2)} - \dfrac{(x-1)(x-1)}{(2x-3)(x+2)(x-1)}$$

$$= \dfrac{(x^2+2x+x+2)-(x^2-x-x+1)}{(2x-3)(x-1)(x+2)}$$

$$= \dfrac{x^2+2x+x+2-x^2+x+x-1)}{(2x-3)(x-1)(x+2)}$$

$$= \dfrac{x^2+3x+2-x^2+2x-1)}{(2x-3)(x-1)(x+2)}$$

$$= \dfrac{5x+1}{(2x-3)(x-1)(x+2)}$$

For my eyes only:

First denominator: The greatest common factor of $2x^2, -5x, 3$ is 1

$2x^2-5x+3$

$6x^2$

$-2x-3x = -5x$

$2x^2-5x+3 = 2x^2-2x-3x+3$

$= 2x(x-1)-3(x-1)$

$= (2x-3)(x-1)$

Second denominator: The greatest common factor of $2x^2, x, -6$ is 1

$2x^2+x-6$

$-12x^2$

$4x-3x = x$

$2x^2+x-6 = 2x^2+4x-3x-6$

$= 2x(x+2)-3(x+2)$

$= (2x-3)(x+2)$

Thus the LCD is

$(2x-3)(x-1)(x+2)$

1. Factor each trinomial or state that it is not factorable over the integers.

   a. $x^2 + 7x + 10$

   i. $6x^2 + 7x + 2$

   b. $x^2 + 2x - 3$

   j. $6x^2 - 7x - 5$

   c. $x^2 - 3x + 2$

   k. $2x^2 + 5x - 3$

   d. $x^2 + 3x - 4$

   l. $4x^2y - 5xy^2 - 6y^3$

   e. $2x^2 - x - 1$

   m. $15a^3b^4 - 14a^2b^5 - ab^6$

   f. $2x^2 - 3x + 1$

   n. $12p^2 + 11pq - 14q^2$

   g. $2x^2 + x - 1$

   o. $54x^3 - 93x^2 + 18x$

   h. $4x^2 + 8x - 5$

   p. $25a^6b^3 + 10a^5b^4 - 15a^4b^5$

2. Factor completely $9x^2 - 25$ (***Extra Credit Question***)

3. Consider the trinomial $x^2 + 4x + 1$.
   a. Show that $x^2 + 4x + 1$ is prime using the techniques of this section.

   b. Expand the product $(x + 2 + \sqrt{3})(x + 2 - \sqrt{3})$ to show that you get $x^2 + 4x + 1$. The "prime" designation for polynomials usually refers to not being able to factor a polynomial with integer coefficients into two or more polynomial factors with integer coefficients.

4. Perform the following operations and simplify your answers.

   a. $\dfrac{3x}{x^2+2x-3} + 2$

   f. $\dfrac{4-x}{1-x} + \dfrac{2x-3}{-5x^2+8x-3}$

   b. $\dfrac{3x}{x^2+2x-3} + \dfrac{1}{x+3}$

   g. $\dfrac{3x}{x^2+2x-3} - \dfrac{1}{x^2-3x+2}$

   c. $\dfrac{x+1}{2x+1} + \dfrac{x}{6x^2+7x+2}$

   h. $\dfrac{5x}{x^2-3x+2} - \dfrac{1}{2x^2-x-1}$

   d. $\dfrac{3x}{x^2+2x-3} - \dfrac{x+2}{x+3}$

   i. $\dfrac{x+1}{2x^2-x-1} + \dfrac{x}{6x^2+7x+2}$

   e. $\dfrac{3x-1}{2x+1} - \dfrac{4-x}{6x^2+7x+2}$

   j. $\dfrac{2x^2+3x+1}{2x^2-3x+1} - \dfrac{3x^2-2x-1}{2x^2+x-1}$

The above problems are multistage. They require many correct logical choices and also at times require patience and care in carrying through subtractions to all terms in a numerator etc. The development of your mental skills used to carry this out successfully will also be very useful in dealing with multistage planning and paying attention to details in many occupations.

Binomial Factoring
Lecture

🖥 **Factoring the Difference of Two Perfect Squares**
http://www.youtube.com/watch?v=cy_n_YfFQlQ (9 min)

To understand binomial factoring we first have to get familiar with the concept of substitution so that we can apply the rules we learn next to any problem of similar type. Substitution is a concept we have been using since the first class when we started with counting. For example if we see the picture below you will be tempted to say "3 apples". You are substituting the image with the numerical and alpha numerical (letters) to represent that picture. This process which we apply daily countless number of times in communicating and in mathematics is called the **substitution process**.

Examples

Let $u = 5, v = -2p, t = 3x, s = a$. Use substitution to rewrite the following algebraic expressions below in terms of the variables $p, x, and\ a$.

1. $u^2v + 4$
2. $(u + v)(u - v)$
3. $(s + t)(s^2 - st + t^2)$
4. $(u - v)(u^2 + uv + v^2)$

Solutions:
Just take the value of the variables given to you and replace them in the expression below.

1. $u^2v + 4 = (5)^2(-2p) + 4 = (25)(-2p) + 4 = -50p + 4$
2. $(u + v)(u - v) = (5 + (-2p))(5 - (-2p)) = (5 - 2p)(5 + 2p)$
   $$= 25 + 10p - 10p - 4p^2 = 25 - 4p^2.$$
3. $(s + t)(s^2 - st + t^2) = (a + 3x)((a)^2 - (a)(3x) + (3x)^2) = (a + 3x)(a^2 - 3ax + 9x^2)$
   Note that $(3x)^2 = (3x)(3x) = 9x^2$. We can expand this out to get: $a^3 - 3a^2x - 9ax^2 + 3xa^2 - 9ax^2 + 27x^3 = a^3 + 27x^3$
4. $(u - v)(u^2 + uv + v^2) = (5 - (-2p))(5^2 + (5)(-2p) + (-2p)^2) = (5 + 2p)(25 - 10p + 4p^2)$
   Note that $(-2p)^2 = (-2p)(-2p) = 4p^2$. If we expand this out, we get $125 - 50p + 20p^2 + 50p - 20p^2 + 8p^3 = 125 + 8p^3$

Let $x = 3a, y = 2b, u = 2x, v = 5y, z = -3, s = 4$. *Use substitution to rewrite the expressions below in terms of the new variables $a, b, t,$ and c.*

1. $s^2 - 3sz + z^2$
2. $(x - y)(x + y)$
3. $(u - 2s)(u + 2s)$
4. $(x - y)(x^2 + xy + y^2)$
5. $(s + x)(s^2 - sx + x^2)$
6. $(a - z)(a + z)$
7. $(x - y)(x + y)(x^2 + y^2)$
8. $(s + x)(s^2 - sx + x^2)$

We will now focus on a few special types of binomials (polynomials with two terms). Let us look at the difference of two squares geometrically first so you can see the motivation for the algebraic patterns.

Assume that the variables in the next few examples represent positive real numbers so that the area interpretation would make sense. The algebraic patterns we will observe are true for all values of the variables.

Difference of Squares

Observation 1

The binomial $a^2 - b^2 = (a - b)(a + b)$.

We can think of a^2 as a square of side length of a units, and think of b^2 as a smaller square of side length b units. Then the quantity $a^2 - b^2$ can be looked at as removing the square of side length b units from the bigger square of side length a units.

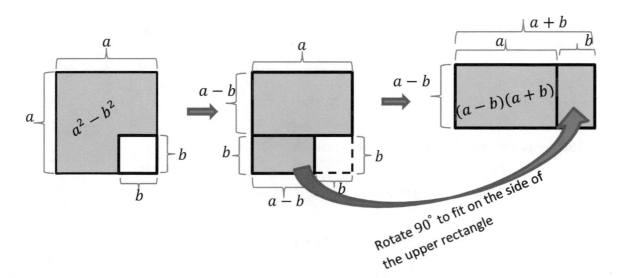

You can see that the area of the region left after you remove the smaller square is the same as the rectangle at the far right. You cut the bottom part of the rectangle and rotate it 90 degrees and paste it on the side as shown in the picture above and that shows you that the

$a^2 - b^2$ area is the same as the $(a - b)(a + b)$ area of the rectangle. So the pattern we observe is that $a^2 - b^2 = (a - b)(a + b)$.

You can see this algebraically as $(a - b)(a + b) = a^2 + ab - ba - b^2 = a^2 - b^2$ using the distributive property of multiplication. So our observation holds true: For all mathematical objects a and b, we have $a^2 - b^2 = (a - b)(a + b)$.

So whenever we have a situation with difference of squares, you need to identify what goes in each of the individual boxes.

$$\left(\square^2 - \square^2\right) = (\square - \square)(\square + \square)$$

Let us do some practice examples to see how this observation helps us.

Practice Examples

Factor the following polynomials completely.

Remember our observation from before that $a^2 - b^2 = (a - b)(a + b)$.

1. $x^2 - y^2 = (x - y)(x + y)$ you can see to use the observation above we had to substitute $a = x$ and $b = y$ in the factors.

In other examples, it might not be as straight forward. Just remember that as we did in other factoring examples, first factor any greatest common factor there may be and then apply your factoring skills. We recommend you always write the difference of squares in the form

$$\left(\square^2 - \square^2\right) = (\square - \square)(\square + \square)$$

2. $25x^2 - 16y^2 = ((5x)^2 - (4y)^2) = (5x - 4y)(5x + 4y)$

3. $49u^2 - 121v^6 = ((7u)^2 - (11v^3)^2) = (7u - 11v^3)(7u + 11v^3)$

4. $20a^2 - 45b^2 = 5(4a^2 - 9b^2) = 5((2a)^2 - (3b)^2) = 5(2a - 3b)(2a + 3b)$

5. $49x^2y^8 - 25w^4z^2 = ((7xy^4)^2 - (5w^2z)^2) = (7xy^4 - 5w^2z)(7xy^4 + 5w^2z)$

6. $18x^3y - 8xy^3 = 2xy(9x^2 - 4y^2) = 2xy((3x)^2 - (2y)^2) = 2xy(3x - 2y)(3x + 2y)$

7. $R^2 - (R - 2)^2 = ((R)^2 - (R - 2)^2) = (R - (R - 2))(R + (R - 2))$

$$= (R - R + 2)(R + R - 2) = 2(2R - 2)$$

$$= 2 \times 2(R - 1) = 4(R - 1)$$

Remember, factoring completely means no factor can be factored any farther.

Application of the difference of squares can be used to do complicated computations as follows

$$37^2 - 7^2 = (37 - 7)(37 + 7) = 30(44) = 1320.$$

In the other direction, if we have say $12 \cdot 8 = (10 + 2)(10 - 2) = 10^2 - 2^2 = 96$. This works well for multiplying numbers that are close to each other and uses perfect squares. For example, $53 \cdot 47 = (50 + 3)(50 - 3) = 2500 - 9 = 2491$.

Video Log 2.5f
Factor the following completely. First identify both quantities that are being squared.

1. $p^2 - 4q^2$
2. $4q^2 - p^2$
3. $9a^6 - 25b^2$
4. $8a^3 - 18ab^2$
5. $12a^3 - 3a$
6. $16a^4 - 81b^4$
7. $1 - x^4$ (Hint: Use the difference of squares twice here!)
8. $(x + 3)^2 - (x - 2)^2$
9. $48^2 - 8^2$
10. Try factoring the sum of two squares in $x^2 + 25$.
    a. First show that $(x + 5)(x + 5)$ does not work
    b. Also explain that this failure also means that $\sqrt{x^2 + 25}$ is not equal to $x + 5$.
    c. What about $\sqrt{x^2 + 10x + 25}$? Factor the radicand and show how this simplifies.

Sum and Difference of Cubes
Lecture

     📺 Factoring the Sum or Difference of Perfect Cube Terms
        http://www.youtube.com/watch?v=2Xvlb_JtvQQ   (12 min)

Observation 2

Consider the binomial $a^3 - b^3$, referred to as a difference of cubes and again we can visualize it physically as a large cube with a smaller cube removed. We think of a^3 as the volume of a cube of side length of a units, and b^3 as the volume of a smaller cube of side length of b units. Then the quantity $a^3 - b^3$ can be looked at as taking the volume of the smaller cube of side length b units from the bigger cube of side length a units. The Diagrams below show you how the remaining part of the bigger cube after remove the smaller cube can be looked at as made of three separate parts. The volumes of these three pieces are: $(a - b)a^2$, $(a - b)ab$, and $(a - b)b^2$ respectively. Therefore we have:

$$a^3 - b^3 = (a - b)a^2 + (a - b)ab + (a - b)b^2 = (a - b)(a^2 + ab + b^2)$$

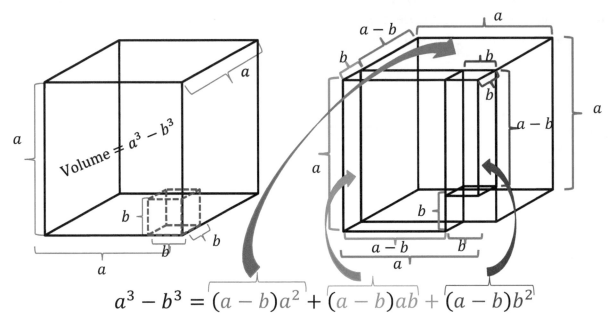

$$a^3 - b^3 = (a - b)a^2 + (a - b)ab + (a - b)b^2$$

Our observation then can be written as

$$a^3 - b^3 = (a - b)(a^2 + ab + b^2)$$

You can also algebraically see that if you distribute

$$(a - b)(a^2 + ab + b^2) = a^3 + a^2b + ab^2 - ba^2 - b^2a - b^3 = a^3 - b^3$$

So our observation is valid for all mathematical objects a, and b, we have

$$a^3 - b^3 = (a - b)(a^2 + ab + b^2).$$

Another way to state the factoring formula for the **difference of two perfect cubes** is :

$$\left(\square^3 - \square^3\right) = \left(\square - \square\right)\left(\square^2 + \square \times \square + \square^2\right)$$

Again just like the difference of squares make sure you identify what goes into the boxes to make it easier to fill in the remainder of the terms.

Let us work with some practice examples

Use the difference of cubes formula $a^3 - b^3 = (a - b)(a^2 + ab + b^2)$ below.

Practice examples

1. $x^3 - y^3 = (x - y)(x^2 + xy + y^2)$ We substituted $a = x$ and $b = y$ in the formula above.

2. $8x^3 - 27y^3 = (2x)^3 - (3y)^3$

    $= (2x - 3y)((2x)^2 + (2x)(3y) + (3y)^2)$

    $= (2x - 3y)(4x^2 + 6xy + 9y^2)$

3. $3x^4y - 24xy^4 = 3xy(x^3 - 8y^3)$

    $= 3xy(x^3 - (2y)^3)$

    $= 3xy(x - 2y)((x)^2 + (x)(2y) + (2y)^2)$

    $= 3xy(x - 2y)(x^2 + 2xy + 4y^2)$

4. $64x^3 - 125b^3 = (4x)^3 - (5b)^3$

    $= (4x - 5b)((4x)^2 + (4x)(5b) + (5b)^2)$

    $= (4x - 5b)(16x^2 + 20xb + 25b^2)$

5. $64a^3 + 125b^3 = (4a)^3 - (-5b)^3$

$$= (4a - (-5b))((4a)^2 + (4a)(-5b) + (-5b)^2)$$

$$= (4a + 5b)(16a^2 - 20ab + 25b^2)$$

Notice that we only had a formula for subtraction of cubes but as mathematicians we do not work hard more than once if necessary, we notice that $(-5b)^3 = -125b^3$ which allows us to use the subtraction formula.

Observation 3

For any mathematical objects a and b we have

$a^3 + b^3 = a^3 - (-b)^3 = (a - (-b))(a^2 + a(-b) + (-b)^2) = (a + b)(a^2 - ab + b^2)$. You can check that the expansion of $(a + b)(a^2 - ab + b^2)$ indeed gives you the sum of cubes.

Or $a^3 + b^3 = (a + b)(a^2 - ab + b^2)$

Another way to state the factoring formula for the **sum of two perfect cubes** is :

$$\left(\square^3 + \square^3\right) = \left(\square + \square\right)\left(\square^2 - \square \times \square + \square^2\right)$$

Video Log 2.5g

1. *Factor the following completely.*

    a. $p^3 - 8q^3$

    b. $4q^3 - 32p^3$

    c. $27a^6 - 125b^3$

    d. $8a^3 - 27b^3c^3$

    e. $p^3 + 8q^3$

    f. $4q^3 + 32p^3$

    g. $27a^6 + 125b^3$

    h. $8a^3 + 27b^3c^3$

2. Show that $\sqrt[3]{x^3 + 8}$ is not equal to $x + 2$.

3. We have learned several methods for factoring trinomials and binomials. Try the following problems. Completely factor the following if possible. If the polynomial does not factor, please indicate so.

a. $x^2 + 8x + 15$	i. $-4t^2 + 8x - 3$ HINT: (Start by factoring out (-1).)
b. $x^2 - x - 2$	j. $4a^2 - 9b^4$
c. $2x^2 + 5x - 3$	k. $2p^2 + 7pq + 5q^2$
d. $4x^2 - 4x - 15$	l. $16x^4 - y^8$
e. $14x^2 + 17x - 6$	m. $12s^2 + 20s - 25$
f. $15x^2 - 24x - 12$	n. $54a^3 - 16b^3$
g. $8x^3y^6 - 1$	o. $8 - 4t$
h. $1 + a^3$	p. $1 - t^4$

Next we revisit the problem of adding and subtracting rational expressions where we need to apply our factoring techniques in order to determine the least common denominator.

Application of Factoring to Sum and Difference of Rational Expressions

Lecture

💻 Application of Factoring http://www.youtube.com/watch?v=fm0NEqFloMA (7 min)

Practice Problems

Combine the rational expressions into a single rational expression.

1. $$\frac{3x - 2}{x^2 - 16} - \frac{2x + 3}{x^2 - 5x + 4}.$$

$$= \frac{3x - 2}{(x - 4)(x + 4)} - \frac{2x + 3}{(x - 4)(x - 1)}$$

$$= \frac{(3x - 2)(x - 1)}{(x - 4)(x + 4)(x - 1)} - \frac{(2x + 3)(x + 4)}{(x - 4)(x - 1)(x + 4)}$$

$$= \frac{(3x^2 - 3x - 2x + 2) - (2x^2 + 8x + 3x + 12)}{(x - 4)(x + 4)(x - 1)}$$

$$= \frac{3x^2 - 5x + 2 - (2x^2 + 11x + 12)}{(x - 4)(x + 4)(x - 1)}$$

$$= \frac{3x^2 - 5x + 2 - 2x^2 - 11x - 12)}{(x - 4)(x + 4)(x - 1)}$$

$$= \frac{x^2 - 16x - 10}{(x - 4)(x + 4)(x - 1)}$$

2. $\dfrac{-2x+1}{x^2+4x+16}+\dfrac{5x^2+3x+4}{x^3-64}-\dfrac{2}{x-4}$

$=\dfrac{-2x+1}{x^2+4x+16}+\dfrac{5x^2+3x+4}{(x-4)(x^2+4x+16)}-\dfrac{2}{x-4}$

$=\dfrac{(-2x+1)(x-4)}{(x^2+4x+16)(x-4)}+\dfrac{(5x^2+3x+4)}{(x-4)(x^2+4x+16)}$

$-\dfrac{2(x^2+4x+16)}{(x-4)(x^2+4x+16)}$

$=\dfrac{(-2x^2+8x+x-4)+(5x^2+3x+4)-(2x^2+8x+32)}{(x-4)(x^2+4x+16)}$

$=\dfrac{3x^2+12x-2x^2-8x-32}{(x-4)(x^2+4x+16)}$

$=\dfrac{x^2+4x-32}{(x-4)(x^2+4x+16)}=\dfrac{(x-4)(x+8)}{(x-4)(x^2+4x+16)}$

Reducing the fraction by dividing out the common $(x-4)$.

$=\dfrac{(x+8)}{(x^2+4x+16)}$

For my eyes only:

Before we can solve the problem we need to factor the denominators.

First Denominator

$x^2+4x+16$ is irreducible or prime over integers.

Second Denominator

$x^3-64=x^3-4^3$

$=(x-4)(x^2+4x+16)$

Third Denominator

$x-4$ is irreducible or prime over integers.

The numerator in the final answer

$x^2+4x-32$

$-32x^2$

$8x-4x$

$x^2+4x-32$

$=x^2+8x-4x-32$

$=x(x+8)-4(x+8)$

$=(x-4)(x+8)$

Video Log 2.5h

Perform the following operations. First factor denominators to find the least common denominator.

1. $\dfrac{5}{x^2-x-6}-\dfrac{3}{x^2+x-2}$

2. $\dfrac{3}{1-x}-\dfrac{4x}{x^2-1}$ (Hint: $(1-x)=-(x-1)$)

3. $\dfrac{3}{2x}+\dfrac{2}{x^2-4}-\dfrac{3}{x^2+2x}$

4. $\dfrac{1}{x^3-8}-\dfrac{x}{x^2+2x+4}$

5. $\dfrac{3}{x^2-9}-\dfrac{5x+2}{x^3-27}$

2.6 Multiplication of Rational and Radical Expressions

Lectures

🖥 Multiplication of Rational Numbers and Expressions
   http://www.youtube.com/watch?v=e-F4CpSXzJ4 (10 min)

We first review multiplication of integers and whole numbers to guide us as we study multiplication of other objects including rational numbers, rational expressions, and radical expressions.

We visualized $2 \times 3 = 6$ as two rows of three objects or as repeated addition as $3 + 3 = 6$ or as two groups of three.

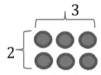

Let us look at some examples to interpret multiplication of rational numbers. Just remember that it is very important to keep track of your whole unit when working with rational numbers.

Example 1 $4 \times \dfrac{1}{2} =?$

Algebraically that would be $\frac{1}{2} + \frac{1}{2} + \frac{1}{2} + \frac{1}{2} = \frac{1+1+1+1}{2} = \frac{4}{2} = 2$.

Remember that 1×4 would be interpreted as 1 group of four, so $\frac{1}{2} \times 4$ would be take half of the four objects which is two whole objects as you see below.

As you can see it is very important when writing the final answer to remember that our one whole here was made up of two pieces. So four pieces makes two complete whole units.

Example 2 $5 \times \dfrac{2}{3}$ Here a whole is made of three pieces and you can see below we have ten of these pieces.

Rearranging the shaded pieces (ten of them total) we can see we have three complete wholes and a third of the next one, or we have ten thirds.

$$5 \times \frac{2}{3} = \frac{10}{3} = 3\frac{1}{3}$$

Example 3 $\dfrac{4}{5} \times \dfrac{2}{3}$ We want to know how much of an object (whole) is in $\dfrac{4}{5}$ of a group which has $\dfrac{2}{3}$ of an object in it. We need to cut the group into 5 equal pieces and take four of these. We draw our area diagram carefully to show what $\dfrac{1}{5}$ of the $\dfrac{2}{3}$ object looks like. Below you see $\dfrac{2}{3}$ of an object is shaded.

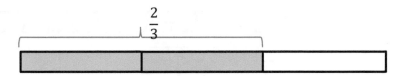

To take $\dfrac{4}{5}$ of this shaded $\dfrac{2}{3}$, we break each third into 5 equal pieces so we can take four fifths of each third making it four fifths of two thirds as shown below.

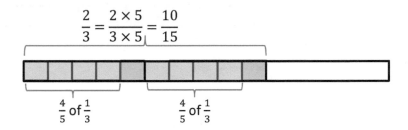

After reorganizing the $\dfrac{4}{5}$ of $\dfrac{2}{3}$ make sure that the unshaded part also has the same divisions of fifths. That will allows us to write our final answer in terms of what part of the whole is shaded to make $\dfrac{4}{5} \times \dfrac{2}{3}$.

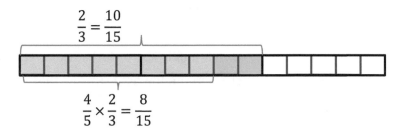

Note that the green shaded region represents $\dfrac{4}{5} \times \dfrac{2}{3}$ and is equal to $\dfrac{8}{15}$th of one object or whole. Algebraically that amounted to multiplying the numerators and multiplying the denominators to get the final answer. The diagrams above give you a motivation behind this algebraic process.

Example 4 $\dfrac{3}{4} \times \dfrac{2}{5}$ Here we have to take three quarters of two fifths.

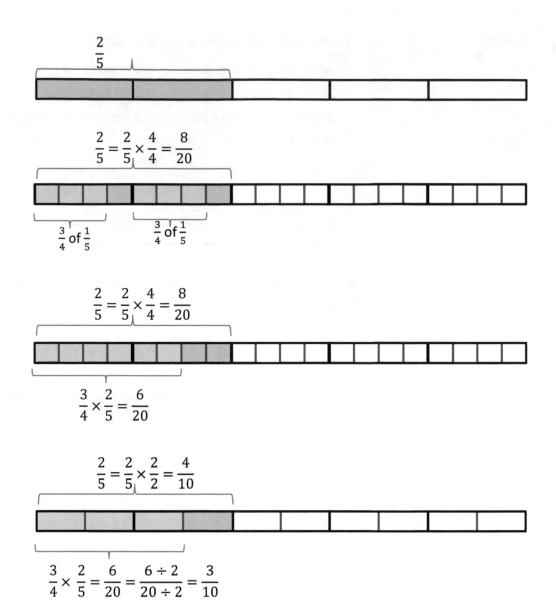

Another way to view this multiplication is that we can think of $\frac{3}{4} \times \frac{2}{5} = \frac{3 \times 2}{4 \times 5}$ and then can write this fraction in the lowest terms or that

$$\frac{3}{4} \times \frac{2}{5} = \frac{3 \times \overset{1}{\cancel{2}}}{\underset{2}{\cancel{4}} \times 5} = \frac{3}{10}$$

Exampe 5   Give an estimate of $2\frac{3}{4} \cdot 3\frac{2}{5}$. Then find the actual value.

A rough estimate here would be $3 \cdot 3 = 9$.

Actual Value

$$2\frac{3}{4} \cdot 3\frac{2}{5}$$

$$= \left(2 + \frac{3}{4}\right)\left(3 + \frac{2}{5}\right)$$

$$= \left(\frac{8}{4} + \frac{3}{4}\right)\left(\frac{15}{5} + \frac{2}{5}\right)$$

$$= \frac{11}{4} \times \frac{17}{5}$$

$$= \frac{187}{20}$$

$$= 9\frac{7}{20}$$

Example 6   Jill brought 60 watermelons to farmers market and sold $\frac{2}{3}$ of them. Of the watermelons she did not sell, she gave $\frac{2}{5}$ to a local food pantry. How many watermelons did she give to the food pantry?

Jill had a third of the 60 watermelons left which is $\frac{1}{3} \cdot \frac{60}{1} = 20$ melons. She gave $\frac{2}{5}$ of these to the food pantry which would be $\frac{2}{5} \cdot \frac{20}{1} = \frac{40}{5} = 8$ watermelons.

> **Note:** *When multiplying two or more rational expressions, the final numerator will be the product of all the factors that make up the numerators, and the final denominator is the product of all the factors making up the denominators of the rational expressions being multiplied. In reducing a product of rational expressions, we can divide out a factor from any numerator with that same factor in any denominator.*

1. Show how to interpret the multiplications below visually using appropriate strip diagrams and algebraically.

Multiplication Problem	Visual interpretation	Algebraic Evaluation
a. 4×3		
b. $3 \times \frac{2}{3}$		
c. $3 \times \frac{1}{2}$		
d. $3\frac{1}{2} \times 2$		
e. $\frac{2}{3} \times 3$		
f. $\frac{1}{4} \times 3$		
g. $\frac{1}{2} \times \frac{4}{5}$		
h. $\frac{2}{3} \times 3\frac{3}{4}$		
i. $\frac{3}{2} \times \frac{2}{3}$		
j. $2\frac{1}{3} \times 1\frac{1}{2}$		
k. $3\frac{3}{4} \times 2\frac{1}{3}$		

2. Evaluate the following multiplications.

  a. $\frac{4}{5} \times \frac{3}{2}$

  b. $\frac{9}{14} \times \frac{2}{3}$

  c. $\frac{5}{12} \times \frac{14}{15}$

  d. $\frac{3}{2} \times \frac{2}{3}$

  e. $6\frac{2}{3} \times 4\frac{1}{4}$

3. Find all statements in the right column that match each of the statements in the left column. It is not necessary that all statements in the right column have a match in the left column.

Algebraic Statement	English Sentence
I. 2×6 II. $\frac{1}{2} \times 2000$ III. $\frac{2}{3} \times 1\frac{1}{2}$	a. Marvin earned $2000 a month, and his friend Michelle earns half has much. How much money does Michelle earn? b. I will need to take two thirds of the flour in that jar to bake my cookies. The jar currently has a pound and a half of flour. How many pounds of flour did I need to bakes my cookies? c. Each package contains six cream puffs. I bought two packages of cream puffs for my friends. How many cream puffs did I buy? d. 50% of the students in class raised $2000 for a fund raiser. e. 50% of the $2000 funds raised will be used for the hunger task force. f. 50% of the total 2000 points in a class come from the in-class exams.

4. John purchased 75 pieces of fruit for a kid's summer camp. Two thirds of the fruit were apples and $\frac{3}{5}$ of these apples were McIntosh variety. How many of the 75 fruit were McIntosh apples?

5. Evaluate the following

  a. 80% of 150

  b. $\frac{1}{2}$ of 300

  c. 250% of 100

  d. We have two and half boxes of Oreo Cookies. Each Box of Oreo's has 36 cookies. How many cookies do we have?

  e. The bank will give Arman 7% simple interest on his $2000 investment.

Multiplication of Rational Expressions
Lecture

🖥 Multiplying Rational Numbers and Expressions
http://www.youtube.com/watch?v=czoI6D3NNeg (12 min)

In general then, if $a, b, c,$ and d are mathematical objects we have studied so far so that $b \neq 0$, and $d \neq 0$, then $\frac{a}{b} \times \frac{c}{d} = \frac{a \times c}{b \times d} = \frac{ac}{bd}$.

Another way to think of it is that you are taking $\frac{a}{b}$ parts of $\frac{c}{d}$, which results in a new fraction $\frac{ac}{bd}$. We can write this fraction in simplest or lowest form (which means the numerator and denominators do not share any common factors).

Note: When we multiply an even number of negative quantities together we get a positive quantity, and an odd number of negative quantities together we get a negative quantity.

Also note that when working with rational expressions or rational numbers, $\frac{-a}{b} = \frac{a}{-b} = -\frac{a}{b}$. The reason for this is equivalent fractions as shown

$$\frac{-a}{b} = \frac{-a \times -1}{b \times -1} = \frac{a}{-b}, \text{ or } -\frac{a}{b} = -1 \times \frac{a}{b} = \frac{-1}{1} \times \frac{a}{b} = \frac{-a}{b}, \text{ or } -\frac{a}{b} = -1 \times \frac{a}{b} = \frac{1}{-1} \times \frac{a}{b} = \frac{a}{-b}.$$

Our multiplication of rational numbers is consistent with our definition of rational numbers.

Recall that in a fraction, e.g., $\frac{5}{7}$, the top number says how many pieces you have when the bottom number of pieces makes a whole object which would be the same as 5 of $\frac{1}{7}$th 's or $5 \times \frac{1}{7}$. With this interpretation we saw that multiplying a rational number by a whole number for example, multiplying $\frac{5}{7}$ by 6 means we'd have six groups of $\frac{5}{7}$ which would also be interpreted as $6 \times \left(5 \times \frac{1}{7}\right) = (6 \times 5) \times \frac{1}{7} = 30 \times \frac{1}{7} = \frac{30}{7}$ (essentially 6 groups of 5 pieces of $\frac{1}{7}$. So this is consistent with what we saw, $6 \times \frac{5}{7} = \frac{6}{1} \times \frac{5}{7} = \frac{6 \times 5}{7} = \frac{30}{7} = \frac{28}{7} + \frac{2}{7} = 4\frac{2}{7}$. When we consider multiplying a rational number by one over a whole number, e.g., $\frac{1}{3}$ of $\frac{5}{7}$ or $\frac{1}{3} \times \frac{5}{7}$, we can view this as taking $\frac{1}{3}$ of five (which is also the same as taking $\frac{1}{3}$ of 1 five times). Now if we focus on $\frac{1}{3}$ of one of the pieces, i.e. $\frac{1}{3}$ of one piece of $\frac{1}{7}$ of a whole object, it is easy to see that we cut one of these $1/7$th of a whole into 3 pieces and each of the smaller pieces would then be $\frac{1}{21}$ of a whole. Now collecting all five of these smaller pieces we have that $\frac{1}{3}$ of $\frac{5}{7}$ is 5/21 of the original whole object. Thus: $\frac{1}{3} \times \frac{5}{7} = \frac{1 \times 5}{3 \times 7} = \frac{5}{21}$. Next if we consider e.g. $\frac{3}{4}$ of something, it is just three times as many pieces as is $\frac{1}{4}$ of the whole, thus $\frac{3}{4} \times \frac{3}{5} = 3 \times \left(\frac{1}{4} \times \frac{3}{5}\right) = 3 \times \frac{3}{20} = \frac{3 \times 3}{20} = \frac{9}{20}$. The net result is that when multiplying fractions, we multiply the tops together and multiply the bottoms together.

Practice examples

Write each product of rational numbers or expressions as a single rational expression in reduced or lowest form.

1. $\dfrac{42}{25} \times \dfrac{65}{56}$

$$\frac{42}{25} \times \frac{65}{56} = \frac{\overset{1}{\cancel{2}} \times 3 \times \overset{1}{\cancel{7}} \times \overset{1}{\cancel{5}} \times 13}{\underset{1}{\cancel{5}} \times 5 \times \underset{2^2}{\cancel{2^3}} \times \cancel{7}} = \frac{3 \times 13}{5 \times 2^2} = \frac{39}{20}$$

2. $\dfrac{24}{-45} \times -\dfrac{30}{9}$

$$\frac{24}{-45} \times -\frac{30}{9} = \frac{24}{-45} \times \frac{30}{-9} = \frac{2^3 \times \overset{1}{\cancel{3}} \times 2 \times \overset{1}{\cancel{3}} \times \overset{1}{\cancel{5}}}{\underset{-1}{\cancel{-3^2}} \times \underset{1}{\cancel{5}} \times (-3^2)} = \frac{2^3 \times 2}{-1 \times (-3^2)} = \frac{16}{9}$$

3. $3\dfrac{2}{9} \times 5\dfrac{3}{5}$

$$= \frac{29}{9} \times \frac{28}{5}$$

$$= \frac{29 \times 2^2 \times 7}{3^2 \times 5}$$

$$= \frac{812}{45}$$

4. $-\dfrac{200}{15} \times \dfrac{18}{60} \times \dfrac{-12}{25}$

$\qquad -\dfrac{200}{15} \times \dfrac{18}{60} \times \dfrac{-12}{25}$

$\qquad = \dfrac{-200}{15} \times \dfrac{18}{60} \times \dfrac{-12}{25}$

$\qquad = \dfrac{-2^3 \times 5^2 \times 2 \times 3^2 \times -2^2 \times 3}{3 \times 5 \times 2^2 \times 3 \times 5 \times 5^2}$

$\qquad = \dfrac{-2^3 \times \overset{1}{\cancel{5^2}} \times 2 \times \overset{1}{\cancel{3^2}} \times \overset{-1}{\cancel{2^2}} \times 3}{\underset{1}{\cancel{3}} \times 5 \times \underset{1}{\cancel{2^2}} \times \underset{1}{\cancel{3}} \times 5 \times \underset{1}{\cancel{5^2}}}$

$\qquad = \dfrac{-2^3 \times 2 \times -1 \times 3}{5 \times 5}$

$\qquad = \dfrac{48}{25}$

$\qquad = 1\dfrac{23}{25}$

5. $\dfrac{a^4 b^{-3}}{b^2 c} \times \dfrac{-a^5 c^7}{b^3 c^5}$

$\qquad = \dfrac{a^4 \times b^{-3} \times -a^5 \times c^7}{b^2 \times c \times b^3 \times c^5}$

$\qquad = \dfrac{-a^9 \times b^{-3} \times c^7}{b^5 \times c^6}$

$\qquad = \dfrac{-a^9 c}{b^8}$

6. $\dfrac{x^2 - 4}{x^2 - 5x} \times \dfrac{x^2 - 4x - 5}{x^2 - 3x + 2}$

$\dfrac{x^2 - 4}{x^2 - 5x} \times \dfrac{x^2 - 4x - 5}{x^2 - 3x + 2}$

$$= \frac{(x-2)(x+2)(x+1)(x-5)}{x(x-5)(x-1)(x-2)}$$

$$= \frac{\overset{1}{\cancel{(x-2)}}(x+2)(x+1)\overset{1}{\cancel{(x-5)}}}{x\underset{1}{\cancel{(x-5)}}(x-1)\underset{1}{\cancel{(x-2)}}}$$

$$= \frac{(x+2)(x+1)}{x(x-1)}$$

7. $\dfrac{8x^2 - 2y^2}{6x^2 + 13xy + 5y^2} \times \dfrac{3x^2 + 2xy - 5y^2}{x^3y - xy^3}$

$= \dfrac{2(2x - y)(2x + y)}{(2x + y)(3x + 5y)} \times \dfrac{(x - y)(3x + 5y)}{xy(x - y)(x + y)}$

$= \dfrac{2(2x - y)\cancel{(2x + y)}^1 \cancel{(x - y)}^1 \cancel{(3x + 5y)}^1}{\cancel{(2x + y)}_1 \cancel{(3x + 5y)}_1 xy \cancel{(x - y)}_1 (x + y)}$

$= \dfrac{2(2x - y)}{xy(x + y)}$

Before we can solve the problem we need factor all the numerators and denominators.

First Numerator

$8x^2 - 2y^2 = 2(4x^2 - y^2)$

$= 2((2x)^2 - (y)^2) = 2(2x - y)(2x + y)$

First Denominator

$6x^2 + 13xy + 5y^2$

$30x^2y^2$

$13xy = 10xy + 3xy$

$6x^2 + 13xy + 5y^2$

$= 6x^2 + 10xy + 3xy + 5y^2$

$= 2x(3x + 5y) + y(3x + 5y$

$= (2x + y)(3x + 5y)$

Second Numerator

$3x^2 + 2xy - 5y^2$

$-15x^2y^2$

$2xy = 5xy - 3xy$

$3x^2 + 2xy - 5y^2$

$= 3x^2 + 5xy - 3xy - 5y^2$

$= x(3x + 5y) - y(3x + 5y)$

$= (x - y)(3x + 5y)$

Second Denominator

$x^3y - xy^3$

$= xy(x^2 - y^2)$

$= xy(x - y)(x + y)$

In summary, when multiplying fractions, we multiply the numerators and multiply the denominators. The result can be simplified by dividing out any factor from any numerator with that same factor in any denominator.

1. Multiply the following rational expressions and write your answers in lowest terms.

a. $\dfrac{14}{25} \times \dfrac{15}{21}$

b. $\dfrac{-4}{9} \times -\dfrac{27}{6}$

c. $\dfrac{14}{15} \times \dfrac{5}{-2}$

d. $\dfrac{100}{-8} \times \dfrac{12}{30} \times \dfrac{-35}{21}$

e. $5\dfrac{4}{7} \times 2\dfrac{1}{2}$

f. $3\dfrac{3}{4} \times 4\dfrac{2}{3}$

g. $\dfrac{a^2 b^3}{b^6} \times \dfrac{a^2 c^3}{bc^5}$

h. $\dfrac{x^2 - 9}{x^2 + 3x - 4} \times \dfrac{x^3 + 64}{3x^2 + 8x - 3}$

i. $\dfrac{x^2 + 2x + 1}{1 - x^2} \times \dfrac{5x^2 - 6x + 1}{5x^2 + 4x - 1}$

j. $\dfrac{x^2 - 9}{x^2 - 2x + 4} \times \dfrac{x^3 - 8}{x^2 - 5x + 6}$

2. Answer True or False and give a justification.

a. $\dfrac{x^2 + 2x + 5}{x^2 + 3x - 1} = \dfrac{\cancel{x^2} + 2x + 5}{\cancel{x^2} + 3x - 1} = \dfrac{2x + 5}{3x - 1}$?

b. $-\dfrac{2}{3} = \dfrac{-2}{-3}$?

c. $\dfrac{x-1}{1-x} = 1$?

Note: Remember that you can only divide or multiply a numerator and the denominator of a rational number or expression by the same nonzero quantity to make them equivalent fractions. When reducing or making a rational expression into its lowest terms it is important to remember to reduce common multiplicative factors on the numerator and denominator and not common additive terms. A common error students make is to cancel additive terms. As an example, consider the fraction

$$\frac{8}{12} = \frac{8 \div 4}{12 \div 4} = \frac{2}{3} \text{ or } \frac{8}{12} = \frac{8 \times 2}{12 \times 2} = \frac{16}{24} \text{ but } \frac{8}{12} \neq \frac{8-4}{12-4} = \frac{4}{8} = \frac{1}{2} \text{ or } \frac{8}{12} \neq \frac{8+2}{12+2} = \frac{10}{14} = \frac{5}{7}$$

When you add or subtract a number from the numerator and denominator the value of the fraction changes and does not preserve equivalency to the original fraction as you see with the counter-examples just given.

Power Rule

Lecture

🖥 Multiplication and Exponents http://www.youtube.com/watch?v=ExausXVXu_E (15 min)

Recall that in Module 1 we defined the terminology of what a base and an exponent are. Our notation was that

For any real number a, and counting number n, $a^n = a \times a \times \ldots \times a$, where you multiply n copies of the factor a.

n times

The number n is called the exponent and the number a is called the base.

We also arrived at some rules for exponents after making observations on some examples. Let us review those rules and see how the operations of addition, subtraction, and multiplication help us simplify exponential expressions.

General Observations: For all integers n, m, and all nonzero real numbers a:

Product Rule: $a^m a^n = a^{n+m}$

Power Rule 1: $(a^m)^n = a^{mn}$

Quotient Rule: $\frac{a^m}{a^n} = a^{m-n}$

Negative Exponent: $a^{-n} = \frac{1}{a^n}$, and $\frac{1}{a^{-n}} = a^n$

Zero Exponent: $a^0 = 1$

Radicals or Fractional Exponents: $\sqrt[n]{a} = a^{\frac{1}{n}}$ (n is a positive integer and a is also positive when n is even.)

Simplify the following and do not leave any negative exponents in the answer.

1. $(2 \times 5)^3$

   $(2 \times 5)^3 = (2 \times 5) \times (2 \times 5) \times (2 \times 5) = (2 \times 2 \times 2) \times (5 \times 5 \times 5)$ by using the associative and commutative properties of multiplication. Thus we have

   $(2 \times 5)^3 = 2^3 \times 5^3 = 8 \times 125 = 1000$

2. $\left(\dfrac{2}{5}\right)^3$

   $\left(\dfrac{2}{5}\right)^3 = \dfrac{2}{5} \times \dfrac{2}{5} \times \dfrac{2}{5} = \dfrac{2 \times 2 \times 2}{5 \times 5 \times 5} = \dfrac{2^3}{5^3} = \dfrac{8}{125}$

Given these examples we can now make two new observations as follows:

Observation: For all integers n and all nonzero real numbers a and b,

Power Rule 2: $(ab)^n = a^n b^n$

Power Rule 3: $\left(\dfrac{a}{b}\right)^n = \dfrac{a^n}{b^n}$

Observation: For all integers n, and all nonzero real numbers a, a negative factor to an odd power remains negative and to an even power becomes positive since any negative term say $-a$, can be written as $-a = -1 \times a$,

$(-a)^n = (-1 \times a\,)^n = (-1)^n a^n$, so that when n is odd $(-a)^n = -a^n$, and when n is even $(-a)^n = a^n$ (based on the value of $(-1)^n$).

So for example $(-2)^3 = -2^3 = -8$ and $(-3)^2 = (-3)(-3) = 3^2 = 9$.

Practice examples

Evaluate and simplify the following. Assume all variables are nonzero real numbers. Do not leave any negative exponents in your answers.

1. $a^{-3} a^5$

   Method 1: We can use the product rule to get $a^{-3+5} = a^2$.

   Method 2: Notice that $a^{-3} a^5 = \dfrac{1}{a^3} \cdot \dfrac{a^5}{1} = \dfrac{a^5}{a^3} = a^{5-3} = a^2$.

What is important to remember when solving any math problem regardless of the method you choose to apply, is that each step is mathematically justified. If you do this, various paths will lead to the same answer. So when you feel you are stuck, just pause, regroup, and pull your resources together and be creative. Don't give up. Also always make sure you know "Why" you are writing or saying or doing a

---

particular step.

2. $(2x^2y^{-3})^{-2}$

Again there are multiple ways to solve this problem. Since we are all different from each other, what comes to one person as a solution may not occur to another person. Also one may think one way is better than another. So choose which method to apply based on what comes naturally to you. Again justify each step and know "Why" you are doing it.

Method 1: Using our power rule we can apply the exponent of -2 to each multiplicative factor in the parentheses. Also, remember negative exponent changes where your base moves to...

$$(2x^2y^{-3})^{-2} = (2)^{-2}(x^2)^{-2}(y^{-3})^{-2} = \frac{1}{2^2}x^{-4}y^6 = \frac{1}{2^2}\frac{1}{x^4}\frac{y^6}{1} = \frac{y^6}{4x^4}$$

Method 2: The outer negative exponent gives us

$$(2x^2y^{-3})^{-2} = \frac{1}{(2x^2y^{-3})^2} = \frac{1}{(2)^2(x^2)^2(y^{-3})^2} = \frac{1}{4x^4y^{-6}} = \frac{y^6}{4x^4}$$

Again remember the y^{-6} moves to the numerator as y^6 from our notation of negative exponents. We can justify this by multiplying numerator and denominator by y^6 which leaves $y^0 = 1$ in the bottom and y^6 on top.

Method 3: We rewrite our expression as

$$(2x^2y^{-3})^{-2} = \left(\frac{2x^2}{y^3}\right)^{-2} = \frac{(2)^{-2}(x^2)^{-2}}{(y^3)^{-2}} = \frac{(2)^{-2}x^{-4}}{y^{-6}} = \frac{y^6}{2^2x^4} = \frac{y^6}{4x^4}$$

Again we used the fact that negative power means take the multiplicative inverse.

3. $\left(\frac{3x^{-4}}{b^3}\right)^{-2}$

$$\left(\frac{3x^{-4}}{b^3}\right)^{-2} = \left(\frac{3}{x^4b^3}\right)^{-2} = \left(\frac{x^4b^3}{3}\right)^{2} = \frac{(x^4)^2(b^3)^2}{(3)^2} = \frac{x^8b^6}{9}$$

4. $\left(\frac{q^{-1}xy^{-2}}{x^{-4}y^3q^{-3}}\right)^{-2}$

$$\left(\frac{q^{-1}xy^{-2}}{x^{-4}y^3q^{-3}}\right)^{-2} = \left(\frac{q^3xx^4}{qy^2y^3}\right)^{-2} = \left(\frac{q^2x^5}{y^5}\right)^{-2} = \left(\frac{y^5}{q^2x^5}\right)^{2} = \frac{(y^5)^2}{(q^2)^2(x^5)^5} = \frac{y^{10}}{q^4x^{10}}$$

5. $\left(\dfrac{3x^{-3}}{y^2}\right)^2\left(-\dfrac{3x^2}{5y^3}\right)^{-3}$

$$\left(\dfrac{3x^{-3}}{y^2}\right)^2\left(-\dfrac{3x^2}{5y^3}\right)^{-3}=\left(\dfrac{3}{x^3y^2}\right)^2\left(-\dfrac{5y^3}{3x^2}\right)^3=\dfrac{3^2}{x^6y^4}\cdot-\dfrac{5^3(y^3)^3}{3^3(x^2)^3}=\dfrac{3^2}{x^6y^4}\cdot-\dfrac{5^3y^9}{3^3x^6}$$

Notice that the negative base in the second expression makes the resulting power negative due to its odd exponent.

So

$$\left(\dfrac{3x^{-3}}{y^2}\right)^2\left(-\dfrac{3x^2}{5y^3}\right)^{-3}=-\dfrac{3^25^3y^9}{x^6y^43^3x^6}=-\dfrac{5^3y^5}{3x^{12}}=-\dfrac{125y^5}{3x^{12}}$$

Video Log 2.6c

1. Evaluate and simplify the following. Write your answer without any negative exponents. Assume that all variables are nonzero real numbers.

   a. $(3b)^2$

   b. $a^2b^3 \times a^3b^2$

   c. $(3x^2y^3)^3$

   d. $\left(\dfrac{2y^3}{3x^2}\right)^4$

   e. $(3a^2b^3)^{-2}$

   f. $\left(\dfrac{2}{3}\right)^{-3}$

   g. $\left(\dfrac{3}{4}\right)^{-2}\times\left(\dfrac{9}{2}\right)^2$

   h. $(a^{-3}b^2)^{-3}$

   i. $(-3a^3b^{-2}c)^3(b^6c^{-4})^2$

   j. $\left(\dfrac{a^{-4}}{b^2}\right)^{-3}$

   k. $\left(\dfrac{x^{-7}}{2y^3}\right)^2\left(-\dfrac{6x^3}{y^{-3}}\right)^2$

   l. $\left(\dfrac{x^{-7}}{2y^3}\right)^{-2}\left(-\dfrac{6x^3}{y^{-3}}\right)^2$

   m. $\left(\dfrac{15x^5y^{-3}}{9x^{-4}y^3}\right)^2$

   n. $\left(\dfrac{-4x^{-2}y^9}{12x^{-3}y^5}\right)^{-2}$

   o. $\left(\dfrac{13345x^{-234}y^{459}}{1002x^{-398}y^{5019}}\right)^0$

Radicals
Lectures

🖥 Review of radicals and fractional powers and simplifying radicals
http://www.youtube.com/watch?v=Ab-epECGrl4 (9 min)

We can also work with radicals and fractional exponents in a manner similar to exponent expressions since we saw that radicals were equivalent to the radicand raised to the exponent of $\frac{1}{index}$, i.e. $\sqrt[n]{a} = a^{\frac{1}{n}}$. All the observations we had for whole number exponents extend to fractional exponents and hence indirectly to radicals as well.

Observations
For all positive real numbers , $\sqrt{a}\sqrt{a} = a^{\frac{1}{2}}a^{\frac{1}{2}} = a^{\frac{1}{2}+\frac{1}{2}} = a^1 = a$.
For all real numbers a, $\sqrt[3]{a}\sqrt[3]{a}\sqrt[3]{a} = a^{\frac{1}{3}}a^{\frac{1}{3}}a^{\frac{1}{3}} = a^{\frac{1}{3}+\frac{1}{3}+\frac{1}{3}} = a^1 = a$.

Another way to look at the above two observations is that for all positive real numbers, $\sqrt{a^2} = \sqrt{aa} = \sqrt{a}\sqrt{a} = a^{\frac{1}{2}}a^{\frac{1}{2}} = a$. (Think about what would happen if a was a negative number, can we still think of $\sqrt{a^2} = \sqrt{aa} = \sqrt{a}\sqrt{a}$?).

For all real numbers a, $\sqrt[3]{a^3} = \sqrt[3]{aaa} = \sqrt[3]{a}\sqrt[3]{a}\sqrt[3]{a} = a^{\frac{1}{3}}a^{\frac{1}{3}}a^{\frac{1}{3}} = a$.

In general, for all positive real numbers a, and all whole numbers , $\sqrt[n]{a^n} = \left(\sqrt[n]{a}\right)^n = a$.

In general for all real numbers a, (pos. and neg.) and all odd whole numbers n,

$$\sqrt[n]{a^n} = \left(\sqrt[n]{a}\right)^n = a.$$

When working with radicals (and fractional exponents) with even index the only way you get a real number is when the radicand is positive (this avoids ambiguous answers). Consider $\sqrt{4}$ which could also be written as $\sqrt{4} = (2^2)^{\frac{1}{2}} = 2^{2\times\frac{1}{2}} = 2^1 = 2$, here 2 is called the principal square root of 4. We could also have written $\sqrt{4}$ as $\sqrt{4} = \sqrt{(-2)^2} = ((-2)^2)^{\frac{1}{2}} = (-2)^{2\times\frac{1}{2}} = (-2)^1 = -2$. Therefore, to avoid this confusion with even powers we define any even index radical of a positive number to be the positive n^{th} root. If we want the negative square root, we indicate this as, e.g. $-\sqrt{4}$. Also note that $\sqrt{-4} = 2i$ is not a real number, notice no real number can be squared to get a negative 4. Therefore $\sqrt{x}$ is not a real number when x is negative since there is no real number that when multiplied by itself two times will be negative. The same holds for ¼ powers and fourth roots since any positive or negative number multiplied by itself four times does not produce a negative result! For odd indexed radicals (or odd denominator fractional power) negative radicands are meaningful, e.g., $\sqrt[3]{-8} = -2$ since $(-2)^3 = -8$.

Odd Root Property: $\sqrt[n]{-a} = -\sqrt[n]{a}$, n is an odd number and a is any real number.

Observation:

$\sqrt[n]{a^n} = (a^n)^{\frac{1}{n}} = a^{n \times \frac{1}{n}} = a$, and that when n is an even number, a has to be a non-negative real number.

Using this observation we have that

Commutative Property of Multiplication

$$\sqrt[3]{a^3} = (a^3)^{\frac{1}{3}} = a^{3 \times \frac{1}{3}} = a^{\frac{1}{3} \times 3} = \left(a^{\frac{1}{3}}\right)^3 = \left(\sqrt[3]{a}\right)^3 = a \text{ for all real numbers } a.$$

Similarly, for all positive real numbers a, $\sqrt{a^2} = \left(\sqrt{a}\right)^2 = a$.

Simplifying Radicals

This also provides a way to simplify radicals if we think about how $\sqrt[n]{a^m} = (a^m)^{\frac{1}{n}} = a^{m \cdot \frac{1}{n}} = a^{\frac{m}{n}}$.

For example, $\sqrt[3]{a^7} = a^{\frac{7}{3}} = a^{2\frac{1}{3}} = a^{2+\frac{1}{3}} = a^2 a^{\frac{1}{3}} = a^2 \sqrt[3]{a}$.

So in $\sqrt[3]{a^7}$, each of the seven factors of a inside the radicand corresponds to an $a^{\frac{1}{3}}$, and groups of three of these correspond to a^1 outside the radicand. Thus if we divide the seven copies into two groups of 3 and 1 left over, the groups of three inside the radicand each simplify to a factor of a outside of the radical and the remaining a^1 is left inside as the radicand. This provides a useful tool for simplifying radicals when the radicand has prime factors raised to an exponent that is greater than or equal to the index of the radical. We could also view this as $\sqrt[3]{a^6 \cdot a} = (a^6)^{\frac{1}{3}} \sqrt[3]{a} = a^2 \sqrt[3]{a}$. We will apply this so that all prime factors in the radicand are raised to exponents less than the index.

Practice examples:

Simplify the algebraic expressions below.

1. $\sqrt[3]{27}$ Since $27 = 3^3$, we have $\sqrt[3]{27} = \sqrt[3]{3^3} = 3$.

2. $\sqrt[4]{x^4}$ The fourth root undoes the four exponent, i.e., $\sqrt[4]{x^4} = (x^4)^{\frac{1}{4}} = x$. For even roots, this will actually return $|x|$ as the result. If x starts out negative, the negative is lost when taking the fourth power and is not recovered in the standard fourth root which is taken to be positive. For example when $x = -2$, $\sqrt[4]{(-2)^4} = \sqrt[4]{16} = +2 = |x|$.

3. $\sqrt[5]{x^7}$ We can simplify this as $\sqrt[5]{x^7} = \sqrt[5]{x^5 x^2} = x^{\frac{5}{5}} \sqrt[5]{x^2} = x \sqrt[5]{x^2}$.

         Or

         We view this as $\sqrt[5]{x^7} = \sqrt[5]{x^5 x^2} = \sqrt[5]{x^5} \sqrt[5]{x^2} = x \sqrt[5]{x^2}$.

4. $\sqrt[3]{x^{12}}$ We can write this as $(x^{12})^{\frac{1}{3}} = x^4$.

         Or as $\sqrt[3]{x^3 x^3 x^3 x^3} = x \cdot x \cdot x \cdot x = x^4$.

         Or as $\sqrt[3]{(x^4)^3} = x^4$.

5. $\sqrt[5]{-a^{13}}$ The negative can be brought out of an odd root as

$$\sqrt[5]{(-1)(a^{13})} = \sqrt[5]{-1} \sqrt[5]{a^{13}} = -1 \sqrt[5]{a^{13}}$$

         Then we can take two groups of five factors of a out as an a^2 and leave the remaining 3 a factors inside to get $\sqrt[5]{-a^{13}} = -a^2 \sqrt[5]{a^3}$.

6. $\sqrt[3]{-32}$ Remember that $32 = 2^5$ (factor 32), and that an odd root with a negative radicand is the same as negative of the root.

$$\sqrt[3]{-32} = -\sqrt[3]{32} = -\sqrt[3]{2^5} = -2^1 \sqrt[3]{2^2} = -2\sqrt[3]{4}$$

         Since $\sqrt[3]{2^5} = 2^{\frac{5}{3}} = 2^{1\frac{2}{3}}$

         Or

         We first note that in an odd root of a negative, the negative comes out of the radicand and also that $32 = 2^5$,   Thus:

$$\sqrt[3]{-32} = -\sqrt[3]{32} = -\sqrt[3]{2^5} = -\sqrt[3]{2^3 2^2} = -\sqrt[3]{2^3} \sqrt[3]{2^2} - 2\sqrt[3]{4}$$

Observations

1. For all real numbers a and b, $\sqrt[n]{ab} = \sqrt[n]{a}\sqrt[n]{b}$ (when n is an even number, then a and b have to be positive real numbers).

2. For all real numbers a and $b \neq 0$, $\sqrt[n]{\dfrac{a}{b}} = \dfrac{\sqrt[n]{a}}{\sqrt[n]{b}}$ (when n is an even number, then a and b have to be positive real numbers).

Practice examples

Simplify the algebraic expressions below. Assume all variables represent positive real numbers.

1. $\sqrt{4x^2}$

We can break this into $\sqrt{4 \cdot x^2} = \sqrt{4} \cdot \sqrt{x^2} = 2x$. ($x$ is assumed to be positive.)

2. $\sqrt[3]{-8y^6x^3}$

The (-) comes out of the odd root, and we have
$\sqrt[3]{-8y^6x^3} = -\sqrt[3]{8} \cdot \sqrt[3]{y^6} \cdot \sqrt[3]{x^3} = -2y^2x$.

3. $\sqrt{-4}$

   $= 2i$ Note that $\sqrt{-1} = $ i.

4. $\sqrt{-x^2}$

We will deal with positive radicands for radicals with even index so that the result is a real number. For this problem though if $x \geq 0$, it can be simplified as $\sqrt{-1} \cdot \sqrt{x^2} = ix$, since the square root of (-1) is i. Other even indexed radicals of negatives, e.g., $\sqrt[4]{-1}$ result in more complicated complex numbers. It is easy to see that this fourth root is not equal to i since $i^4 = i^2 \cdot i^2 = (-1)(-1) = 1$. For this course we will always work with positive radicands with even roots.

5. $\sqrt[4]{x^9}$

We rewrite this as $\sqrt[4]{x^8x} = x^2 \sqrt[4]{x}$ since $(x^8)^{\left(\frac{1}{4}\right)} = x^2$.

6. $\sqrt{125x^5}$

   $\sqrt{125x^5} = \sqrt{5^3x^5}$

   Remember that square root means the index is 2.

   Therefore, we have $\dfrac{3}{2} = 1\dfrac{1}{2}$ and $\dfrac{5}{2} = 2\dfrac{1}{2}$ giving us

   $\sqrt{125x^5} = \sqrt{5^3x^5} = 5^1x^2 \sqrt{5^1x^1} = 5x^2 \sqrt{5x}$.

   Also we could write this as $\sqrt{5^2 \cdot 5 \cdot x^4 \cdot x} = 5x^2 \sqrt{5x}$.

7. $\sqrt{12x^3y^6}$

We look for perfect square powers in the radicand that can be computed with the result co

Thus $\sqrt{12x^3y^6} = \sqrt{3 \cdot 2^2 \cdot x \cdot x^2 \cdot y^6} = \sqrt{3} \cdot 2 \cdot \sqrt{x} \cdot x \cdot y^3 = 2xy^3 \sqrt{3x}$.

8. $\sqrt{3x}\,\sqrt{3x^4}$

   We can rewrite $\sqrt{3x}\,\sqrt{3x^4}$

   $= \sqrt{3x3x^4}$

   $= \sqrt{9x^5}$

   $= \sqrt{9}\,\sqrt{x^4x}$

   $= \sqrt{9}\,\sqrt{x^4}\,\sqrt{x}$

   $= 3x^2\,\sqrt{x}$

9. $\sqrt[3]{6x^4y^5}\sqrt[3]{9x^2y^2}$

   $= \sqrt[3]{54x^6y^7}$

   $= \sqrt[3]{2\cdot 27\cdot x^6\cdot y^6\cdot y}$

   $= 3x^2y^2\,\sqrt[3]{2y}$

So you can observe that all the properties for whole number exponents apply to rational exponents and thus appropriately to radical expressions as well.

Multiplying Radicals

Lecture

🖥 Simplifying and Multiplying Radicals Continued
http://www.youtube.com/watch?v=xSEpcZdcBHc (9 min)

More Practice examples

Simplify the following.

1.
   $$\sqrt{3}\sqrt{3}$$
   $$\sqrt{3}\sqrt{3} = \sqrt{3\times 3} = \sqrt{3^2} = 3$$

2.
   $$\sqrt{32x}$$
   $$\sqrt{32x} = \sqrt{2^5x^1} = 2^2\sqrt{2x}$$
   OR
   $$\sqrt{2^5x^1} = (2^5x^1)^{\frac{1}{2}} = 2^{\frac{5}{2}}x^{\frac{1}{2}}$$
   $$= 2^{2\frac{1}{2}}x^{\frac{1}{2}}$$
   $$= 2^2\sqrt{2}\sqrt{x}$$
   $$= 4\sqrt{2x}$$

3. $\sqrt[3]{-243x^7}$ We first take the cube root of (-1) outside the radical.

Then note that $\frac{5}{3} = 1 + \frac{2}{3}$, and $\frac{7}{3} = 2 + \frac{2}{3}$. Or you can think

$$\sqrt[3]{-243x^7} = -\sqrt[3]{3^5 x^7}$$
$$= -3^1 x^2 \sqrt[3]{3^2 x^1}$$
$$= -3x^2 \sqrt[3]{9x}$$

of it as cube root (which means index is 3). The cube root of 3 factors of "3" is "3" outside the radical and 2 factors of "3" remain inside the radical. Likewise two groups of 3 factors of "x" go outside the radical as x^2 and one factor of "x" remains inside the radical.

4. $\sqrt[3]{125b^3 a^5}$

$$\sqrt[3]{125b^3 a^5} = \sqrt[3]{5^3 b^3 a^3 a^2} = 5^{3 \times \frac{1}{3}} b^{3 \times \frac{1}{3}} a^{3 \times \frac{1}{3}} a^{2 \times \frac{1}{3}} = 5^1 b^1 a^1 a^{\frac{2}{3}} = 5ba \sqrt[3]{a^2}.$$

Eventually you should be able to simplify the exponents in your head by noticing how the index divides into the exponent of the base of each factor in the radicand.

5. $3\sqrt{y} \times 2\sqrt{y}$

$$3\sqrt{y} \times 2\sqrt{y} = 3 \times 2 \times \sqrt{y \times y} = 6\sqrt{y^2} = 6y$$

Remember the associative and commutative property of multiplication is what allowed us to multiply the 3 and the 2. We also used the fact $a^{\frac{1}{n}} b^{\frac{1}{n}} = (ab)^{\frac{1}{n}}$ allows us to multiply the radicands under a single radical $\sqrt{y}\sqrt{y} = \sqrt{y \times y}$.

The example below asks you to draw upon your knowledge of using the distributive property of multiplication over addition and subtraction.

6. $(2\sqrt{x} - 3)(5 + 3\sqrt{x})$ We expand this using the distributive property of multiplication over addition and subtraction to get:

$$(2\sqrt{x} - 3)(5 + 3\sqrt{x}) = 10\sqrt{x} + 6x - 15 - 9\sqrt{x} = \sqrt{x} + 6x - 15.$$

7. $(2 + \sqrt{3})(2 - \sqrt{3})$

$$(2 + \sqrt{3})(2 - \sqrt{3}) = 2 \times 2 + 2 \times (-\sqrt{3}) + \sqrt{3} \times 2 + \sqrt{3} \times (-\sqrt{3})$$
$$= 4 - 2\sqrt{3} + 2\sqrt{3} - \sqrt{3 \times 3}$$
$$= 4 - 3$$
$$= 1$$

Notice that we multiplied two expressions similar to the factors in a difference of squares $((a - b)(a + b) = a^2 - b^2$) As we saw earlier, this makes the two middle terms sum to zero which leaves the final answer without any radical terms. The factors $(2 + \sqrt{3})$ and $(2 - \sqrt{3})$ are called **conjugates** of each other.

Playing

Recall that the product and quotient rules for multiplying or dividing the same base raised to integer exponents means we add or subtract the exponents respectively. These rules were developed for integer exponents, but they extend to rational exponents and radicals as well. Just remember, you must have the same base or same radicand.

Practice Examples

Simplify to a base raised to a single power and to a simplified radical. Assume that all the variables are positive real numbers.

1. $a^{\frac{1}{5}}a^{\frac{2}{3}}$ We add the exponents to get $a^{\frac{1}{5}+\frac{2}{3}} = a^{\frac{3}{15}+\frac{10}{15}} = a^{\frac{13}{15}}$ as a radical
$= \sqrt[15]{a^{13}}$.

2. $\dfrac{x^{\frac{5}{3}}}{x^{\frac{1}{2}}}$ We subtract exponents to get $x^{\frac{5}{3}-\frac{1}{2}} = x^{\frac{10}{6}-\frac{3}{6}} = x^{\frac{7}{6}} = x^1 \cdot x^{\frac{1}{6}}$ also
$= x\sqrt[6]{x}$.

3. $a^{\frac{2}{3}}a^{\frac{1}{2}}$ $= a^{\frac{2}{3}+\frac{1}{2}} = a^{\frac{2\times 2}{3\times 2}+\frac{1\times 3}{2\times 3}} = a^{\frac{4+3}{6}} = a^{\frac{7}{6}} = a^{1\frac{1}{6}} = a^1 a^{\frac{1}{6}} = a\sqrt[6]{a}$

4. $\sqrt[3]{a}\;\sqrt[4]{a^3}$ We first convert the radicals to rational exponents and then add the exponents. $\sqrt[3]{a}\;\sqrt[4]{a^3} = a^{\frac{1}{3}}a^{\frac{3}{4}} = a^{\frac{1}{3}+\frac{3}{4}} = a^{\frac{1\times 4}{3\times 4}+\frac{3\times 3}{4\times 3}} = a^{\frac{4+9}{12}} = a^{\frac{13}{12}} = a^{1\frac{1}{12}} = a\sqrt[12]{a}$

5. $\dfrac{a^{\frac{2}{3}}}{a^{\frac{3}{4}}}$ We subtract exponents: $a^{\frac{2}{3}-\frac{3}{4}} = a^{\frac{2\times 4}{3\times 4}-\frac{3\times 3}{4\times 3}} = a^{\frac{8-9}{12}} = a^{-\frac{1}{12}} = \dfrac{1}{a^{\frac{1}{12}}} =$
$\dfrac{1}{\sqrt[12]{a}}$

6. $\dfrac{\sqrt[3]{a^2}}{\sqrt[4]{a^3}}$ We switch to exponent expression to get $\dfrac{\sqrt[3]{a^2}}{\sqrt[4]{a^3}} = \dfrac{a^{\frac{2}{3}}}{a^{\frac{3}{4}}}$ which is done in #
5.

Video Log 2.6d

1. Assume that all the variables are positive real numbers. Simplify the following and write your final answer as one radical term.

a. $a^{\frac{1}{2}}a^{\frac{1}{2}}$	l. $\left(\sqrt{2a^5y^7}\right)\left(\sqrt{8ay^2}\right)$
b. $\sqrt{a}\sqrt{a}$	m. $\left(-5ab\sqrt[3]{a^6b^3}\right)\left(7\sqrt[3]{a^9b^6}\right)$
c. $5\sqrt{ab} \times 7\sqrt{ab}$	n. $\left(3\sqrt{a^5b^3}\right)\left(\sqrt{40a^2b^6}\right)$
d. $12a\sqrt{b} \times 7b\sqrt{a}$	o. $\sqrt[3]{a^5}\sqrt[5]{a^3}$
e. $a^{\frac{2}{3}}a^{\frac{1}{2}}$	p. $\sqrt[3]{25}\sqrt{5}$ (Write using a base of 5.)
f. $\sqrt{a^3}\sqrt{a}$	q. $\sqrt[5]{8}\sqrt[3]{4}$
g. $x^{\frac{5}{4}}x^{-\frac{2}{3}}$	r. $\sqrt[3]{x^7}\sqrt[5]{x^8}$
h. $\dfrac{x^{\frac{5}{4}}}{x^{-\frac{1}{2}}}$	s. $\left(2\sqrt[3]{27a}\right)\left(\sqrt[3]{24a^3b^5}\right)$
i. $\sqrt{2}\sqrt{6}$	t. $\left(9\sqrt[5]{2a^4b^6}\right)\left(\sqrt{16a^2b^4}\right)$
j. $\sqrt{4ab}\sqrt{2ab^4}$	u. $\left(-\sqrt{5a}\right)\left(-2\sqrt{15a^3b^2}\right)\left(\sqrt{3a^2b^3c^{11}}\right)$
k. $\left(\sqrt{4a^3b^2}\right)\left(\sqrt{2ab}\right)$	

2. Simplify the following.

a. $\sqrt{25}$	e. $\sqrt[3]{125x^7}$	i. $\sqrt[4]{32a^{15}b^4}$
b. $\sqrt[3]{125}$	f. $\sqrt{125x^5}$	j. $\sqrt{32a^5}\sqrt{4a^3b}$
c. $\sqrt{125}$	g. $3\sqrt{x} \times 2\sqrt{x}$	k. $\left(2+4\sqrt{3}\right)\left(3+5\sqrt{2}\right)$
d. $\sqrt{48}$	h. $\sqrt[3]{-8a^3b^7}$	l. $\left(3-2\sqrt{3}\right)\left(3+2\sqrt{3}\right)$

Rationalizing Denominators of Radical Expressions
Lecture

💻 Rationalizing Denominators of Radical Expressions
http://www.youtube.com/watRch?v=BM7KwGKZBbs (8 min)

Terminology

For any real numbers a and b, the terms $a + b\sqrt{c}$ and $a - b\sqrt{c}$ are called **conjugates** of each other, and their product is $(a + b\sqrt{c})(a - b\sqrt{c}) = a^2 - b^2 c$.

This terminology applies to complex numbers as well. For any complex number of the form $a + bi$, $a - bi$ is called its conjugate and vice versa. Remember that $\sqrt{-1} = i$ and $i^2 = -1$. Thus, $2 - 3i$ and $2 + 3i$ are complex conjugates of each other.

__Note__ if square root two-term factors of the type $a + b\sqrt{c}$ or $a - b\sqrt{c}$ appear in a numerator or a denominator in a fractional expression we can create an equivalent fraction by multiplying by the conjugate expression on the top and bottom. The resulting expression will end up not having a radical term in the original location. We often use this process to rationalize (eliminate a square root radical from) the denominator of such an expression.

Convention on simplifying radical expressions.

Recall you can write all rational expressions in lowest terms by dividing any common factor from the numerator and denominator. Once this is achieved:

   a. Simplify the rational expression as much as possible such that all the prime factors in the remaining expression within the radicand should be raised to exponents less than the radical index.
   b. There should be no fraction within the radicand.
   c. There should be no radical in the denominator if possible.

We've dealt with (a.) already. Item (b.) is handled e.g., by $\sqrt[n]{\dfrac{a}{b}} = \dfrac{\sqrt[n]{a}}{\sqrt[n]{b}}$, but this leaves us with a radical term in the denominator which we prefer not to have.

The following examples demonstrate how to eliminate radicals from the single- and two-term denominators. This is called **rationalizing the denominator**.

Practice Examples

Rationalize the denominator so that your final answer does not have radical terms in the denominator. We do this by multiplying top and bottom by the conjugate expression of the bottom.

1. $$\frac{3 + \sqrt{2}}{2 - \sqrt{3}}$$

    The conjugate of $2 - \sqrt{3}$ is $2 + \sqrt{3}$. So multiply the numerator and denominator by $2 + \sqrt{3}$.

    $$\frac{3 + \sqrt{2}}{2 - \sqrt{3}} = \frac{\left(3 + \sqrt{2}\right)\left(2 + \sqrt{3}\right)}{\left(2 - \sqrt{3}\right)\left(2 + \sqrt{3}\right)}$$

    Now use distributive property of multiplication over addition and subtraction to simplify.

    $$= \frac{3 \times 2 + 3 \times \sqrt{3} + \sqrt{2} \times 2 + \sqrt{2} \times \sqrt{3}}{2 \times 2 + 2 \times \sqrt{3} - \sqrt{3} \times 2 - \sqrt{3} \times \sqrt{3}}$$

    $$= \frac{6 + 3\sqrt{3} + 2\sqrt{2} + \sqrt{6}}{4 + 2\sqrt{3} - 2\sqrt{3} - 3}$$

    $$= \frac{6 + 3\sqrt{3} + 2\sqrt{2} + \sqrt{6}}{4 - 3}$$

    $$= 6 + 3\sqrt{3} + 2\sqrt{2} + \sqrt{6}$$

2. $$\frac{3 + 2\sqrt{x}}{2 - 3\sqrt{x}}$$

    The conjugate of $2 - 3\sqrt{x}$ is $2 + 3\sqrt{x}$. So multiply the numerator and denominator by $2 + 3\sqrt{x}$.

    $$\frac{3 + 2\sqrt{x}}{2 - 3\sqrt{x}} = \frac{\left(3 + 2\sqrt{x}\right)\left(2 + 3\sqrt{x}\right)}{\left(2 - 3\sqrt{x}\right)\left(2 + 3\sqrt{x}\right)}$$

    Now use distributive property of multiplication over addition and subtraction to simplify.

    $$= \frac{3 \times 2 + 3 \times 3\sqrt{x} + 2\sqrt{x} \times 2 + 2\sqrt{x} \times 3\sqrt{x}}{2 \times 2 + 2 \times 3\sqrt{x} - 3\sqrt{x} \times 2 - 3\sqrt{x} \times 3\sqrt{x}}$$

    $$= \frac{6 + 9\sqrt{x} + 4\sqrt{x} + 6\sqrt{x^2}}{4 + 6\sqrt{x} - 6\sqrt{x} - 9\sqrt{x^2}}$$

    $$= \frac{6 + 13\sqrt{x} + 6x}{4 - 9x}$$

3. $\dfrac{3-2i}{4+5i}$ This example shows how to divide complex numbers. We multiply top and bottom by $4-5i$, (the conjugate of $4+5i$). Remember that $i = \sqrt{-1}$, and $i^2 = -1$.

$$\dfrac{3-2i}{4+5i} = \dfrac{(3-2i)(4-5i)}{(4+5i)(4-5i)}$$

$$= \dfrac{3\times 4 + 3\times(-5i) - 2i\times 4 - 2i\times(-5i)}{4\times 4 + 4\times(-5i) + 5i\times 4 + 5i\times(-5i)}$$

$$= \dfrac{12 - 15i - 8i + 10i^2}{16 - 20i + 20i - 25i^2}$$

$$= \dfrac{12 - 23i - 10}{16 + 25}$$

Note that $10i^2 = 10(-1) = -10, and -25i^2 = -25(-1) = 25$

$$= \dfrac{2-23i}{41}$$

$$= \dfrac{2}{41} - \dfrac{23}{42}i$$

(when we write complex numbers we always want them to appear in the form $a + bi$)

The problems below have single term denominators. Here we multiply the numerator and denominator by a radical expression to make all the factors in the bottom radicand be raised to powers that are multiples of the index. In this way the denominator radical will be eliminated. Thus for a square root radical, we need to make the radicand in the bottom a perfect square, for a cube root radical we need to make the radicand in the bottom a perfect cube.

4. $\sqrt{\dfrac{1}{2}}$

$\dfrac{\sqrt{1}}{\sqrt{2}} = \dfrac{1}{\sqrt{2}}.$

$$\sqrt{\dfrac{1}{2}} = \dfrac{1\times\sqrt{2}}{\sqrt{2}\times\sqrt{2}} = \dfrac{\sqrt{2}}{\sqrt{4}} = \dfrac{\sqrt{2}}{2}$$

5. $\dfrac{3x}{\sqrt{12x^3}}$

Simplify the radicals and
write the rational expression
in lowest terms.

$$= \dfrac{3x}{\sqrt{2^2 \cdot 3 \cdot x^2 \cdot x}}$$

$$= \dfrac{3x}{2x\sqrt{3x}}$$

$$= \dfrac{3\cancel{x}}{2\cancel{x}\sqrt{3x}}$$

$$= \dfrac{3}{2\sqrt{3x}}$$

$$= \dfrac{3\sqrt{3x}}{2\sqrt{3x}\sqrt{3x}}$$

$$= \dfrac{3\sqrt{3x}}{2\sqrt{9x^2}}$$

$$= \dfrac{\cancel{3}\sqrt{3x}}{2 \cdot \cancel{3}x}$$

$$= \dfrac{\sqrt{3x}}{2x}$$

6. $\dfrac{2x^2}{\sqrt[3]{24x^8y^4}}$

Simplify the radicals and write the rational expression in lowest terms.

$= \dfrac{2x^2}{\sqrt[3]{2^3 \times 3x^8y^4}}$ (Remember $\sqrt[3]{2^3} = 2$, $\sqrt[3]{x^8} = x^{\frac{8}{3}} = x^{2\frac{2}{3}} = x^2 \sqrt[3]{x^2}$,

and , $\sqrt[3]{y^4} = y^{\frac{4}{3}} = y^{1\frac{1}{3}} = y \sqrt[3]{y}$)

$= \dfrac{2x^2}{2x^2y \sqrt[3]{3x^2y}}$

$= \dfrac{\overset{1}{\cancel{2x^2}}}{\cancel{2x^2}y \sqrt[3]{3x^2y}}$

$= \dfrac{1}{y\sqrt[3]{3x^2y}}$

$= \dfrac{1 \times \sqrt[3]{3^2xy^2}}{y\sqrt[3]{3x^2y} \times \sqrt[3]{3^2xy^2}}$

$= \dfrac{\sqrt[3]{3^2xy^2}}{y\sqrt[3]{3^3x^3y^3}}$

$= \dfrac{\sqrt[3]{9xy^2}}{y \times 3xy}$

$= \dfrac{\sqrt[3]{9xy^2}}{3xy^2}$

7.
$$\sqrt[3]{\dfrac{2x^4}{3y^2}}$$

$$= \dfrac{\sqrt[3]{2x^4}}{\sqrt[3]{3y^2}}$$

$$= \dfrac{x\sqrt[3]{2x}}{\sqrt[3]{3y^2}}$$

$$= \dfrac{x\sqrt[3]{2x} \times \sqrt[3]{3^2 y}}{\sqrt[3]{3y^2} \times \sqrt[3]{3^2 y}}$$

In order to get rid of the cube root from the denominator we need to multiply numerator and denominator by $\sqrt[3]{3^2 y}$.

$$= \dfrac{x\sqrt[3]{18xy}}{\sqrt[3]{3^3 y^3}}$$

$$= \dfrac{x\sqrt[3]{18xy}}{3y}$$

8.
$$\dfrac{\sqrt[3]{4}}{\sqrt[3]{2x^2}}$$

$$= \dfrac{\sqrt[3]{2^2}}{\sqrt[3]{2x^2}}$$

$$= \dfrac{\sqrt[3]{2^2} \times \sqrt[3]{2^2 x}}{\sqrt[3]{2x^2} \times \sqrt[3]{2^2 x}}$$

$$= \dfrac{\sqrt[3]{2^4 x}}{\sqrt[3]{2^3 x^3}}$$

$$= \dfrac{2\sqrt[3]{2x}}{2x}$$

Note: You can divide numerator and denominator by 2 to write the rational expression in lowest terms.

$$= \dfrac{\sqrt[3]{2x}}{x}$$

9. $$\dfrac{\sqrt[5]{2y^7}}{\sqrt[5]{x^2}}$$

$$= \dfrac{y\sqrt[5]{2y^2}}{\sqrt[5]{x^2}}$$

$$= \dfrac{y\sqrt[5]{2y^2} \times \sqrt[5]{x^3}}{\sqrt[5]{x^2} \times \sqrt[5]{x^3}}$$

$$= \dfrac{y\sqrt[5]{2y^2 x^3}}{\sqrt[5]{x^5}}$$

$$= \dfrac{y\sqrt[5]{2y^2 x^3}}{x}$$

10. $$\sqrt[3]{\dfrac{3x^2}{4y}}$$

$$\sqrt[3]{\dfrac{3x^2}{4y}}$$ Note we can work inside the cube root before taking the cube root of each of the numerator and denominators separately.

$$= \sqrt[3]{\dfrac{3x^2(2y^2)}{4y(2y^2)}}$$ We need to make the denominator a perfect cube so that the cube root radical will go away. Multiplying both the numerator and denominator by $2y^2$ will accomplish our goal.

$$= \sqrt[3]{\dfrac{6x^2 y^2}{8y^3}}$$

$$= \dfrac{\sqrt[3]{6x^2 y^2}}{2y}$$

11. $$3y\sqrt{8x^3 y} + 5xy\sqrt{2xy} - x\sqrt[3]{3y} - x\sqrt{2xy^3} + \sqrt[3]{24x^3 y}$$

$$= 3y\sqrt{2^3 x^3 y} + 5xy\sqrt{2xy} - x\sqrt[3]{3y} - x\sqrt{2xy^3} + \sqrt[3]{2^3 \times 3x^3 y}$$

$$= 3y \times 2x\sqrt{2xy} + 5xy\sqrt{2xy} - x\sqrt[3]{3y} - xy\sqrt{2xy} + 2x\sqrt[3]{3y}$$

$$= 6xy\sqrt{2xy} + 5xy\sqrt{2xy} - xy\sqrt{2xy} - x\sqrt[3]{3y} + 2x\sqrt[3]{3y}$$

Add like terms.

$$= 10xy\sqrt{2xy} + x\sqrt[3]{3y}$$

Video Log 2.6e

1. Simplify the following radicals and do not leave any radicals in the denominator.

a. $\frac{1}{\sqrt{5}}$	k. $\sqrt[3]{\dfrac{54x^{-3}y}{6x^{-1}y^7}}$
b. $\dfrac{1}{\sqrt{2x^3}}$	
c. $\dfrac{\sqrt{2x}}{\sqrt{27}}$	l. $\dfrac{y^{\frac{1}{2}}y^{\frac{2}{3}}}{y^{\frac{3}{4}}}$
d. $\dfrac{4}{\sqrt[3]{5}}$	m. $\dfrac{2-3\sqrt{5}}{2+3\sqrt{5}}$
e. $\dfrac{1}{\sqrt[3]{4x^2}}$	n. $\dfrac{1+4\sqrt{3}}{2-5\sqrt{2}}$
f. $\dfrac{1}{\sqrt[4]{9x}}$	o. $\dfrac{2+7i}{3+2i}$
g. $\sqrt[3]{-8a^7}$	p. $\dfrac{2+3\sqrt{x}}{3-2\sqrt{x}}$
h. $\sqrt[3]{5x^3y^{10}}\sqrt[3]{25x^2y^2}$	q. $\dfrac{3x-\sqrt{2}}{2+\sqrt{x}}$
i. $\sqrt{3}\sqrt[3]{9}$	r. $\dfrac{2\sqrt{3}-5\sqrt{x}}{3\sqrt{x}-2\sqrt{3}}$
Note that one of these is a square root and the other a cube root! Switch to exponent notation first and then convert back to a radical.	s. $\dfrac{x-y}{2\sqrt{x}-3y}$
j. $\sqrt[3]{x^2}\sqrt[5]{x^4}$	

2.7 Division
Lecture

🖥 Introduction to Division http://www.youtube.com/watch?v=7gZ4yW1nr9Y (13 min)

We have not formally studied division yet, but have worked with it briefly when dealing with equivalent rational numbers and expressions. We introduced subtraction as the inverse process of addition and will now view division as the inverse process of multiplication. Since we looked at multiplication of whole numbers as repeated addition, then division can be considered as repeated subtraction. Thus when we had a groups of b objects, the total number is $a \times b = T$ objects. In the problem $T \div b$ we start with the total set of objects and "divide" it into groups of size b with the result being the number of groups which is a. This is the "how many groups" model for division.

Terminology

Division is a binary operation denoted by the symbol $\div$. We say for any mathematical objects $a, b \neq 0$, and c, you have studied so far we say $a \div b = c$ if and only $a = b \times c$.

In the notation $a \div b = c$, a is called the **dividend,** b is called the **divisor** and the result of the division c is called the **quotient.** We say that b divides a completely if and only if b is a factor of a.

Another way to represent division is using the fraction bar as in the notation $a \div b = \frac{a}{b}$. When we work with whole number division there are two ways we can interpret division corresponding to the different roles of the factors in multiplication $A \times B = A$ groups of size B. One way is to ask "How many groups" and the second interpretation is to ask "How many in each group".

These two ways to interpret the result of division are demonstrated in the problem $6 \div 2$ below:

First Interpretation of the problem $6 \div 2$: $2 \times ? = 6$: "How many in each group" interpretation: Wanting 2 rows of objects for a total of 6 objects, and asking how many objects in each row. Or, if 6 cookies are to be divided equally between Paul and Laura, how many cookies does each person get?

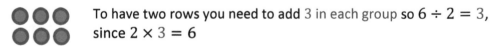 To have two rows you need to add 3 in each group so $6 \div 2 = 3$, since $2 \times 3 = 6$

Second Interpretation of the problem $6 \div 2$: $? \times 2 = 6$: "How many groups" interpretation: Wanting 2 objects in each row for a total of 6 objects, and asking how many rows total. Or, how many servings of two cookies each are there in a bag of 6 cookies?

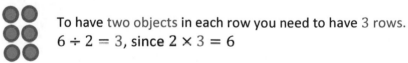 To have two objects in each row you need to have 3 rows. $6 \div 2 = 3$, since $2 \times 3 = 6$

You can see the context of the two different interpretations of division in the practice examples below.

1. How do you distribute 12 marbles equally among 3 people?
2. If we have 12 marbles and each person has to have 3 marbles, then at most, how many people can we give marbles to?

Solutions

1. In order to distribute 12 marbles equally among 3 people we start giving one marble per person until we exhaust them all. You can see we start giving 1st marble to the first person, the second marble to the second person and so on. By the time we are done each person has gotten 4 marbles since $12 - 3 - 3 - 3 - 3 = 0$ or that $12 - (4 \times 3) = 0$ or $12 = 4 \times 3$. Therefore $12 \div 3 = 4$ and we have put 4 marbles in each person's possession. This is the how many in each group interpretation.

2. In order to distribute 12 marbles so that each person gets 3 marbles we start with giving three marbles to the first person, the next three to the next person and so on. By the time all marbles are exhausted we have repeated the subtraction of a group of 3, four times, so we needed 4 people. Therefore $12 - 3 - 3 - 3 - 3 = 0$ or that $12 - (3 \times 4) = 0$ or $12 = 3 \times 4$. Therefore $12 \div 3 = 4$ and we need 4 people so that each can be given 3 marbles. This is the how many groups interpretation.

More Examples

3. **How many groups:** If we had 1236 eggs and wanted to know how many dozen eggs this is, we'd be asking how many groups of 12 are there in 1236 eggs.
   The answer is 103.
   $(1200 + 36) = 100$ dozen $+ 3$ dozen.
   In this model of division, we can compute the answer by repeated subtraction of groups of the given size.

4. **How many in a group:** If we had 1236 eggs and need to divide them up for 12 families, how many eggs should go to each family?

   The answer is the same as $1236 \div 12 = 103$, but here it is not 103 groups of 12 eggs, but 12 groups of 103 eggs.

We don't usually think about it, but when dividing we are always answering either how many groups or how many in a group. Most college students have also come to associate fractions with division. E.g., we often read the fraction 2/3 as 2 divided by 3. Recall that by definition, the fraction 2/3 means the fractional part of a whole that has been cut into 3 equal pieces and 2/3 is just two of those pieces. As a division problem $2 \div 3$ could be the number in each group when two whole objects is divided equally into three groups. We see that if we cut each of the wholes into three equal pieces, we could put one of these three pieces from each of the two whole objects to each group. Thus each group ends up with $\frac{2}{3}$ of a whole object. This shows that division of two whole numbers $a \div b$ is equivalent to the fraction definition of $\frac{a}{b}$.

The answer to a division problem can take many forms as shown in the next few problems:

5. If you had 5 marbles and wanted to share them equally amongst 3 friends, then how many should you give each friend?

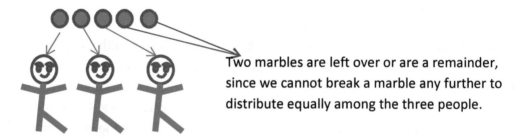

Two marbles are left over or are a remainder, since we cannot break a marble any further to distribute equally among the three people.

Each friend will get only one marble and there would be two left (a remainder of 2) because we cannot break marbles into parts, or $5 \div 3 = 1R2$. 1 is called the quotient and 2 is called the remainder. The division of $5 \div 3$ can be used to write 5 using the quotient and remainder as follows $5 = 1 \times 3 + 2$.

6. If you had 5 chocolates that you wanted to distribute equally amongst 3 friends, how much chocolate does each friend get?

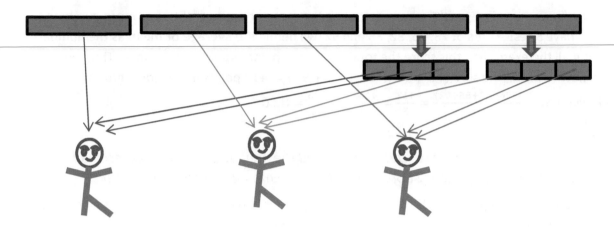

Each person must get 1 full candy bar and $\frac{2}{3}$ of another candy bar and there is no left over so $5 \div 3 = 1\frac{2}{3} = 1 + \frac{2}{3}$.

7. If you had 5 dollars and wanted to share them equally amongst 3 friends, how many should you give each friend?

Again we can start by giving each person a $1. Then we can change the remaining two dollars to quarters so there are 8 quarters, and we give 2 quarters to each person. That is an additional 50 cents. Then there remain 2 more quarters. We can split the two quarters into five dimes. We can give each person an additional dime. Now each own one dollar and 60 cents. We break the remaining 2 dimes into four nickels. We can give person one nickel. Now each person has one dollar and 65 cents. The remaining nickel we can break into pennies. We can give each person one penny. Now there are 2 pennies left over. So each friend received $1.66, because money cannot be divided into units any smaller than a penny. Our answer would be $1.66 per person with 2 pennies left over.

If were working with decimal numbers, $5 \div 3 = \frac{5}{3} = 1.\overline{6}$ if we write the answer in decimal form. We will talk more about how to do this later.

8. If $9.36 is the cost of three pizzas, then what is the cost of one pizza?

The cost of one pizza is $\$9.36 \div 3 = \frac{\$9.36}{3} = \frac{\$9.36 \times 100}{3 \times 100} = \frac{\$936}{3 \times 100} = \frac{\$312}{100} = \$3.12$.

When doing division, the form of the answer depends on the context. For example if wanted to solve the problem where you have $9.36 and want to buy pizzas that cost $3 each, the division result is that three pizzas can be purchased with $0.36 left over as a remainder. $\$9.36 \div \$3 = 3 \; with \; remainder \; \$0.36$.

9. What is Alex's average test score if he earned 78, 76, 82, 85 and 92 on each of his five tests respectively (all tests were out of 100 points).

We use the "how many in a group" when computing the mean or average of two or more numbers. Thus if we have 5 test scores of 78, 76, 82, 85 and 92, we define the **average or mean** as the number such that if all the exams had this score the total number of points would be the same. Thus we want to know how to divide the sum $(78 + 76 + 82 + 85 + 92) = 413$ points into 5 equal groups. The mean is given by $\frac{(78+76+82+85+92)}{5} = \frac{413}{5} = \frac{413 \times 2}{5 \times 2} = \frac{826}{10} = 82.6$

Note: *A slightly different measure of average is called the* **median** *score and represents the score that is halfway through the list of scores when they are put in increasing order.*

The list of scores from the problem above in an increasing order is $76, 78, 82, 85, 92$. Halfway through would be the middle or third score. Thus the median of this set of scores is 82. When there is an even number of numbers, the median is computed as the average of the two middle scores. Thus the median of the set of 4 scores $34, 66, 67, 70$ is the average of 66 and 67 which is 66.5 .

In general the answer to a division of two whole numbers can take many different forms. The answer could be written as a whole number with a remainder, as a rational number, or as a decimal number depending on the context. The result of the division will always answer either how many groups or how many in a group.

Playing

We can extend this concept of division to all the mathematical objects you studied in Module 1 Below are few examples.

1. $6 \div 3$

$$6 \div 3 = \frac{6}{3} = 2$$

2. Evaluate $(3x^2 + 4x + 1) \div (3x + 1)$

$$(3x^2 + 4x + 1) \div (3x + 1) = \frac{3x^2+4x+1}{3x+1}.$$

$$\frac{(3x + 1)(x + 1)}{3x + 1} = x + 1$$

Note we divided numerator and denominator by the factor $(3x + 1)$ to write our answer in lowest terms.

3. If $(x) = 3x^2 + 4x + 1$, and $g(x) = 3x + 1$, then $f(x) \div g(x)$.

We have $f(x) \div g(x) = \frac{f(x)}{g(x)} = \frac{3x^2 + 4x + 1}{3x + 1}$, which is defined for all x, such that $g(x) \neq 0$, or that $3x + 1 \neq 0$. So in this case also, $\frac{f(x)}{g(x)} = x + 1$, but the restriction that $3x + 1$ cannot be equal zero remains.

4. $\left(3\sqrt{2} + 5\right) \div \left(5\sqrt{3} + 2\right)$

$\left(3\sqrt{2} + 5\right) \div \left(5\sqrt{3} + 2\right) = \frac{3\sqrt{2} + 5}{5\sqrt{3} + 2}$.

Here we can simplify as we saw earlier by multiplying top and bottom by the conjugate expression $(5\sqrt{3} - 2)$ will remove the radical term from the denominator.

$\left(3\sqrt{2} + 5\right) \div \left(5\sqrt{3} + 2\right)$

$= \frac{\left(3\sqrt{2} + 5\right)\left(5\sqrt{3} - 2\right)}{\left(5\sqrt{3} + 2\right)\left(5\sqrt{3} - 2\right)}$

$= \frac{15\sqrt{6} - 6\sqrt{2} + 25\sqrt{3} - 10}{75 - 4}$

$= \frac{15\sqrt{6} - 6\sqrt{2} + 25\sqrt{3} - 10}{71}$

Division of Rational numbers

We have seen some of the divisions previously.

Lecture

 Introduction to Division of Rational Numbers
http://www.youtube.com/watch?v=9LTICGxqwKE   (10 min)

Visual interpretation of division of rational numbers

1.

$$4 \div \frac{1}{2}$$

Remember $\frac{1}{2}$ can be visualized as one part of two or as the shaded part below.

Now to answer the question $4 \div \frac{1}{2}$ we need to see how many of these shaded objects fit into 4 whole objects. So let us draw the 4 whole and count. You can see that two $\frac{1}{2}$ fit into each whole giving is a total of eight halves.

So you can see that $4 \div \frac{1}{2} = 4 \times \frac{2}{1} = 8$.

> *Note: The problem of dividing any collection of T objects into groups of size $\frac{1}{n}$ of an object is the "How many Groups" question. The answer is achieved just as above and means that division by a unit fraction $\frac{1}{n}$ is equivalent to multiplying by n. Thus division by $\frac{1}{n}$ is equivalent to multiplying by the multiplicative inverse or reciprocal of this divisor.*

2. $\dfrac{4}{5} \div \dfrac{2}{3}$

In order to see how many $\dfrac{2}{3}$ fit into $\dfrac{4}{5}$ we need to make the pieces of equal size which means we would have write them as $\dfrac{4}{5} = \dfrac{4 \times 3}{5 \times 3} = \dfrac{12}{15}$ and $\dfrac{2}{3} = \dfrac{2 \times 5}{3 \times 5} = \dfrac{10}{15}$. We want to know how many groups of $\dfrac{10}{15}$ can be gotten out of $\dfrac{12}{15}$. So we get one whole group of $\dfrac{10}{15}$ with $\dfrac{2}{15}$ remaining. These remaining two pieces is $\dfrac{1}{5}$ of another group and hence there are $1\dfrac{2}{10}$ or $1\dfrac{1}{5}$ groups of $\dfrac{2}{3}$ in $\dfrac{4}{5}$.

One group of $\dfrac{4}{5}$ which is made up of 12 pieces.

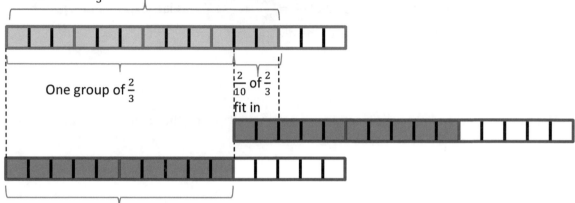

One group of $\dfrac{2}{3}$

$\dfrac{2}{10}$ of $\dfrac{2}{3}$ fit in

One group of $\dfrac{2}{3}$ which is made up of 10 pieces.

If we use the observation from the previous problem that division by a number is the same as multiplying by the reciprocal or multiplicative inverse of the divisor, we will get the same result $1\dfrac{1}{5}$ as shown below.

$$\dfrac{4}{5} \div \dfrac{2}{3} = \dfrac{4}{5} \times \dfrac{3}{2} = \dfrac{12}{10} = 1\dfrac{2}{10} = 1\dfrac{1}{5}$$

or get

$$\dfrac{4}{5} \div \dfrac{2}{3} = \dfrac{4}{5} \times \dfrac{3}{2} = \dfrac{12}{10} = \dfrac{6}{5} = 1\dfrac{1}{5}$$

Another way to see **division as "invert and multiply" or "multiply by the reciprocal"** is to write the fraction division as a fraction of fractions and then multiply the top and bottom fractions by the reciprocal of the bottom as shown below.

$$\dfrac{a}{b} \div \dfrac{c}{d} = \dfrac{\dfrac{a}{b}}{\dfrac{c}{d}} = \dfrac{\dfrac{a}{b} \cdot \dfrac{d}{c}}{\dfrac{c}{d} \cdot \dfrac{d}{c}} = \dfrac{\dfrac{a}{b} \cdot \dfrac{d}{c}}{1} = \dfrac{a}{b} \cdot \dfrac{d}{c}$$

3. $\dfrac{5}{2} \div \dfrac{3}{7}$

This is interpreted as how many groups of $\frac{3}{7}$ are in $\frac{5}{2}$ of some whole. An example might be how many groups of $\frac{3}{7}$ c of sugar can one measure out of $\frac{5}{2}$ cups of sugar. If we first convert to a common denominator of 2×7 we have the equivalent problem of

$\frac{35}{14} \div \frac{6}{14}$. This says we have 35 pieces (each of size $\frac{1}{14}$ of a whole) and want to know how many groups of 6 pieces this will make. Thus the answer is $\frac{5}{2} \div \frac{3}{7} = \frac{35}{6} = 5\frac{5}{6}$. If you look at the factors in the original problem here, you see that $\frac{35}{6} = \frac{5 \times 7}{2 \times 3} = \frac{5}{2} \times \frac{7}{3}$. This last expression is just the dividend multiplied by the reciprocal of the divisor.

4. $4\dfrac{5}{6} \div 2\dfrac{1}{4}$

We first convert to improper fractions and then multiply by the reciprocal. Thus:

$$\left(\frac{24}{6} + \frac{5}{6}\right) \div \left(\frac{8}{4} + \frac{1}{4}\right)$$

$$= \frac{29}{6} \div \frac{9}{4}$$

$$= \frac{29}{6} \cdot \frac{4}{9} = \frac{29 \cdot 2 \cdot \cancel{2}}{\cancel{2} \cdot 3 \cdot 9} = \frac{58}{27} = \frac{54}{27} + \frac{4}{27} = 2\frac{4}{27}$$

As with multiplication, this pattern for division of whole numbers extends to all rational expressions.

Observation: In general, $\dfrac{a}{b} \div \dfrac{c}{d} = \dfrac{a}{b} \times \dfrac{d}{c} = \dfrac{ad}{bc}$, or dividing is the same as multiplying by the multiplicative inverse (or reciprocal) of the divisor for all mathematical objects studied so far.

1. Show how to interpret the divisions below visually using appropriate strip diagrams and algebraically.

Multiplication Problem	Visual interpretation	Algebraic Evaluation
a. $6 \div 2$		
b. $3 \div \frac{1}{3}$		
c. $3 \div \frac{1}{2}$		
d. $3\frac{1}{2} \div \frac{1}{2}$		
e. $3 \div 2$		
f. $3\frac{1}{2} \div 2$		
g. $\frac{4}{15} \div \frac{2}{5}$		

2. Describe two scenarios where division is used. One with the how many groups and the other with how many in a group interpretation. E.g., in determining how many eggs out of 85 total that each of five families will get is a how many in a group problem. $85 \div 5 = 17$ eggs for each family.

3. Answer true or false and justify your answer.

    a. $4 \div \frac{1}{2} = \frac{4}{1} \div \frac{1}{2} = \frac{4 \times 2}{1 \times 2} \div \frac{1}{2} = \frac{8}{2} \div \frac{1}{2} = \frac{8 \div 1}{2 \div 2} = 8$

    b. $\frac{a}{b} \div \frac{c}{d} = \frac{a \div c}{b \div d}$

    c. $14 \div 0 = 0$

    d. $0 \div 14 = 0$

4. State the reciprocal of each number below.

    a. $\frac{2}{5}$ b. 17 c. $-\frac{1}{3}$ d. π

5. Express each situation as a division problem and evaluate the answer.

   a. Hans has picked 85 cobs of sweet corn and will sell it in bags of 6 cobs each. How many

       bags will Hans need and how many cobs will remain?

   b. John has $8.75. How many 45 cent peppers can he buy?

   c. A class of 25 students purchased a block of lottery tickets and won $2.5 million dollars. If

       shared evenly, how many dollars would each student get?

6. Simplify the division problems. Convert improper fractions to mixed numbers.

   a. $\frac{3}{4} \div \frac{2}{3}$ b. $\frac{5}{2} \div \frac{25}{8}$ c. $3\frac{2}{3} \div 1\frac{1}{4}$

7. Simplify $\left(2 + \sqrt{3}\right) \div \left(3 - \sqrt{6}\right)$ and rationalize the denominator.

8. Simplify $\frac{f}{g}(x)$ when $f(x) = x^2 - 4$ and $g(x) = x^2 - 3x - 10$ and also state the domain of

   the function $\frac{f}{g}$.

Division of Decimal Numbers and Rational Expressions
Lecture

💻 Division of Decimal Numbers and Rational Expressions
   http://www.youtube.com/watch?v=BGReDOGObbk (7 min)

Practice Examples

1. $288 \div 12$

2. $(6x^2 + 11x + 3) \div (2x + 3)$

3. $\sqrt{3} \div \sqrt{2}$

4. $\frac{x^2 - 9}{x^2 + 2x + 4} \div \frac{x^2 - 5x + 6}{x^3 - 8}$

5. $\frac{8x^2 - 2y^2}{6x^2 + 13xy + 5y^2} \div \frac{x^3y - xy^3}{3x^2 + 2xy - 5y^2}$

6. $\frac{32.5}{0.25}$

Solutions

1.
$$288 \div 12 = \frac{288}{12} = \frac{2^5 \times 3^2}{2^2 \times 3} = 2^3 \times 3 = 24$$

2. $(6x^2 + 11x + 3) \div (2x + 3)$

$$= \frac{6x^2 + 11x + 3}{2x + 3}$$

$$= \frac{\overset{1}{\cancel{(3x + 1)}}\cancel{(2x + 3)}}{\underset{1}{\cancel{(2x + 3)}}}$$

$$= 3x + 1$$

3.
$$\sqrt{3} \div \sqrt{2} = \frac{\sqrt{3}}{\sqrt{2}}$$

$$\frac{\sqrt{3}}{\sqrt{2}} = \frac{\sqrt{3} \times \sqrt{2}}{\sqrt{2} \times \sqrt{2}} = \frac{\sqrt{6}}{2}$$

For My Eyes Only

Before we can solve the problem we need factor all the numerators and denominators.

First Numerator

$$6x^2 + 11x + 3$$

$$18x$$

$$11x = 9x + 2x$$

$$6x^2 + 11x + 3 = 6x^2 + 9x + 2x + 3$$
$$= 3x(2x + 3) + 1(2x + 3)$$
$$= (3x + 1)(2x + 3)$$

We rationalize the denominator (multiply by $\frac{\sqrt{2}}{\sqrt{2}}$) to get:

4. $\dfrac{x^2-9}{x^2+2x+4} \div \dfrac{x^2-5x+6}{x^3-8}$

$$\dfrac{x^2-9}{x^2+2x+4} \div \dfrac{x^2-5x+6}{x^3-8}$$

$$= \dfrac{x^2-9}{\underset{1}{x^2+2x+4}} \times \dfrac{x^3-8}{\underset{1}{x^2-5x+6}} \qquad 1$$

$$= \dfrac{(x-3)(x+3) \times (x-2)(x^2+2x+4)}{\underset{1}{(x^2+2x+4)} \times \underset{1}{(x-3)}\underset{1}{(x-2)}}$$

$$= \dfrac{x+3}{1}$$

$$= x+3$$

5. $$\frac{8x^2 - 2y^2}{6x^2 + 13xy + 5y^2} \div \frac{x^3y - xy^3}{3x^2 + 2xy - 5y^2}$$

$$\frac{8x^2 - 2y^2}{6x^2 + 13xy + 5y^2} \div \frac{x^3y - xy^3}{3x^2 + 2xy - 5y^2}$$

$$= \frac{8x^2 - 2y^2}{6x^2 + 13xy + 5y^2} \times \frac{3x^2 + 2xy - 5y^2}{x^3y - xy^3}$$

$$= \frac{2(2x - y)(2x + y)}{(2x + y)(3x + 5y)} \times \frac{(x - y)(3x + 5y)}{xy(x - y)(x + y)}$$

$$= \frac{2(2x - y)\overset{1}{\cancel{(2x + y)}}\overset{1}{\cancel{(x - y)}}\overset{1}{\cancel{(3x + 5y)}}}{\cancel{(2x + y)}\cancel{(3x + 5y)}xy\cancel{(x - y)}(x + y)}$$

$$= \frac{2(2x - y)}{xy(x + y)}$$

Before we can solve the problem we need factor all the numerators and denominators.

First Numerator

$8x^2 - 2y^2 = 2(4x^2 - y^2)$
$= 2((2x)^2 - (y)^2) = 2(2x - y)(2x + y)$

First Denominator

$6x^2 + 13xy + 5y^2$

$30x^2y^2$

$13xy = 10xy + 3xy$

$6x^2 + 13xy + 5y^2$
$= 6x^2 + 10xy + 3xy + 5y^2$
$= 2x(3x + 5y) + y(3x + 5y)$
$= (2x + y)(3x + 5y)$

Second Numerator

$3x^2 + 2xy - 5y^2$

$-15x^2y^2$

$2xy = 5xy - 3xy$

$3x^2 + 2xy - 5y^2$
$= 3x^2 + 5xy - 3xy - 5y^2$
$= x(3x + 5y) - y(3x + 5y)$
$= (x - y)(3x + 5y)$

Second Denominator

$x^3y - xy^3 = xy(x^2 - y^2)$
$= xy(x - y)(x + y)$

The numerator in the final answer does not factor.

6. $\dfrac{32.5}{0.25}$ Here we can eliminate the decimal aspect simply by multiplying top and bottom by 100 to get

$$\frac{32.5 \times 100}{0.25 \times 100} = \frac{3250}{25} = \frac{2 \times 13 \times 5^3}{5^2} = 2 \times 13 \times 5 = 130.$$

We could also use the long division method as we'll soon review to get this result.

1. Perform the following divisions and write your answers in lowest terms.

a) $250 \div 5$

b) $720 \div 9$

c) $0.072 \div 90$

d) $0.072 \div 0.009$

e) $240{,}000 \div 60$

f) $\dfrac{1960}{35}$

g) $\dfrac{12.6}{0.02}$

h) $\dfrac{2\sqrt{24}}{\sqrt{32}}$

i) $(3x^2 - 2x - 1) \div (3x + 1)$

j) $\dfrac{x^2-4}{x^2+3x-4} \div \dfrac{x^2-3x-10}{x^2-16}$

k) $\dfrac{x^2-9}{x^2+3x-4} \div \dfrac{3x^2+8x-3}{x^3+64}$

l) $\dfrac{x^2+2x+1}{1-x^2} \div \dfrac{5x^2+4x-1}{5x^2-6x+1}$

m) $\dfrac{x^2-9}{x^2-2x+4} \div \dfrac{x^2-5x+6}{x^3-8}$

Division Algorithm

Lecture

🖥 Division Algorithm for Decimal Numbers and Polynomials
  http://www.youtube.com/watch?v=XXr0ixy8PfA (8 min)

Let a and b be any two mathematical objects where b is the divisor and $b \neq 0$. If we set c to be the quotient of $a \div b$, and let r to be the remainder, then we have

$$a \div b = c + \frac{r}{b} \text{ and } a = c \times b + r.$$

Here we start with a objects and divide into c groups with b objects in a group and $r < b$ objects remain. In fact the remainder r is such that $0 \leq r < b$.

You can see that when $r = 0$ then b is a factor of a, and we say a is divisible by b.

Notice that division is repeated subtraction. So when in Module 1 when we wrote fractions as mixed numbers it was really writing a division problem in the form of quotient plus the remainder. For example, in the problem $7 \div 3$ the remainder arrives when we can no longer subtract a whole 3. If the remainder is zero then we are done dividing. If we have a nonzero remainder, it would have to be 1 or 2. If we have more than 2 remaining, we can subtract more three's. So $7 \div 3 = 2 + \frac{1}{3}$. So 2 is referred to as quotient and 1 the remainder.

When we divide two natural numbers, the result can be viewed as a natural number quotient with a natural number remainder. Or the quotient can be computed as either a mixed number fraction or as a terminating, or as a nonterminating decimal with repeating pattern and no remainder.

The long division algorithm that you learned in primary school is based on removing divisor-sized groups from the dividend. This process of division works with decimal numbers and other mathematical objects as is shown in the examples below.

Examples

1. $276 \div 6$

We start long division by removing as many groups of 6 from 27 as we can. Then we can continue to remove groups of 6 from 36 until we have none left or there is a remainder less than 6.

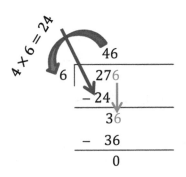

2. $278 \div 12$

We can start by removing 2 groups of 12 from 27. Then continue removing 3 groups of 12 from 38. Leaving a remainder of 2.

$$
\begin{array}{r}
23 \\
12\overline{\smash)278} \\
-\ 24 \\
\hline
38 \\
-\ 36 \\
\hline
2
\end{array}
$$

3. $5 \div 3$

We get $5 - 3 = 2$ and 2 is smaller than three so $5 \div 3$ has a quotient of 1 since only one group of 3 could be taken out and 2 would be the remainder. But if we want to know how many objects there would be in each of three groups, we can take the remainder of 2 and divide it into three equal pieces, one for each group. If we do this in terms of fractions, we want $\frac{1}{3}$ of the two-piece remainder for each group i.e., $\frac{1}{3} \cdot 2 = \frac{2}{3}$ piece for each group and $5 \div 3 = 1\frac{2}{3}$.

If we do this in terms of decimals, we can write our remainder of 2 as $2 = \frac{20}{10}$ and we can put $\frac{6}{10}$ into each group leaving $\frac{2}{10}$ remaining.

So now $5 \div 3 = \frac{5}{3} = 1 + \frac{20}{10} \div 3 = 1 + \frac{6}{10} + \frac{\frac{2}{10}}{3} = 1.6 + \frac{\frac{2}{10}}{3}$.

If we view the remaining $\frac{2}{10}$ as $\frac{20}{100}$ we can put $\frac{6}{100}$ into each group leaving $\frac{2}{100}$ as the remainder and:

$5 \div 3 = 1 + \frac{6}{10} + \left(\frac{20}{100} \div 3\right) = 1 + \frac{6}{10} + \frac{6}{100} + \frac{\frac{2}{100}}{3} = 1.66 + \frac{0.02}{3}$.

We can continue this process until it is terminated or we find a repeating pattern as it exists in this example. Note as we go on and on the remainder term gets smaller and smaller and in the limit it approach zero so we drop it and write $5 \div 3$ as:

$5 \div 3 = 1.666 \ldots = 1.\overline{6}$.

The bar on the head of 6 indicates that the digit 6 is repeated infinitely. This process of division is a bit cumbersome. The long division algorithm for dividing whole and decimal numbers streamlines the process as shown below.

The first zero we put after the decimal number 5 and carry down is from rewriting the remainder of 2 as $\frac{20}{10}$ and the second zero is from writing the next remainder as $\frac{2}{10} = \frac{20}{100}$.

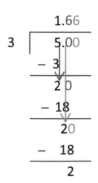

We can continue on and the pattern of 6's keeps repeating.

4. $0.324 \div 12$

$$0.324 \div 12 = \frac{0.324}{12} = \frac{324}{12} \times \frac{1}{1000}$$

You can see that we start subtracting groups of 12 but since the number is smaller than one we have subtract tenths or hundredths times groups of 12 as shown below. The division shown on the left shows you how you can retain the place values but we could also have done the same problem as shown on the right where you have to remember to move the decimal point the appropriate number of places.

```
          0.027
    ┌──────────
12  │   0.324
    │  − 0.0
    │  ──────────
    │    0.32
    │  − 0.24
    │  ──────────
    │    0.084
    │  − 0.084
    │  ──────────
    │    0.000
```

```
        .027.
    ┌──────────
12  │   324
    │  − 24
    │  ──────────
    │    84
    │  − 84
    │  ──────────
    │     0
```

5. $3 \div 7$

As we showed earlier, the remainder at each subtraction step can only be the digit 0, 1, 2, 3, 4, 5, or 6. That means that after six steps or earlier, we will get a remainder that was obtained earlier. This means that the decimals in the quotient cycle through a set of six or fewer digits. Therefore $3 \div 7$ is a repeating decimal. This will happen when converting any fraction to a decimal. Therefore all fractions are either repeating decimals, or terminating decimals. The number of repeating digits is always at most one less than the divisor.

```
        0.4285714
    ┌──────────
7   │   30
    │  − 28
    │  ──────────
    │    20
    │  −  14
    │  ──────────
    │    60
    │  −  56
    │  ──────────
    │    40
    │  −35
    │  ──────────
    │    50
    │  −49
    │  ──────────
    │    10
    │  −7
    │  ──────────
    │    30
    │  −28
    │  ──────────
```

Note: $3 \div 7 = \frac{3}{7}$

$$= \frac{30}{7 \times 10}$$

$$= \frac{30}{7} \times \frac{1}{10}$$

This fact allows us to divide 30 by 7, and then move the decimal one to the left. Continue the process until the repeating pattern is visible.

The final answer is $3 \div 7 = 0.\overline{428571}$

2

6. Compute $(6.4 \times 10^{-11}) \div (1.6 \times 10^{23})$

Recall that

$(6.4 \times 10^{-11}) \div (1.6 \times 10^{23})$

$= \dfrac{6.4 \times 10^{-11}}{1.6 \times 10^{23}}$

$= \dfrac{6.4}{1.6} \times \dfrac{10^{-11}}{10^{23}}$

$= \dfrac{6.4}{1.6} \times 10^{-34}$ Note that $\dfrac{6.4}{1.6} = \dfrac{6.4 \times 10}{1.6 \times 10} = \dfrac{64}{16}$.

$= \dfrac{64}{16} \times 10^{-34}$

$= 4 \times 10^{-34}$

7. Use division to convert the ratio or fraction $\dfrac{23}{47}$ into a percentage. Round to the nearest tenth of a percent.

Recall that $\dfrac{23}{47} = 23 \div 47$. After long division we get the quotient to be about 0.4893 which is 48.93% or 48.9% when rounded to the nearest tenth of a percent.

```
              0.4893
      47 |  23.0
           - 188
           ─────
             420
           - 376
           ─────
             440
           - 423
           ─────
             170
           - 141
           ─────
             290
```

8. The table shows the how many students are male and female and traditional age and returning adults at a small college.

400 students Total	Male	Female
Traditional Age	150	175
Returning Adult	25	50

a. What percent of the students are Male?

175 out of 400 are male. Thus $\dfrac{175}{400} = \dfrac{175 \div 4}{400 \div 4} = \dfrac{43.75}{100} = 43.75\%$ are male students

b. What percent of the students are traditional aged?

325 of 400 students are traditional age. Thus $\dfrac{325}{400} = \dfrac{81.25}{100} = 81.25\%$ are traditional aged students.

Playing

Lecture

🖥 Division Algorithm for Decimals & Polynomials
  http://www.youtube.com/watch?v=PQrlt8PhFAE (11 min)

Let us look at the long division of whole numbers and how that might help with long division of polynomials.

1. $676 \div 32 = (6 \times 10^2 + 7 \times 10 + 6) \div (3 \times 10 + 2)$

2. $(6x^2 + 7x + 6) \div (3x + 2)$

   Look at the similarity of the solutions to problem number 7 and 8.

$$
\begin{array}{r}
21. \\
32 \enclose{longdiv}{676.} \\
-64 \\
\hline
36 \\
-32 \\
\hline
4
\end{array}
$$

Quotient 21
Remainder 4

$$
\begin{array}{r}
2x + 1 \\
(3x + 2) \enclose{longdiv}{6x^2 + 7x + 6} \\
-(6x^2 + 4x) \\
\hline
3x + 6 \\
-(3x + 2) \\
\hline
4
\end{array}
$$

Quotient $2x + 1$
Remainder is 4

3. $(2x^3 - 5x^2 + x - 10) \div (x^2 - 4x + 1)$

As you saw above the long division process can be extended to dividing polynomials where the dividend must be of degree at least as large as the divisor and the result will be a polynomial quotient and a remainder will be left at the end. In the first line, we seek to subtract out all of the x^3 terms. Thus we multiply the divisor by $2x$ so that upon subtraction, the x^3 terms will disappear. It is important to **subtract** all the terms in the second line and this is why we put the second line in parentheses.

After this we remove the remaining x^2 terms by multiplying the divisor by 3 and subtracting. When the remaining terms have degree lower than the divisor, we stop and these terms are the remainder in the problem. The result would then be stated as $(2x^3 - 5x^2 + x - 10) \div (x^2 - 4x + 1) = 2x + 3 \ with \ remainder \ 11x - 3$.

$$
\begin{array}{r}
2x + 3 \\
(x^2 - 4x + 1) \overline{\smash{\big)}\ 2x^3 - 5x^2\ + x - 10} \\
\underline{-(2x^3 - 8x^2 + 2x)} \\
3x^2\ -\ x - 10 \\
\underline{-(3x^2 - 12x + 3)} \\
11x - 13
\end{array}
$$

Quotient $2x + 3$
Remainder $11x - 13$

$$(2x^3 - 5x^2 + x - 10) \div (x^2 - 4x + 1) = \frac{2x^3 - 5x^2 + x - 10}{x^2 - 4x + 1} = 2x + 3 + \frac{11x - 13}{x^2 - 4x + 1}$$

4. $(4x^4 - x^2 - 6x - 14) \div (2x^2 - x - 3)$

Since in the dividend the x^3 term has a coefficient of zero we put a place holder so as to not forget that place value. You don't have to worry about this part in decimal number division. Also don't forget that once you put the first term in the quotient to multiply the entire divisor by it to get the first row and so on.

$$
\begin{array}{r}
2x^2 + x + 3 \\
2x^2 - x - 3 \overline{\smash{\big)}\ 4x^4 + 0x^3\ - x^2 - 6x - 14} \\
\underline{-(4x^4 - 2x^3 - 6x^2)} \\
2x^3 + 5x^2 - 6x - 14 \\
\underline{-(2x^3 - 1x^2 - 3x)} \\
6x^2 - 3x - 14 \\
\underline{-(6x^2 - 3x - 9)} \\
-5
\end{array}
$$

Quotient:$2x^2 + x + 3$
Remainder :-5

$$(4x^4 - x^2 - 6x - 14) \div (2x^2 - x - 3) = 2x^2 + x + 3 - \frac{5}{2x^2 - x - 3}$$

1. Use the division algorithms to perform the following divisions. Write your final answer in the form Quotient $+ \dfrac{\text{Remainder}}{\text{Divisor}}$.

a. $800 \div 4$	e. $8x^2 \div 4$
b. $862 \div 21$	f. $(8x^2 + 6x + 2) \div (2x + 1)$
c. $802 \div 21$	g. $(8x^2 + 2) \div (2x + 1)$
d. $411 \div 24$	h. $(4x^2 + x + 1) \div (2x + 4)$

What are the differences or similarities between a & e, between b & f, between c & g, and between d & h?

i. $34.9 \div 2.5$

j. $98.7 \div 0.13$

k. $0.000987 \div 0.2$

l. $(-9x^5 + 12x^4 - 4x^3 - 3x^2 + 5x + 2) \div (-3x + 2)$

m. $(2x^2 + 8x^3 + 3x - 1) \div (2x - 3)$

n. $(5x^3 + 22x^2 - 4) \div (x - 1)$ (Hint: Remember to add a $0x$ in the dividend!)

o. $(5x^2 + 10x^3 + 2x - 10) \div (2x^2 + 3x - 5)$

p. $(15x^6 + 10x^3 + 2x^4 - 7) \div (3x^3 - 2x - 1)$

q. $(3x^4 - 2x^2 + 5x - 1) \div (3x^2 - 2)$

2. Find the repeating decimal that represents $\dfrac{17}{13}$. (Hint: The repeating pattern has 6 digits repeat.)

3. Use division to write the number below in scientific notation.
   a. $(9.3 \times 10^7) \div (3 \times 10^4)$
   b. $(2.5 \times 10^{-23}) \div (5 \times 10^{-12})$

2.8 Order of Operations

Now that we have learned about all the arithmetic operations individually, we can talk about what to do when two or more operations appear in the same problem. Mathematicians have a convention on how to read and the order in which to evaluate arithmetic operations when more than one operation is being performed, so that no matter who reads the problem the same answer is generated. This convention of operations is to read the problem left to right and use the mnemonic device PEMDAS (Please Excuse My Dear Aunt Sally) which dictates the following order of evaluating multiple operations in a complicated expression.

Lecture

💻 Order of Operations http://www.youtube.com/watch?v=iHvTbraDV38 (11 min)

1. **P**arentheses (First simplify within parentheses or any grouping symbol such as a radical, numerator or denominator of a fraction and within absolute value symbols.)
2. **E**xponents (Evaluate bases raised to exponents before multiplication or division. Thus $2 \cdot 3^2 = 2 \cdot 9 = 18$ and $-4^3 = -(4^3) = -64$.)
3. **M**ultiplication/**D**ivision (from left to right as they appear)
4. **A**ddition/**S**ubtraction (also from left to right as they appear)

Practice Examples

Evaluate the following

1.	$2 + 3 \times 5 - 10$ $= 2 + 15 - 10$ $= 17 - 10$ $= 7$	Read left to right and $\times$ will come first then do addition/subtraction.
2.	$20 \div 4 \times 3 - 2 + 3^2$ $= 20 \div 4 \times 3 - 2 + 9$ $= 5 \times 3 - 2 + 9$ $= 15 - 2 + 9$ $= 13 + 9$ $= 22$	Read left to right and compute exponents first, $\times / \div$ depending on which one comes first and then addition/subtraction.
3.	$2 - 5 \times 4 + 3$ $= 2 - 20 + 3$ $= -18 + 3$ $= -15$	Notice the difference between this problem and the next, how the parentheses change the outcome. Here we do multiplication first then addition/subtraction.
4.	$(2 - 5) \times 4 + 3$ $= -3 \times 4 + 3$	Here we do within parentheses first, then multiplication, and

	$= -12 + 3$ $= -9$	finally addition.
5.	$(3 - 2^2)^2 + 5$ $= (3 - 4)^2 + 5$ $= (-1)^2 + 5$ $= 1 + 5$ $= 6$	Within parentheses first, then the exponent outside of the parentheses, then addition.
6.	$\sqrt{2^2 + 3^2}$ $= \sqrt{4 + 9}$ $= \sqrt{13}$	Don't forget that radicals are fractional exponents.
7.	$\dfrac{\frac{2}{3} + 5}{5^2 - 4}$ $= \dfrac{\frac{2}{3} + \frac{15}{3}}{25 - 4}$ $= \dfrac{\frac{17}{3}}{21}$ $= \dfrac{\frac{17}{3}}{\frac{21}{1}}$ $= \dfrac{17}{3} \times \dfrac{1}{21}$ $= \dfrac{17}{63}$	Evaluate the denominator and numerator like they were two separate orders of operations problems and then simplify.

| 8. | $$\frac{\dfrac{2}{3}+\dfrac{1}{5}}{\dfrac{4}{5}-\dfrac{2}{3}}$$ $$=\frac{\dfrac{10}{15}+\dfrac{3}{15}}{\dfrac{12}{15}-\dfrac{10}{15}}$$ $$=\frac{\dfrac{13}{15}}{\dfrac{2}{15}}$$ $$=\frac{13}{15}\times\frac{15}{2}$$ Recall that we can divide numerator denominator by 15 to rewrite the final answer in lowest terms $$=\frac{13}{2}$$ | Evaluate the denominator and numerator like they were two separate orders of operations problems and then simplify. Alternative method to solve this problem is multiply the numerator and denominator by the common denominator across all the fractions that appear in the numerator and the denominator and then simplify. $$\frac{\dfrac{2}{3}+\dfrac{1}{5}}{\dfrac{4}{5}-\dfrac{2}{3}}=$$ $$\frac{\left(\dfrac{2}{3}+\dfrac{1}{5}\right)\times\dfrac{15}{1}}{\left(\dfrac{4}{5}-\dfrac{2}{3}\right)\times\dfrac{15}{1}}$$ $$=\frac{\dfrac{2}{3}\times\dfrac{\cancel{15}^{5}}{1}+\dfrac{1}{5}\times\dfrac{\cancel{15}^{3}}{1}}{\dfrac{4}{5}\times\dfrac{\cancel{15}^{3}}{1}-\dfrac{2}{3}\times\dfrac{\cancel{15}^{5}}{1}}$$ $$=\frac{10+3}{12-10}$$ $$=\frac{13}{2}$$ |
| 9. | $$\frac{3^2+2\times5-10}{\sqrt{25}-3\times2}$$ $$=\frac{9+2\times5-10}{5-3\times2}$$ $$=\frac{9+10-10}{5-6}$$ $$=\frac{19-10}{-1}$$ $$=\frac{9}{-1}=-9$$ | Evaluate the denominator and numerator like they were two separate orders of operations problems and then simplify. |

10.	$\dfrac{-7 + (3 \times 2 - 4)^2}{3^2 - 4 + 2 \times 5}$	Evaluate the denominator and numerator like they were two separate orders of operations problems and then simplify.
	$= \dfrac{-7 + (6 - 4)^2}{9 - 4 + 10}$	
	$= \dfrac{-7 + (2)^2}{5 + 10}$	
	$= \dfrac{-7 + 4}{15}$	
	$= \dfrac{-3}{15}$	
	$= \dfrac{-1}{5} = -\dfrac{1}{5}$	
11.	$\dfrac{-5^2 - (3 - 2^2)^3}{3^2 - 5 + 5 \times 2}$	Evaluate the denominator and numerator like they were two separate orders of operations problems and then simplify.
	$= \dfrac{-25 - (3 - 4)^3}{9 - 5 + 10}$	
	$= \dfrac{-25 - (-1)^3}{4 + 10}$	
	$= \dfrac{-25 + 1}{14}$	
	$= \dfrac{-24}{14}$	
	$= \dfrac{-12}{7}$	

Examples of evaluating algebraic quantities involving absolute value and other radicals

Find the value of each of the following.

1.	$3\lvert 5 - 8 \rvert - 12$	Absolute value is in the same place in the hierarchy as the parentheses are.
	$= 3\lvert -3 \rvert - 12$	
	$= 3(3) - 12$	
	$= 9 - 12$	
	$= -3$	

2.	$3\lvert 2-7 \rvert - \dfrac{15}{3}$ $= 3\lvert -5 \rvert - \dfrac{15}{3}$ $= 3(5) - \dfrac{15}{3}$ $= 15 - 5$ $= 10$	Absolute value is a grouping symbol and is in the same place in the hierarchy as parentheses are.
3.	$3\sqrt{36} - 5\sqrt[3]{8} + 3 \times 4 - \dfrac{12}{3}$ $3(6) - 5(2) + 3 \times 4 - \dfrac{12}{3}$ $= 18 - 10 + 12 - 4$ $= 8 + 12 - 4$ $= 20 - 4$ $= 16$	Remember radicals are fractional exponents and therefore are in the same place in the hierarchy as the exponents are.
4.	$3\lvert 2 \times 3^2 - 8 \times 3 \rvert - 5 \times 2^2$ $= 3\lvert 2 \times 9 - 24 \rvert - 5 \times 2^2$ $= 3\lvert 18 - 24 \rvert - 5 \times 2^2$ $= 3\lvert -6 \rvert - 5 \times 2^2$ $= 3(6) - 5 \times 4$ $= 18 - 20$ $= -2$	Absolute value is in the same place in the hierarchy as the parentheses are. Remember radicals are fractional exponents and therefore are in the same place in the hierarchy as the exponents are.

1. Simplify the following.

   a. $3 + 2 \times 7 - 9$

   b. $100 \div 2 \times 5 - 7^2 + 9$

   c. $11 - 3 \times 6 + 8$

   d. $21 - 6 \times 2 - 3$

   e. $(21 - 6) \times 2 - 3$

   f. $(5^2 - 10)^2 + 7$

   g. $\sqrt{5^2 - 3^2}$

   h. $\dfrac{\frac{2}{5} + 1}{3^2 - 4}$

   i. $\dfrac{\frac{1}{2} - \frac{1}{7}}{\frac{3}{7} - \frac{1}{2}}$

   j. $\dfrac{-7 + |3^2 - 5|}{(4-3)^2 - 3}$

   k. $2|13 - 5| - 17$

   l. $|3 \times 2^2 - 7 \times 5| - 8 \times 3^2$

   m. $\dfrac{-7 + (3 \times 2 - 4)^2}{3^2 - 4 + 2 \times 5}$

   n. $\dfrac{-5^2 - (3 - 2^2)^3}{3^2 - 5 + 5 \times 2}$

   o. $\dfrac{2 + 3 \times 5 \div 2}{2 \times 3 - 10 \div 2}$

2. Consider the two operations of reducing prices for a 20% off sale and adding 5.5% sales tax.
   a. Show taking the 20% reduction followed by the 5.5% tax addition corresponds to first multiplying by 0.8 and then by 1.055.
   b. Does it matter which operation is done first? What property of real numbers does this relate to?

Complex Fractions
Lecture

⌨ **Complex Fractions** http://www.youtube.com/watch?v=_epR6si0ncc (4 min)

Complex fraction refers to when a fraction contains fractions within the numerator or the denominator, e.g., $\dfrac{\frac{3}{x} - 2}{\frac{2}{x^2} - 1}$. The steps for evaluation or simplification are to simplify numerator and denominator individually as fractions and then invert the denominator and multiply. Basically, pay attention to order of operations.

1. $\dfrac{\dfrac{1}{2} - 3}{\dfrac{1}{3} - 2}$

$= \dfrac{\dfrac{-5}{2}}{\dfrac{-5}{3}}$

$= \dfrac{-5}{2} \times \dfrac{3}{-5}$

$= \dfrac{3}{2}$

Numerator

$\dfrac{1}{2} - 3 = \dfrac{1}{2} - \dfrac{3 \times 2}{1 \times 2} = \dfrac{1}{2} - \dfrac{6}{2} = \dfrac{-5}{2}$

Denominator

$\dfrac{1}{3} - 2 = \dfrac{1}{3} - \dfrac{2 \times 3}{1 \times 3} = \dfrac{1}{3} - \dfrac{6}{3} = \dfrac{-5}{3}$

2. $\dfrac{\dfrac{3}{x+1} - 2}{5}$

$= \dfrac{\dfrac{1 - 2x}{x+1}}{\dfrac{5}{1}}$

$= \dfrac{1 - 2x}{x+1} \cdot \dfrac{1}{5}$

$= \dfrac{1 - 2x}{5(x+1)}$

Numerator

$\dfrac{3}{x+1} - 2 = \dfrac{3}{x+1} - \dfrac{2(x+1)}{x+1}$

$= \dfrac{3 - 2x - 2}{x+1}$

$= \dfrac{1 - 2x}{x+1}$

3.

$$\frac{\frac{3}{x} - 2}{\frac{2}{x^2} - 1}$$

$$= \frac{\frac{3 - 2x}{x}}{\frac{2 - x^2}{x^2}}$$

$$= \frac{3 - 2x}{x} \times \frac{x^2}{2 - x^2}$$

$$= \frac{(3 - 2x)x^2}{x(2 - x^2)}$$

$$= \frac{(3 - 2x)x}{(2 - x^2)}$$

Final answer is in lowest terms that we get by dividing numerator and denominator by an x.

Numerator

$$\frac{3}{x} - 2 \ = \frac{3}{x} - \frac{2}{1}$$

$$= \frac{3}{x} - \frac{2x}{x}$$

$$= \frac{3 - 2x}{x}$$

Denominator

$$\frac{2}{x^2} - 1 \ = \frac{2}{x^2} - \frac{x^2}{x^2}$$

$$= \frac{2 - x^2}{x^2}$$

4.

$$\frac{\frac{4}{x + 1} - 3}{\frac{1}{x - 1} - 2}$$

$$= \frac{\frac{(1 - 3x)}{(x + 1)}}{\frac{(3 - 2x)}{(x - 1)}}$$

$$= \frac{(1 - 3x)}{(x + 1)} \times \frac{(x - 1)}{(3 - 2x)}$$

$$= \frac{(1 - 3x)(x - 1)}{(x + 1)(3 - 2x)}$$

Numerator

$$\frac{4}{x + 1} - 3 \ = \frac{4}{x + 1}$$

$$- \frac{3(x + 1)}{1(x + 1)}$$

$$= \frac{4 - 3x - 3}{x + 1}$$

$$= \frac{1 - 3x}{x + 1}$$

Denominator

$$\frac{1}{x - 1} - 2 \ = \frac{1}{x - 1}$$

$$- \frac{2(x - 1)}{1(x - 1)}$$

$$= \frac{1 - 2x + 2}{x - 1}$$

$$= \frac{3 - 2x}{x - 1}$$

5. $$\frac{\dfrac{1}{a^2}-\dfrac{1}{b^2}}{\dfrac{a}{b}-\dfrac{b}{a}}$$

Alternative method to solve these problems is to multiply both the top and bottom expressions in the problems by the least common multiple of all the denominators of the top and bottom. This alternate method is shown below.

$$\frac{\dfrac{1}{a^2}-\dfrac{1}{b^2}}{\dfrac{a}{b}-\dfrac{b}{a}}$$

$$=\frac{\dfrac{1\times b^2}{a^2\times b^2}-\dfrac{1\times a^2}{b^2\times a^2}}{\dfrac{a\times a}{b\times a}-\dfrac{b\times b}{a\times b}}$$

$$=\frac{\dfrac{b^2-a^2}{a^2b^2}}{\dfrac{a^2-b^2}{ab}}$$

$$=\frac{b^2-a^2}{a^2b^2}\times\frac{ab}{a^2-b^2}$$

$$=\frac{-1\overset{1}{\cancel{(a^2-b^2)}}\times\overset{1}{\cancel{ab}}}{\underset{ab}{\cancel{a^2b^2}}\times\underset{1}{\cancel{(a^2-b^2)}}}$$

Note: $b^2-a^2=-1(a^2-b^2)$, then divide out common factors of (a^2-b^2).

$$=-\frac{1}{ab}$$

Alternate method In this problem we multiply the top and bottom expressions by the LCD which is a^2b^2 to get the same result.

$$\frac{\left(\dfrac{1}{a^2}-\dfrac{1}{b^2}\right)\cdot\dfrac{a^2b^2}{1}}{\left(\dfrac{a}{b}-\dfrac{b}{a}\right)\cdot\dfrac{a^2b^2}{1}}$$

$$=\frac{b^2-a^2}{a^3b-ab^3}$$

$$=\frac{b^2-a^2}{-ab(b^2-a^2)}$$

$$=-\frac{1}{ab}$$

1. Simplify the following complex fractions.

a. $\dfrac{\frac{3}{4} - \frac{1}{5}}{\frac{1}{2} + \frac{1}{5}}$

g. $\dfrac{\frac{2}{x+1} - \frac{3x}{x-1}}{\frac{1}{x-1} + x}$

b. $\dfrac{\frac{2}{3} - \frac{3}{4}}{\frac{3}{5} - 1}$

h. $\dfrac{\frac{3x}{x+2} - 2}{3}$

c. $\dfrac{\frac{1}{a} - \frac{1}{b}}{\frac{1}{a} + \frac{1}{b}}$

i. $\dfrac{\frac{1}{x} - \frac{1}{x+1}}{\frac{1}{x-1} - \frac{1}{x}}$

d. $\dfrac{\frac{a}{x} - \frac{b}{y}}{\frac{a}{x} + \frac{b}{y}}$

j. $\dfrac{\frac{1}{1} - \frac{1}{3+x}}{\frac{1}{x+2} - \frac{1}{2}}$

e. $\dfrac{x - \frac{4}{x}}{\frac{1}{2} + \frac{1}{x}}$

k. Show that dividing mixed numbers, e.g. $7\frac{1}{3} \div 3\frac{1}{2}$ comes down to simplifying a complex fraction.

f. $\dfrac{x^{-1} + x^{-2}y}{x^{-2} + y^{-1}}$

l. Simplify $\dfrac{1}{\frac{1}{R_1} + \frac{1}{R_2}}$.

Extra Credit

2. Simplify:

$$\dfrac{1 - \dfrac{1}{1 - \frac{1}{x}}}{1 + \dfrac{1}{1 + \frac{1}{x}}}$$

3. Find what is
   a. A continued fraction
   b. The Golden Ratio and find examples in real life where golden ratio appears.

This completes Module 2 on the arithmetic operations applied to mathematical objects you studied in Module 1.

Module 3: Solving Equations and Inequalities

Introduction

You can think of this module as an application of material you have learned so far. This module will show you how mathematics builds upon itself by using the definitions of objects and arithmetic operations from modules one and two to find solutions of complicated equations and inequalities of various kinds.

In a sentence, you can think of this module as an undoing process to find all the value(s) of the variable(s) involved that make a given equation or inequality a true statement. We will first develop some terminology and conventions to represent our solutions before attempting to solve equations. We present material in a way to show you that the process of solving equations and inequalities is really not that much different than what you did in Module 2.

Remember to be mindful of the process and become aware of your thought processes while attempting these problems.

3.1 A Brief History of Equations and Inequalities

For centuries mathematicians have been solving equations and inequalities. Although they did not always appear in the form you are used to seeing them. Sometimes mathematicians wrote the equations using language like "a number and two is 3," meaning that $x + 2 = 3$. There was also a time when mathematicians did not accept negative numbers, so great care was taken to write an equation so that negative numbers did not appear in an equation or an inequality.

Lecture

🖥 Introduction to Equations and Inequalities (11 min)

http://www.youtube.com/watch?v=vZ2mjSUvneQ

Equations and Inequalities

An **equation** is a statement asserting the equality of two mathematical objects.
An **inequality** is statement asserting that one mathematical object is larger than or equal to, or less than or equal to another mathematical object.

Note: Inequalities can only be used to relate objects from an ordered set such as the real numbers or integers, but not the complex numbers.

The symbol to signify equality of two mathematical objects is $=$.

The symbols used to signify inequalities of different types are $<, >, \leq$, and $\geq$.

The symbols above can be used as follows:

1. The equation $a = b$ signifies that the mathematical object a is equal to the mathematical object b.
2. The inequality $a < b$ signifies that the mathematical object a is smaller than or less than the mathematical object b.
3. The inequality $a > b$ signifies that the mathematical object a is bigger than or greater than the mathematical object b.
4. The inequality $a \leq b$ signifies that the mathematical object a is smaller than or equal to, or less than or equal to, the mathematical object b.
5. The inequality $a \geq b$ signifies that the mathematical object a is bigger than or equal to, or greater than or equal to, the mathematical object b.

The symbols above are our shorthand way of writing comparisons between two mathematical objects. In this way, you can see how mathematics is a symbolic language.

To create an example of an equation or an inequality, take one or more objects that you have studied so far and combine them using arithmetic tools learned in module 2 on the left hand side. Then write an equal to or an inequality sign and then a similar combination of objects on the right hand side. All real number solutions to an equation or inequality in one variable can be represented on a real number line. All real number solutions to an equation or inequality in two variables can be represented as points or regions in a 2-dimensional Cartesian coordinate system which we will study in Module 4.

Examples of different types of equations using objects you have seen so far.

1. $2x + 4 = 3$

2. $\frac{2}{3}x - 3 = \frac{5}{x} + 2$

3. $y = \frac{3x + 1}{2x - 3}$

4. $3x^2 - 4x + 1 = 5x^2 - 5x - 2$

5. $\sqrt{3 - 2x} = 2$

6. $\frac{2}{x - 1} - \frac{3x}{x + 1} = \frac{2x - 1}{x^2 - 1}$

7. $\sqrt{3 - 2x} = 5\sqrt{x} - 1$

8. $|3 - x| = 2$

Examples of different types of inequalities using objects you have seen so far.

1. $2x + 4 \geq 3 - x$

2. $\frac{2}{3}x - 3 < \frac{5}{x} + 2$

3. $y < \frac{3x + 1}{2x - 3}$

4. $3x^2 - 4x + 1 > 5$

5. $\sqrt{3 - 2x} < 5$

6. $|3 - x| \geq 2$

Terminology

Any number(s) when substituted for the variable(s) in the original equation or inequality that results in a true statement is called a <u>solution </u>to that equation or inequality.

The process in which we use mathematical properties of equality or inequality respectively to isolate the variable by itself is called <u>solving</u> the equation or inequality.

Solving an equation or an inequality is like untying a knot or undoing what was done to the variable to get it into its current state. The undoing process will involve applying the inverse of operations that you learned in module 2. I.e. when a variable is multiplied by a number, we'll apply division by that number as one of the steps in isolating the variable. The skill you develop for deciding where to begin to unravel an equation or inequality will come with practice and patience. When stuck, you can make a list of all the available tools or operations in your "for my eyes" column, and then select a tool or operation which will begin the process of isolating the variable of interest.

Terminology

An equation that is true for all values of the variable is called an identity.

The equation $x \times x = x^2$ is an identity. Both sides of the equal sign yield the same number for any real number value of x.

Terminology

An equation in which you end up with a false statement for all values of the variable is said to have "No Solution".

The equation $x + 1 = x$ has no solution as no real number can be equal to one more than itself.

Terminology

Certain tools used in the process of isolating the variable can sometimes lead us to a value of the variable that makes the original equation false. Such a solution is called an extraneous solution and we will need to watch out for these "false" solutions whenever we use those tools.

As a simple example, consider the equation $x = 4$ which has only one answer, i.e., $x = 4$. Now multiply both sides of the equation by $(x - 1)$ to get $x(x - 1) = 4(x - 1)$. This new equation is still true at $x = 4$, but it is also true at $x = 1$ which we'd call an extraneous solution. Multiplying both sides of an equation by an expression in the variable, can lead to extraneous solutions. We'll see several other tools that can lead to extraneous solutions later as we develop them.

There are many operations that can show up in an equation, e.g., $+$, $-$, $\times$, $\div$, $\sqrt{}$, $(\ )^n$, $|\ \ |$, $-$. To unravel them you have to develop mastery in identifying what tools or operations can be used to undo each of these.

If you look at the equation $\frac{2}{x} + 3x = 3 - x$, we can say that $x = 0$ can never be a solution as it will make the denominator zero. Also, in the equation $\sqrt{2 - x} = 5$ we know that any real solution can't be bigger than 2 or else the radicand will be negative and the left side will be a complex number. In this course, these restrictions of "no division by zero" and "even roots only of non-negative numbers" will sometimes restrict what solutions are possible. So always pay attention that any solution you find makes sense in the original formulation of the equation or inequality.

Once you find the solution to an inequality you may choose to represent your answers in the form of an algebraic inequality in which you have the variable isolated on one side and a number on the other side. For example, a solution may be represented by the inequality $2 < x$ or equivalently as $x > 2$.

Solutions to inequalities can also be represented <u>graphically on a number line.</u> You draw a number line and then plot your solutions on the number line. For example $2 < x$ is graphically represented by the open circle and red arrow on the number line graph below. Our number lines will always be oriented so the right side goes off in the positive direction and the left side off to large negative numbers.

$$0 \qquad 2$$

Another way to express solutions to inequalities is through interval notation. This format for describing intervals of numbers is most easily expressed by reading from a number line graph of a solution. Interval notation has a precise format using the appropriate brackets following the convention shown below.

Interval Notation

Lecture

🖥 Interval Notation (14 min)

http://www.youtube.com/watch?v=P1IIz3XtJLs

Notation

1. Round brackets or parenthesis such as "(" or ")" are used to enclose endpoints of intervals when the endpoint(s) is not included in the solution as shown below.

2. Square brackets such as "[" or "]" are used to enclose endpoints of intervals that are included in the set of numbers.

The examples below show how interval notation, graphing on a number line, and algebraic expressions are used to describe the various types of intervals of numbers that we will see as solutions.

1. Algebraic: $\qquad x < a$ (which is the same as $a > x$)

    Interval Notation: $\qquad (-\infty, a)$ | *Note: The symbol $-\infty$ is used to represent negative infinity meaning all numbers to the left of the number a.*

    Graphical:

    $$a$$

2. Algebraic: $\qquad x \leq a$ (which is the same as $a \geq x$)

    Interval Notation: $\qquad (-\infty, a]$

    Graphical:

    $$a$$

---

3. Algebraic: $x > a$ (which is the same as $a < x$)

    Interval Notation: (a, ∞)

    > Note: The symbol ∞ is used to represent positive infinity meaning all numbers to the right of the number **a**.

    Graphical:

    ```
                                    a
    ◄─────────────────────○══════════►
    ```

4. Algebraic: $x \geq a$ (which is the same as $a \leq x$)

    Interval Notation: $[a, \infty)$

    Graphical:

    ```
                                    a
    ◄─────────────────────●══════════►
    ```

5. Algebraic: $a < x < b$

    Interval Notation: (a, b)

    Graphical:

    ```
                    a                           b
    ◄──────────────○═══════════════════════════○──────────►
    ```

6. Algebraic: $a \leq x \leq b$

    Interval Notation: $[a, b]$

    Graphical:

    ```
                    a                           b
    ◄──────────────●═══════════════════════════●──────────►
    ```

7. Algebraic: $a \leq x < b$

    Interval Notation: $[a, b)$

    Graphical:

    ```
                    a                           b
    ◄──────────────●═══════════════════════════○──────────►
    ```

8. Algebraic: $a < x \leq b$

    Interval Notation: $(a, b]$

    Graphical:

    ```
                    a                           b
    ◄──────────────○═══════════════════════════●──────────►
    ```

9. Algebraic: Given any $a < b$, the set of numbers: $x < a$ or $x > b$

    Interval Notation: $(-\infty, a) \cup (b, \infty)$

    Graphical:

    ```
                        a       b
    ◄═══════════════○───────○═══════════►
    ```

10. Algebraic: Given any $a < b$, the set of numbers: $x \le a$ or $x \ge b$

     Interval Notation: $(-\infty, a] \cup [b, \infty)$

     Graphical:

11. Algebraic: Given any $a < b$, the set of numbers: $x < b$ and $x > a$

     Interval Notation: (a, b) *Note: The shorthand for the algebraic statement here is $a < x < b$ as seen in #7.*

     Graphical:

12. Algebraic: Given any $a < b$, the set of numbers: $x \le b$ and $x \ge a$

     Interval Notation: $[a, b]$

     Graphical:

13. Algebraic: Given any $a < b$, the set of numbers: $x < a$ and $x > b$

     No Solution

     Interval Notation: You cannot have a number smaller than a and at the same time be bigger than b.

     Graphical:

14. Algebraic: Given any $a < b$, the set of numbers: $x \le a$ and $x \ge b$

     Interval Notation: No Solution same reason as above.

     Graphical:

15. Algebraic: Given any $a < b$, the set of numbers: $x \ge a$ or $x \le b$

     Interval Notation: $(-\infty, \infty)$.

     Graphical:

Practice Problems

Represent the solutions to the following algebraic inequalities on the number line, and then also write the corresponding interval notation.

1.

   Algebraic: $x < -\dfrac{3}{4}$

   Interval Notation: $\left(-\infty, -\dfrac{3}{4}\right)$

   Graphical:
   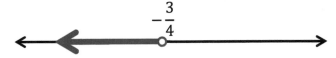

2.

   Algebraic: $x \leq 5$

   Interval Notation: $(-\infty, 5]$

   Graphical:

3.

   Algebraic: $x > -4$

   Interval Notation: $(-4, \infty)$

   Graphical:
   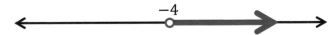

4.

   Algebraic: $x \geq 100$

   Interval Notation: $[100, \infty)$

   Graphical:

5.

Algebraic: $-\dfrac{2}{3} < x < \dfrac{2}{3}$

Interval Notation: $\left(-\dfrac{2}{3}, \dfrac{2}{3}\right)$

Graphical:

6.

Algebraic: $3 \leq x \leq 12$

Interval Notation: $[3,12]$

Graphical:

7.

Algebraic: $x < -2$ or $x > 2$

Interval Notation: $(-\infty, -2) \cup (2, \infty)$

Graphical:

8.

Algebraic: $x \leq \dfrac{3}{2}$ or $x \geq \dfrac{5}{3}$

Interval Notation: $\left(-\infty, \dfrac{3}{2}\right] \cup \left[\dfrac{5}{3}, \infty\right)$

Graphical:

9.

Algebraic: $x < \dfrac{1}{5}$ and $x > -\dfrac{1}{5}$

Interval Notation: $\left(-\dfrac{1}{5}, \dfrac{1}{5}\right)$

Graphical:

10.   Algebraic: $x \leq -30$ and $x \geq -40$

       Interval Notation: $[-40, -30]$

       Graphical:

11.   Algebraic: $x < -2$ and $x > 5$

       Interval Notation: No solution, no number can be smaller than -2 and at the same time be bigger than 5.

       Graphical:

12.   Algebraic: $x \leq 4$ and $x \geq 10$

       Interval Notation: No solution, no number can be smaller or equal to 4 and at the same time
       Graphical: be bigger than or equal to 10

13.   Algebraic: $x \geq -3$ or $x < 2$

       Interval Notation: $(-\infty, \infty)$

       Graphical:

Notice that since we are including every number above or equal to -3, the number 2 gets included even though the second inequality is all numbers below 2. The numbers below -3 get included due the second inequality. Therefore all real numbers either are below 2 or they satisfy that they are greater than or equal to -3. Notice the difference between the "or" statements and the "and" statements.

Note: *When working with "and" statements all numbers that make the solution set must satisfy all the statements, whereas in the "or" statements as long a number satisfies at least one of the statements it is included in the solution set.*

Fill in the empty columns appropriately with an algebraic inequalities, interval notation, or a number line, as needed. Use the format shown in the practice problems.

	Algebraic	Interval Notation	Graphical
1.	$x < 5$		
2.		$(-\infty, 3)$	
3.		$(-4, 2)$	
4.	$7 \leq x \leq 10$		[number line: closed dots at 7 and 10, segment shaded between]
5.	$7 < x \leq 10$		
6.	$x \leq 5$ and $x \geq -2$		
7.	$x < -3$ and $x > 3$		
8.	$\dfrac{1}{3} < x$ or $\dfrac{4}{5} \geq x$		
9.	$x \leq -3$ or $x > 5$		[number line: closed dot at -3 with ray left, open dot at 5 with ray right]
10.			[number line: closed dot at 1 with ray left, open dot at 5 with ray right]
11.		$\left(-\dfrac{1}{3}, \dfrac{1}{2}\right] \cup [4, 10]$	
12.	$x \leq -2$ or $x < 3$		

3.2 Solving Equations and Inequalities

There are many types of equations and inequalities that you will learn to solve. Before we begin, let's review some basic properties of equality and inequality that support two basic solving tools.

Properties of Equalities and Inequalities

Lecture

💻 Additive Property of Equalities and Inequalities (10 min)

http://www.youtube.com/watch?v=Emlxj6Xj4w0

Note that if $-2 < 5$, then, if we add 4 to both sides, we also have $-2 + 4 < 5 + 4$, or $2 < 9$ similarly if we subtract a 4 from both sides you will notice that $-2 - 4 < 5 - 4$, or $-6 < 1$. So adding or subtracting the same number from both sides of an inequality preserves the inequality. The same can be said for equations where if the left and right sides of an equation are equal to each other for some value of x, then adding or subtracting the same quantity from both sides of the equation will preserve the equality of the two sides for that same value of x. This can be visualized on a number line as shown below. Adding or subtracting a constant c from both sides of the equation simply shifts both sides of the equation left or right c units which preserves the equality.

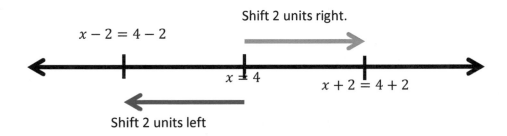

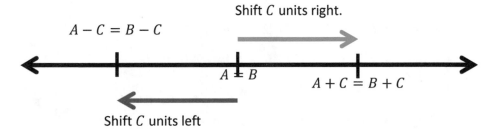

Note that for inequalities, adding or subtracting c moves both sides of the inequality left or right c units and preserves the left-right orientation of the two objects as shown below.

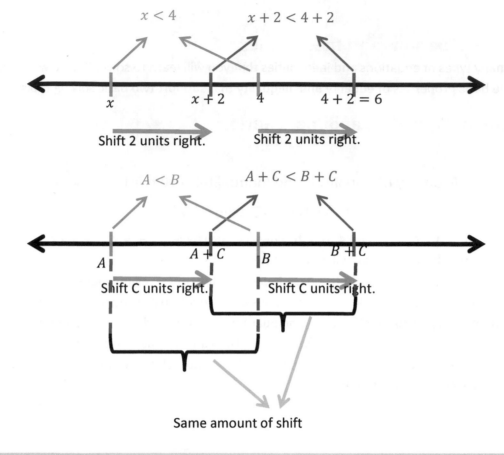

Same amount of shift

Observations

Addition/Subtraction Property

You can add or subtract the same number on both sides of an equation or an inequality to get an equivalent equation or inequality. For example,

If $A = B$, then $A + C = B + C$ and $A - C = B - C$ for all C.

If $A < B$, then $A + C < B + C$ and $A - C < B - C$ for all C.

If $A > B$, then $A + C > B + C$ and $A - C > B - C$ for all C.

If $A \leq B$, then $A + C \leq B + C$ and $A - C \leq B - C$ for all C.

If $A \geq B$, then $A + C \geq B + C$ and $A - C \geq B - C$ for all C.

In each example we take an equation or an inequality and convert it into equivalent equation or inequality using the properties above. Equivalent means they have the same solution sets.

Equations	Inequalities
1. $x + 5 = 3$ Equivalent Equations $x + 5 - 5 = 3 - 5$ $x = -2$	1. $x + 5 > 3$ Equivalent Inequalities $x + 5 - 5 > 3 - 5$ $x > -2$
2. $R + C = P$ Equivalent Equations $R + C - C = P - C$ $R = P - C$	2. $R + C < P$ Equivalent Inequalities $R + C - C < P - C$ $R < P - C$
3. $Ax + B = C$ Equivalent Equations $Ax + B - B = -B + C$ $Ax = -B + C$	3. $Ax + B \geq C$ Equivalent Inequalities $Ax + B - B \geq -B + C$ $Ax \geq -B + C$
4. $\sqrt{4x - 7} - 5 = 3$ Equivalent Equations $\sqrt{4x - 7} - 5 + 5 = 3 + 5$ $\sqrt{4x - 7} = 8$	4. $\sqrt{4x - 7} - 5 \leq 3$ Equivalent Inequalities $\sqrt{4x - 7} - 5 + 5 \leq 3 + 5$ $\sqrt{4x - 7} \leq 8$
5. $\dfrac{3x - 11}{x^2 - 1} - 4 = 58$ Equivalent Equations $\dfrac{3x - 11}{x^2 - 1} - 4 + 4 = 58 + 4$ $\dfrac{3x - 11}{x^2 - 1} = 62$	5. $\dfrac{3x - 11}{x^2 - 1} - 4 > 58$ Equivalent Inequalities $\dfrac{3x - 11}{x^2 - 1} - 4 + 4 > 58 + 4$ $\dfrac{3x - 11}{x^2 - 1} > 62$

🖥 Multiplicative Property of Equalities and Inequalities (8 min)

http://www.youtube.com/watch?v=IUaQxG8Vn-8

When an equation is true for some value of x, it remains true when you multiply or divide both sides by the same nonzero number. With inequalities, multiplying or dividing by a positive number corresponds to stretching or compressing all points on a number line by the same factor. Thus $-2 < 3$ when multiplied on both sides by 2 gives $-2 \times 2 < 3 \times 2$, or $-4 < 6$. So multiplying by a positive number on both sides preserves the inequality. This is illustrated below in the number line representation of this example. Stretching or compressing the number line keeps the left-right orientation the same.

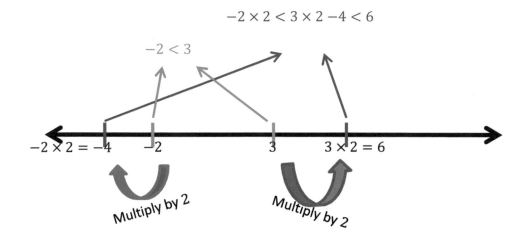

However, if we multiply both sides of an inequality by a negative number, e.g., by (-2), see what happens to $-2 < 3$,
$-2 \times (-2) > 3 \times (-2)$, or $4 > -6$ on the number line.

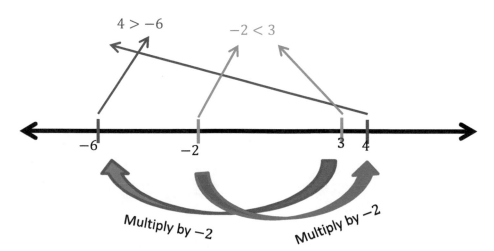

The left-right orientation gets reversed! $-2 \times (-2) > 3 \times (-2)$, or $4 > -6$ and the inequality is reversed when we multiply any inequality by a negative number. Division by a positive number just shrinks the number line without changing the direction of an inequality. Division by a negative two shrinks and also reverses the direction of inequality, e.g., $8 < 10$, and $\frac{8}{2} < \frac{10}{2}$, or $4 < 5$, but $\frac{8}{-2} > \frac{10}{-2}$, or $-4 > -5$.

Multiplication/Division Property

You can multiply or divide both sides of an equation by the same non-zero number or quantity to get an equivalent equation.

If $A = B$, then $AC = BC$, and $\frac{A}{C} = \frac{B}{C}$ for all $C \neq 0$.

You can multiply or divide both sides of an inequality by the same positive number to get an equivalent inequality. However, when you multiply or divide both sides of an inequality by the same negative number, you need to switch the direction of the inequality to obtain an equivalent inequality statement.

If $A < B$, then $AC < BC$, and $\frac{A}{C} < \frac{B}{C}$ for all $C > 0$.

If $A < B$, then $AC > BC$, and $\frac{A}{C} > \frac{B}{C}$ for all $C < 0$.

In the following examples we convert an equation or an inequality into an equivalent equation or inequality using the properties above.

Equations	Inequalities
1. $3x = -5$	1. $3x < -5$
Equivalent Equations	Equivalent Inequalities
$\frac{3x}{3} = -\frac{5}{3}$ or $x = -\frac{5}{3}$	$\frac{3x}{3} < -\frac{5}{3}$ or $x < -\frac{5}{3}$
2. $-PQ = R + C$,	2. $-PQ < R + C$,
with $P \neq 0$, real number	with $P > 0$, $(-P$ is negative. $)$
Equivalent Equations	Equivalent Inequalities
$\frac{-PQ}{-P} = \frac{R+C}{-P}$ or	$\frac{-PQ}{-P} > \frac{R+C}{-P}$ or
$Q = -\frac{R}{P} - \frac{C}{P}$	$Q > -\frac{R}{P} - \frac{C}{P}$

3. $Ax + B = C$, with real number $A \neq 0$.

Equivalent Equations

$Ax + B - B = -B + C$

$Ax = -B + C$

$\dfrac{Ax}{A} = \dfrac{-B + C}{A}$

$x = -\dfrac{B}{A} + \dfrac{C}{A}$

3. $Ax + B \geq C$, with real number $A \neq 0$.

Equivalent Inequalities

$Ax + B - B \geq -B + C$

$Ax \geq -B + C$ (be careful when dividing)

if $A > 0$	if $A < 0$
$\dfrac{Ax}{A} \geq \dfrac{-B + C}{A},$	$\dfrac{Ax}{A} \leq \dfrac{-B + C}{A},$
$x \geq \dfrac{-B}{A} + \dfrac{C}{A}$	$x \leq \dfrac{-B}{A} + \dfrac{C}{A}$

4. $3|9x - 1| = 2$

Equivalent Equations

$\dfrac{3|9x - 1|}{3} = \dfrac{2}{3}$

$|9x - 1| = \dfrac{2}{3}$

4. $3|9x - 1| \geq 2$

Equivalent Inequalities

$\dfrac{3|9x - 1|}{3} \geq \dfrac{2}{3}$

$|9x - 1| \geq \dfrac{2}{3}$

5. $5(x - 1)^2 = 7$

Equivalent Equations

$\dfrac{5(x - 1)^2}{5} = \dfrac{7}{5}$

$(x - 1)^2 = \dfrac{7}{5}$

5. $5(x - 1)^2 < 7$

Equivalent Inequalities

$\dfrac{5(x - 1)^2}{5} < \dfrac{7}{5}$

$(x - 1)^2 < \dfrac{7}{5}$

Basic Undoing Strategies

Solving Equations and Inequalities (12 min)

http://www.youtube.com/watch?v=9Ky4kZA1unE

Solving Equations and Inequalities (8 min)

http://www.youtube.com/watch?v=kRbOrSNxKy0

Solving Equations (11 min)

http://www.youtube.com/watch?v=6oGn22clCwA

Below is a summary of tools that can be used to undo operations to isolate a variable. Make sure you really understand these concepts and tools.

1. Addition undoes subtraction.
   Examples

   If $x - 3 = 5$, then $x - 3 + 3 = 5 + 3$ or $x = 8$

   $x - 3 < 5$ then $x - 3 + 3 < 5 + 3$ or $x < 8$

2. Subtraction undoes addition.
   Examples

   $x + 3.5 = 7.8$ then $x + 3.5 - 3.5 = 7.8 - 3.5$ or $x = 4.3$

   $x + 3\frac{1}{3} \geq 5\frac{1}{2}$ then $x + 3\frac{1}{3} - 3\frac{1}{3} \geq 5\frac{1}{2} - 3\frac{1}{3}$ or $x \geq 2\frac{1}{6}$

3. Multiplication undoes division.
   Examples

   If $\frac{x}{3} = 5$, then $\frac{x}{3} \times 3 = 5 \times 3$, or that $x = 15$.

   If $\frac{x}{3} > 5$, then $\frac{x}{3} \times 3 > 5 \times 3$, or that $x > 15$.

   If $-\frac{2}{3}x = 5$, then $\left(-\frac{3}{2}\right)\left(-\frac{2}{3}\right)x = \left(-\frac{3}{2}\right)\left(\frac{5}{1}\right)$ or $x = -\frac{15}{2} = -7\frac{1}{2}$

   If $-\frac{2}{3}x < 5$, then $\left(-\frac{3}{2}\right)\left(-\frac{2}{3}\right)x > \left(-\frac{3}{2}\right)\left(\frac{5}{1}\right)$ or $x > -\frac{15}{2}$ (remember to switch the inequality if you are multiplying by a negative number)

4. Division undoes multiplication.
   Examples

   If $3x = 5$, then $\frac{3x}{3} = \frac{5}{3}$, or that $x = \frac{5}{3}$.
   If $3x < 5$, then $\frac{3x}{3} < \frac{5}{3}$, or that $x < \frac{5}{3}$.
   If $-5x \geq 2$, then $\frac{-5x}{-5} \leq \frac{2}{-5}$ or $x \leq -\frac{2}{5}$ (Remember to switch the inequality when dividing by a negative number!)

5. Undoing with multiple steps
   a. $3x + 5 = 3 - 7x$ Collecting the x terms on the left we have

      $3x + 5 + 7x - 5 = 3 - 7x + 7x - 5$ or $10x = -2$ or $x = -\frac{2}{10}$ or $x = -\frac{1}{5}$.

   b. $3.5x - 7 \leq 6x + 3$ Collecting the x terms on the right we have

      $3.5x - 7 - 3.5x - 3 \leq 6x + 3 - 3.5x - 3$ or $-10 \leq 2.5x$ or $-\frac{10}{2.5} \leq x$ or $-4 \leq x$ or

      $x \geq -4$.

---

6. When working with fractions, we convert all denominators to the least common denominator and then determine what values of the variable make the numerators equal. We also need to exclude any value of the variable that makes the bottom zero!

Example

Solve for x, $\dfrac{5}{x-1} + \dfrac{3x}{x^2-1} = -\dfrac{2}{x+1}$ where $(x \neq 1, -1)$

Factor the denominators leading to

$$\frac{5}{x-1} + \frac{3x}{(x-1)(x+1)} = -\frac{2}{x+1}$$

$$\frac{5(x+1)}{(x-1)(x+1)} + \frac{3x}{(x-1)(x+1)} = -\frac{2(x-1)}{(x+1)(x-1)}$$

$$\frac{5(x+1)+3x}{(x-1)(x+1)} = -\frac{2(x-1)}{(x+1)(x-1)}$$

The two above fractions with the same denominator are equivalent if and only if their numerators are equal (don't forget to exclude solutions that make denominator equal to zero).

$$5(x+1) + 3x = -2(x-1)$$
$$5x + 5 + 3x = -2x + 2$$
$$8x + 5 = -2x + 2$$
$$8x + 2x + 5 - 5 = -2x + 2x + 2 - 5$$
$$10x = -3$$
$$x = \frac{-3}{10}$$

7. Squaring undoes square roots. (Squaring both sides can introduce extraneous answers so remember to check your answers! This will be dealt with more completely in section 3.4.)

Example: Solve for x, $\sqrt{x+1} = 5$

$$\left(\sqrt{x+1}\right)^2 = 5^2$$
$$x + 1 = 25$$
$$x = 24$$
Check $\sqrt{24+1} = \sqrt{25} = 5$ ✔

8. Taking the square root undoes the squaring operation.

   There are two real even roots to any positive number, positive and negative (or $\pm$ square root). This will also be dealt with more fully in section 3.4.

   Example

   Solve for x, $(x + 2)^2 = 5$. Start by taking the square root on both sides. Be aware that there are always two square roots of any positive number, thus on one side we put in a $\pm$ to account for both.

   $$\sqrt{(x + 2)^2} = \pm\sqrt{5}$$
   $$x + 2 = \sqrt{5} \text{ or } x + 2 = -\sqrt{5}$$

   Finally: $x = -2 + \sqrt{5}$ or $x = -2 - \sqrt{5}$.

9. In general, an nth power is unraveled by taking an nth root (or $1/n^{\text{th}}$ power, keep track of odd and even root property)

   Example

   Solve for x, $(x + 2)^5 = 7$

   $$\sqrt[5]{(x + 2)^5} = \sqrt[5]{7} \quad \text{(There is only one solution given that 5}^{\text{th}} \text{ root is an odd root.)}$$
   $$x + 2 = \sqrt[5]{7}$$
   $$x + 2 - 2 = -2 + \sqrt[5]{7}$$
   $$x = -2 + \sqrt[5]{7}$$

   Check and make sure your solution works

10. In general, an nth root (or $1/n^{\text{th}}$ power) is unraveled by taking the nth power.

   Solve for x, $\sqrt[3]{2x - 1} = 4$

   $$\left(\sqrt[3]{2x - 1}\right)^3 = 4^3$$
   $$2x - 1 = 64$$
   $$2x - 1 + 1 = 64 + 1$$
   $$2x = 65$$
   $$x = \frac{65}{2}$$

   Check and make sure your solution works... $x = \frac{65}{2} \rightarrow \sqrt[3]{2 \cdot \frac{65}{2} - 1} = \sqrt[3]{65 - 1} = \sqrt[3]{64} = 4$, OK!

Remember the even and odd root properties, ($\sqrt[odd]{x^{odd}} = x$ and $\sqrt[evem]{x^{even}} = \pm x$) Also check your answer to make sure you do not have any extraneous solutions when raising both sides to an even power and when multiplying by variable expressions that can possibly be equal to zero. If you get stuck while trying to solve an equation, look to your toolbox of methods for simplifying expressions and converting equations to equivalent equations. (There should be at least four tools in your box at this point.) You should make note card with these methods that you can refer to whenever you get stuck. Sometimes there may not be a tool in your box and you may need a new tool. In this course, we will introduce you to several more tools for solving equations. Your instructor's box of tools should be ample to solve any equation at this level, so seek help after you've tried your toolkit and are still stuck. Just try out each tool/method to see if it might help in a "For My Eyes" column.

We will solve equations and inequality problems side by side for a while so you can see how the tools for each are mostly the same with a few important differences, e.g., when dividing an inequality by a negative number, you must reverse the direction of all inequalities.

Practice examples

Solve the following equations and inequalities for the indicated variables. Express the solution set of all inequalities in 3 ways, algebraically, graphically, and using interval notation.

1. **Equation** $x + 3 = -5$

   Here we have to undo addition so we use subtraction.

   $$x + 3 - 3 = -5 - 3$$
   $$x = -8$$

   Solution: $x = -8$

   Check: $-8 + 3 = -5$ ✓

   Inequality $x + 3 < -5$

   Method 1 Here we have to undo addition so we use subtraction.

   $$x + 3 - 3 < -5 - 3$$
   $$x < -8$$

   Algebraic:
   $$x < -8$$

   Interval Notation:
   $$(-\infty, -8)$$

   Graphically:

Method 2 Solve the inequality $x + 3 < -5$ like an equation and use test points.
$$x + 3 - 3 = -5 - 3, \text{ or } x = -8$$
The only critical number is $x = -8$ which divides the real number line into two separate intervals. We need to check a single point from each interval to see if that interval is part of the solution. Using $x = 0$ and $x = -10$ as test points, we see that for $x = 0$, 3 is not less than -5 and for $x = -10$, -7 is less than -5. We also check the critical number $x = -8$ and see that the inequality is false, and thus the solution is the interval to the left of -8.

Algebraic: $x < -8$ Graphical solution:

Interval Notation:$(-\infty, -8)$

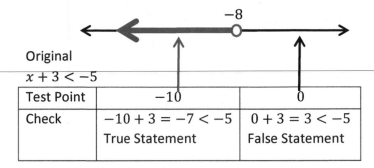

Original

$x + 3 < -5$

Test Point	-10	0
Check	$-10 + 3 = -7 < -5$	$0 + 3 = 3 < -5$
	True Statement	False Statement

Notice that if $x < -8$, then $x + 3 < -8 + 3$ or that $x + 3 < -5$. Thus for any real number smaller than -8, adding a 3 to it will keep the number smaller than -5 and for any real number bigger than -8 adding a 3 to it will make it bigger than -5. That is why using one test point below and one above -8 to check the validity of our inequality is enough.

When solving inequalities, we will work with method 1 when possible and sometimes, when advantageous, we will use method 2. You can decide which method you like best and use that method. Remember that there is not a fixed recipe; there are multiple correct ways to apply your algebra tool kit to solve most problems. As long as you can justify each and every step as a mathematically correct process, you can use it no matter what method someone else uses. What comes naturally to you is what you will retain longer.

2. **Equation** $x - 3.4 = -5.6$

   Addition undoes subtraction

$$x - 3.4 + 3.4 = -5.6 + 3.4$$

$$x = -2.2$$

   Solution: $x = -2.2$

   Check: $-2.2 - 3.4 = -5.6$ ✔

Inequality $x - 3.4 < -5.6$

Addition undoes subtraction

$$x - 3.4 + 3.4 < -5.6 + 3.4$$

$$x < -2.2$$

Algebraic: $x < -2.2$

Interval Notation: $(-\infty, -2.2)$

Graphically:

3. **Equation** $x - \frac{1}{2} = 7$

Addition undoes subtraction

$$x - \frac{1}{2} + \frac{1}{2} = 7 + \frac{1}{2}$$

$$x = \frac{7 \times 2}{1 \times 2} + \frac{1}{2}$$

$$x = \frac{14 + 1}{2}$$

Solution: $x = \frac{15}{2} = 7\frac{1}{2}$

Check:

$$\frac{15}{2} - \frac{1}{2} = \frac{14}{2} = 7 \checkmark$$

Inequality

$$x - \frac{1}{2} \geq 7$$

Addition undoes subtraction

$$x - \frac{1}{2} + \frac{1}{2} \geq 7 + \frac{1}{2}$$

$$x \geq \frac{7 \times 2}{1 \times 2} + \frac{1}{2}$$

$$x \geq \frac{14 + 1}{2} = \frac{15}{2} = 7\frac{1}{2}$$

Algebraic: $x \geq \frac{15}{2}$

Interval Notation: $\left[\frac{15}{2}, \infty\right)$

Graphical

4. **Equation** $x - \frac{1}{2} = \frac{7}{3}$

Addition undoes subtraction

$$x - \frac{1}{2} + \frac{1}{2} = \frac{7}{3} + \frac{1}{2}$$

$$x = \frac{7 \times 2}{3 \times 2} + \frac{1 \times 3}{2 \times 3} = \frac{14 + 3}{6}$$

$$x = \frac{17}{6}$$

Solution: $x = \frac{17}{6}$

Check:

$$\frac{17}{6} - \frac{1}{2} = \frac{17}{6} - \frac{1 \times 3}{2 \times 3}$$

$$= \frac{17}{6} - \frac{3}{6} = \frac{14}{6} = \frac{7}{3} \checkmark$$

Inequality $x - \frac{1}{2} \geq \frac{7}{3}$

Addition undoes subtraction

$$x - \frac{1}{2} + \frac{1}{2} \geq \frac{7}{3} + \frac{1}{2}$$

$$x \geq \frac{7 \times 2}{3 \times 2} + \frac{1 \times 3}{2 \times 3} = \frac{14 + 3}{6} = \frac{17}{6}$$

$$x \geq \frac{17}{6}$$

Algebraic: $x \geq \frac{17}{6}$

Interval Notation: $\left[\frac{17}{6}, \infty\right)$

Graphically:

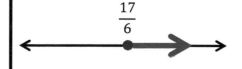

---

5. **Equation** $2x = 7$

Division or multiplying by multiplicative inverse will undo multiplication.

$$\frac{2x}{2} = \frac{7}{2}$$

Solution: $x = \frac{7}{2}$

Check:

$$2 \times \frac{7}{2} = 7 \checkmark$$

Inequality $2x \leq 7$

Division or multiplying by multiplicative inverse will undo multiplication. Just watch out for the negative numbers.

$$\frac{2x}{2} \leq \frac{7}{2}$$

Algebraic: $x \leq \frac{7}{2}$

Interval Notation: $\left(-\infty, \frac{7}{2}\right]$

Graphically:

6. **Equation** $-\frac{2}{3}t = \frac{5}{2}$

Division undoes multiplication or multiplication by multiplicative inverse.

$$\left(-\frac{3}{2}\right) \times \left(-\frac{2}{3}\right)t = \left(-\frac{3}{2}\right) \times \frac{5}{2}$$

Solution:

$$t = -\frac{15}{4}$$

Check:

$$-\frac{2}{3} \times -\frac{15}{4} = \frac{30}{12} = \frac{5}{2} \checkmark$$

Inequality $-\frac{2}{3}t < \frac{5}{2}$

Division undoes multiplication or multiplication by multiplicative inverse.

$$\left(-\frac{3}{2}\right) \times \left(-\frac{2}{3}\right)t > \left(-\frac{3}{2}\right) \times \frac{5}{2}$$

Reverse the inequality sign since we multiplied both sides by a negative

Algebraic: $t > -\frac{15}{4}$

Interval Notation: $\left(-\frac{15}{4}, \infty\right)$

Graphically:

$$-\frac{15}{4}$$

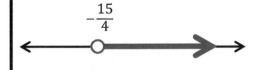

7. **Equation** $2u - \frac{1}{2} = \frac{7}{3}$

Addition undoes subtraction.

$$2u - \frac{1}{2} + \frac{1}{2} = \frac{7}{3} + \frac{1}{2}$$

$$2u = \frac{7 \times 2}{3 \times 2} + \frac{1 \times 3}{2 \times 3} = \frac{14 + 3}{6} = \frac{17}{6}$$

Division or multiplying by multiplicative inverse will undo multiplication

$$\frac{1}{2} \times 2u = \frac{1}{2} \times \frac{17}{6} = \frac{17}{12}$$

Solution: $u = \frac{17}{12}$

Check:

$$2\left(\frac{17}{12}\right) - \frac{1}{2} = \frac{17}{6} - \frac{1}{2}$$

$$= \frac{17}{6} - \frac{1 \times 3}{2 \times 3}$$

$$= \frac{17}{6} - \frac{3}{6} = \frac{14}{6} = \frac{7}{3} \checkmark$$

Inequality $2u - \frac{1}{2} \geq \frac{7}{3}$

Addition undoes subtraction.

$$2u - \frac{1}{2} + \frac{1}{2} \geq \frac{7}{3} + \frac{1}{2}$$

$$2u \geq \frac{7 \times 2}{3 \times 2} + \frac{1 \times 3}{2 \times 3} = \frac{14 + 3}{6} = \frac{17}{6}$$

Division or multiplying by multiplicative inverse will undo multiplication

$$\frac{1}{2} \times 2u \geq \frac{1}{2} \times \frac{17}{6} = \frac{17}{12}$$

Algebraic: $u \geq \frac{17}{12}$

Interval Notation: $\left[\frac{17}{12}, \infty\right)$

Graphically:

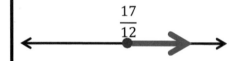

$\frac{17}{12}$

8. **Equation** $\quad -2x - 3 = 7$

$$-2x - 3 + 3 = 7 + 3$$

$$-2x = 10$$

$$\frac{-2x}{-2} = \frac{10}{-2}$$

Solution: $x = -5$

Check: $-2 \times (-5) - 3 = 10 - 3 = 7 \checkmark$

Inequality $\quad -2x - 3 \leq 7$

$$-2x - 3 + 3 \leq 7 + 3$$

$$-2x \leq 10$$

$$\frac{-2x}{-2} \geq \frac{10}{-2}$$

Algebraic: $x \geq -5$

Interval Notation: $[-5, \infty)$

Graphically:

-5

9. Equation $2.5x + 4.5 = -5.6$

$$2.5x + 4.5 - 4.5 = -5.6 - 4.5$$

$$2.5x = -10.1$$

$$\frac{2.5x}{2.5} = -\frac{10.1}{2.5}$$

$$x = -4.04$$

Check: $2.5(-4.04) + 4.5$
$$= -10.1 + 4.5$$
$$= -5.6 ✔$$

Inequality $2.5x + 4.5 > -5.6$

$$2.5x + 4.5 - 4.5 > -5.6 - 4.5$$

$$2.5x > -10.1$$

$$\frac{2.5x}{2.5} > -\frac{10.1}{2.5}$$

$$x > -4.04$$

Algebraic: $x > -4.04$

Interval Notation: $(-4.04, \infty)$

Graphically:

10. Equation $-2x - 3 = 7 + x$

Move terms so that all variable terms come to one side, and number terms to other side. You could perform multiple operations in one step as shown below (using associative and commutative property or addition and subtraction).

$$-2x - x - 3 + 3 = 7 + 3 + x - x$$
$$-3x = 10$$

Solution: $x = -\frac{10}{3}$

Check:

$$-2\left(-\frac{10}{3}\right) - 3 = \frac{20}{3} - \frac{9}{3} = \frac{11}{3}$$

and $7 + \left(-\frac{10}{3}\right) = \frac{21}{3} - \frac{10}{3} = \frac{11}{3}$ ✔

Inequality $-2x - 3 > 7 + x$

Steps are similar to the equation solving.
$$-2x - x - 3 + 3 > 7 + 3 + x - x$$

$$-3x > 10$$

$$\frac{-3x}{-3} < \frac{10}{-3}$$
$$\frac{-3x}{-3} < \frac{10}{-3}$$

Algebraic: $x < -\frac{10}{3}$

Interval Notation: $\left(-\infty, -\frac{10}{3}\right)$

Graphically:

11. **Equation** $-2.5x + 3 = 5.7x - 8.5$

Move terms so that all variable terms come to one side, and number terms to other side.

$$-2.5x - 5.7x + 3 = 5.7x - 8.5 - 5.7x$$

$$-8.2x + 3 = -8.5$$

$$-8.2x + 3 - 3 = -8.5 - 3$$

$$-8.2x = -11.5$$

$$\frac{-8.2x}{-8.2} = \frac{-11.5}{-8.2}$$

$$x = \frac{11.5}{8.2}$$

$$x = \frac{115}{82}$$

Inequality $-2.5x + 3 \geq 5.7x - 8.5$

Steps are similar to the equation solving just watch out for change of signs when dividing by -8.2 .

$$-2.5x - 5.7x + 3 \geq 5.7x - 8.5 - 5.7x$$

$$-8.2x + 3 \geq -8.5$$

$$-8.2x + 3 - 3 \geq -8.5 - 3$$

$$-8.2x \geq -11.5$$

$$\frac{-8.2x}{-8.2} \leq \frac{-11.5}{-8.2}$$

$$x \leq \frac{11.5}{8.2}$$

$$x \leq \frac{115}{82}$$

Algebraic: $x \leq \frac{115}{82}$

Interval Notation $\left(-\infty, \frac{115}{82}\right]$

Graphically:

$$\frac{115}{82}$$

---

12. **Equation** $-2(3x - 5) + 5x = 4(x - 3)$

Distribute through and then collect terms on each side.

$$-6x + 10 + 5x = 4x - 12$$

$$-x + 10 = 4x - 12$$

Isolate x on the right side (or left is ok too)

$$-x + 10 + x + 12 = 4x - 12 + x + 12$$

$$22 = 5x$$

$$\frac{22}{5} = x \ \ or \ \ x = \frac{22}{5}.$$

Inequality $-2(3x - 5) + 5x < 4(x - 3)$

Proceed exactly as for the equation:

$$-6x + 10 + 5x < 4x - 12$$

$$-x + 10 < 4x - 12$$

Isolate x on the right side (or left is ok too)

$$-x + 10 + x + 12 < 4x - 12 + x + 12$$

$$22 < 5x$$

$$\frac{22}{5} < x \ \ or \ \ x > \frac{22}{5}$$

Algebraic: $x > \frac{22}{5}$

Interval Notation: $\left(\frac{22}{5}, \infty\right)$

Graphically:

$$\frac{22}{5}$$

In the next equation and inequality we pay careful attention to the process.

13. **Equation** $2 - \frac{1}{x+1} = \frac{7}{3}$

Note that since the variable term is in the denominator, we need to restrict x so that $x \neq -1$. If we do not, we will end up having zero in the denominator and division by zero doesn't make sense. When you encounter a problem you do not remember how to solve, follow your instinct or intuition. Consider all of your available tools and proceed from there.

$$2 - \frac{1}{x+1} = \frac{7}{3}$$

We cannot compare fractions unless they have the same units or denominators. So we start by converting all the terms to equivalent terms all having the least common denominator. The LCD is $(x+1)3$.

$$\frac{2(3(x+1))}{1(3(x+1))} - \frac{1(3)}{(x+1)(3)} = \frac{7(x+1)}{3(x+1)}$$

Now combine the numerator terms on each side.

$$\frac{2(3x+3) - 3}{3(x+1)} = \frac{7x+7}{3(x+1)}$$

$$\frac{6x+6-3}{3(x+1)} = \frac{7x+7}{3(x+1)}$$

$$\frac{6x+3}{3(x+1)} = \frac{7x+7}{3(x+1)}$$

We know that two fractions with the same denominator can only be equal to each other if their numerators are equal. Therefore we can conclude that $6x + 3 = 7x + 7$. We solve this as:

$$6x + 3 - 3 = 7x + 7 - 3$$

$$6x = 7x + 4$$

$$6x - 7x = 7x - 7x + 4$$

$$-x = 4 \quad and \quad x = -4$$

(Note that this is not $x = -1$, which was excluded.)

Solution: $x = -4$

Check:

$$2 - \frac{1}{-4+1} = 2 - \frac{1}{-3} = \frac{2(-3)}{1(-3)} - \frac{1}{-3} = \frac{-6-1}{-3} = \frac{-7}{-3} = \frac{7}{3} \checkmark$$

Now for a related inequality-

Inequality $2 - \frac{1}{x+1} \geq \frac{7}{3}$

We still have the restriction that $x \neq -1$. We start as for the equation and simplify each side with the same denominator.

$$\frac{2(3(x+1))}{1(3(x+1))} - \frac{1(3)}{(x+1)(3)} \geq \frac{7(x+1)}{3(x+1)}$$

$$\frac{2(3x+3) - 3}{3(x+1)} \geq \frac{7x+7}{3(x+1)}$$

$$\frac{6x+6-3}{3(x+1)} \geq \frac{7x+7}{3(x+1)}$$

$$\frac{6x+3}{3(x+1)} \geq \frac{7x+7}{3(x+1)}$$

Here we need to be careful. We can't simply multiply both sides by $3(x+1)$ because this quantity is negative for some x-values and positive for others. This would require us to switch the direction of the inequality for some x-values. We use the critical number method of finding values of x where the equation is true. Also need to include as critical numbers any x-values where any of the factors in the denominator switch sign. This is due to the fact that the order of inequality changes when dividing by a negative, but not by a positive. Thus $x = -1$ is a critical number. Then we plot these "critical values" on a number line and test the intervals in between them to see where the original inequality is true and where it is false.

Already we know $x = -1$ is a critical value.

In addition, the **equation** is true when the numerators are equal. We already solved this problem and found the solution for equality to be $x = -4$.

We have critical points on the real line at $x = -4$ and at $x = -1$. The plot below shows these plotted and test points are used to see which of the three intervals of the real number line make the original inequality true. Also, since the inequality is $\geq$, the equality with $x = -4$ means we include -4 in that interval. The value $x = -1$ endpoint is excluded due to division by zero.

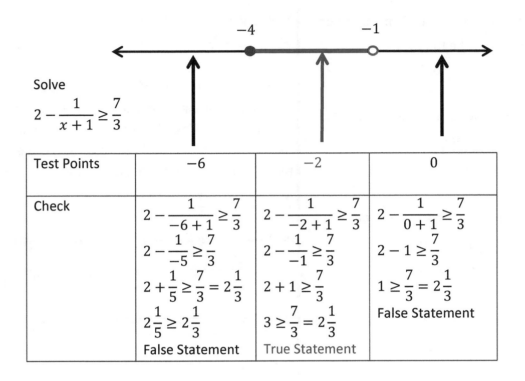

Solve

$$2 - \frac{1}{x+1} \geq \frac{7}{3}$$

Test Points	-6	-2	0
Check	$2 - \dfrac{1}{-6+1} \geq \dfrac{7}{3}$ $2 - \dfrac{1}{-5} \geq \dfrac{7}{3}$ $2 + \dfrac{1}{5} \geq \dfrac{7}{3} = 2\dfrac{1}{3}$ $2\dfrac{1}{5} \geq 2\dfrac{1}{3}$ False Statement	$2 - \dfrac{1}{-2+1} \geq \dfrac{7}{3}$ $2 - \dfrac{1}{-1} \geq \dfrac{7}{3}$ $2 + 1 \geq \dfrac{7}{3}$ $3 \geq \dfrac{7}{3} = 2\dfrac{1}{3}$ True Statement	$2 - \dfrac{1}{0+1} \geq \dfrac{7}{3}$ $2 - 1 \geq \dfrac{7}{3}$ $1 \geq \dfrac{7}{3} = 2\dfrac{1}{3}$ False Statement

The Solution
Algebraically: $-4 \leq x < -1$
Interval Notation: $[-4, -1)$

Graphically:

-4 -1

14. **Equation** $|3x - 4| = \frac{5}{3}$

To undo absolute value you have to look at its meaning. We know that absolute value refers to distance from zero. The only way to have the number $(3x - 4)$ be $\frac{5}{3}$ of a unit from zero would be to have:

$$3x - 4 = \frac{5}{3} \quad \text{or} \quad 3x - 4 = -\frac{5}{3}.$$

Solving each of the equations, we get:
$$3x - 4 + 4 = \frac{5}{3} + 4$$
$$\textbf{or} \ \ 3x - 4 + 4 = -\frac{5}{3} + 4$$

Continue as: $3x = \frac{5}{3} + \frac{12}{3}$ **or**

$3x = -\frac{5}{3} + \frac{12}{3}$

$3x = \frac{17}{3}$ **or** $3x = \frac{7}{3}$

Finally $\div 3$:

$$\left(\frac{1}{3}\right)3x = \left(\frac{1}{3}\right)\frac{17}{3} \quad \textbf{or} \quad \left(\frac{1}{3}\right)3x = \left(\frac{1}{3}\right)\frac{7}{3}$$

Solution:
$$x = \frac{17}{9} \quad \textbf{or} \quad x = \frac{7}{9}$$

Check:
$$\left|3\left(\frac{17}{9}\right) - 4\right| = \left|\frac{17}{3} - \frac{12}{3}\right| = \frac{5}{3} \ \checkmark$$
$$\left|3\left(\frac{7}{9}\right) - 4\right| = \left|\frac{7}{3} - \frac{12}{3}\right| = \left|-\frac{5}{3}\right|$$
$$= \frac{5}{3} \ \checkmark$$

Inequality $|3x - 4| > \frac{5}{3}$

We can use our test point method here as well. We locate all x-values where the corresponding equation is true or undefined (critical x-values).

Solving these we get as before:
$$x = \frac{17}{9} \quad \text{or} \quad x = \frac{7}{9}$$

These are the only critical numbers for this inequality. Plotting these and checking each of the three intervals with a test point, we obtain the graphical solution below. Here we exclude the endpoints since the inequality was $<$.

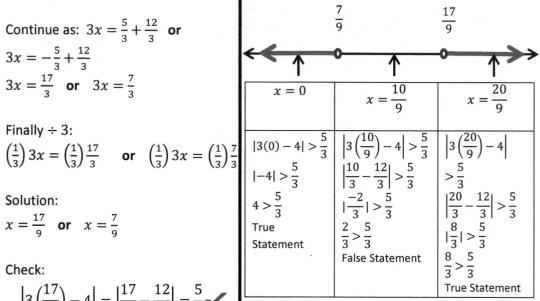

$x = 0$	$x = \frac{10}{9}$	$x = \frac{20}{9}$
$\|3(0) - 4\| > \frac{5}{3}$	$\left\|3\left(\frac{10}{9}\right) - 4\right\| > \frac{5}{3}$	$\left\|3\left(\frac{20}{9}\right) - 4\right\|$
$\|-4\| > \frac{5}{3}$	$\left\|\frac{10}{3} - \frac{12}{3}\right\| > \frac{5}{3}$	$> \frac{5}{3}$
$4 > \frac{5}{3}$	$\|\frac{-2}{3}\| > \frac{5}{3}$	$\left\|\frac{20}{3} - \frac{12}{3}\right\| > \frac{5}{3}$
True	$\frac{2}{3} > \frac{5}{3}$	$\|\frac{8}{3}\| > \frac{5}{3}$
Statement	False Statement	$\frac{8}{3} > \frac{5}{3}$
		True Statement

Solution:

Interval Notation: $\left(-\infty, \frac{7}{9}\right) \cup \left(\frac{17}{9}, \infty\right)$

Algebraic: $x < \frac{7}{9}$ or $x > \frac{17}{9}$

Graphically:

1. Solve the following equations and inequalities for the respective variables. If an equation is an identity, or has no solution, or has an extraneous solution, please state so. For all the inequalities write the solution in algebraic notation, interval notation, and represent the solutions graphically on a number line.

Equation	Inequality
a. $3x - 5 = 2x + 6$	a. $3x - 5 < 2x + 6$
b. $5 + 2x = x - 9$	b. $5 + 2x \leq x - 9$
c. $11 + 2t = t - 3$	c. $11 + 2t > t - 3$
d. $11 + 2t = 7t - 8$	d. $11 + 2t \leq 7t - 8$
e. $7x - 5 = 2x + 6$	e. $7x - 5 < 2x + 6$
f. $3x + 4.5 = -8.5$	f. $3x + 4.5 > -8.5$
g. $2.3x - 5.6 = 7.4 - 4.2x$	g. $2.3x - 5.6 \leq 7.4 - 4.2x$
h. $5(1 - x) = 3 - 2(3x - 7)$	h. $5(1 - x) < 3 - 2(3x - 7)$
i. $5(1 - x) = 3 - 4(3x - 7)$	i. $5(1 - x) > 3 - 4(3x - 7)$
j. $2(x + 1) - 4x = 3(x - 1) - 5x$	j. $2(x + 1) - 4x \geq 3(x - 1) - 5x$
k. $5(1 - x) = 1 - x - 4(x - 1)$	k. $5(1 - x) \leq 1 - x - 4(x - 1)$
l. $5 + \frac{2}{3}x = \frac{3}{2}x - 9$	l. $5 + \frac{2}{3}x \geq \frac{3}{2}x - 9$
What are the similarity and differences between the corresponding equations and inequalities?	

Equation	Inequality
m. $\|x\| = \frac{5}{2}$	m. $\|x\| < \frac{5}{2}$
n. $\|3 - 4x\| = 9$	n. $\|3 - 4x\| \leq 9$
o. $\|2x - 1\| = \frac{5}{2}$	o. $\|2x - 1\| > \frac{5}{2}$
p. $\|1 - 8x\| = 9$	p. $\|1 - 8x\| > 9$
q. $\|2x - 1\| + 3 = 7$	q. $\|2x - 1\| + 3 \geq 7$
r. $\|2x - 1\| - 3 = \frac{5}{2}$	r. $\|2x - 1\| - 3 \leq \frac{5}{2}$
s. $\dfrac{2}{x-1} = 5$	s. $\dfrac{2}{x-1} < 5$

What are the similarity and differences between the corresponding equations and inequalities?

2. Solve the following equations and inequalities for the respective variables. If an equation is an identity, or has no solution, or has an extraneous solution, please state so.

a. $\dfrac{5}{x+1} - \dfrac{2}{3} = 7$

b. $3(x + 1) - 2 = \dfrac{4}{3}(2x - 1)$

c. $\dfrac{3}{x+2} - \dfrac{1}{3x^2+5x-2} = -\dfrac{2}{3x-1}$

d. $\dfrac{2x-4}{x^2-1} = \dfrac{2}{x+1} - \dfrac{1}{x-1}$

e. $(x + 1)^3 = -8$

f. $x^2 = 9$

g. $(2x + 3)^2 = 9$

h. $(5x - 1)^2 - 2 = 7$

3. Solve the equations below for the designated variables.

a. Solve for y, $Ax + By = C$

b. Solve for q, $\dfrac{p}{q} = rt$

c. Solve for F, $T = \dfrac{5}{9}(F - 32)$

d. Solve for T, $D = RT$

e. Solve for x, $y = mx + b$

f. Solve for f, $\dfrac{1}{p} = \dfrac{1}{f} + \dfrac{1}{q}$

4. Below are some equations and inequalities students have solved. Please read them carefully to see if their work is correct or incorrect. If incorrect, please explain what property or mathematical principles are misapplied and at what step.

Equation	Inequality
a. $-4x - 5 = 3x - 1$ $-5 = -1 - 4x + 3x$ $-4 = x$	b. $-4x - 5 < 3x - 1$ $-7x < 4$ Algebraic Solution: $x < -\frac{4}{7}$ Interval notation $\left(-\frac{4}{7}, -\infty\right)$ Graphical Solutions: $-\frac{4}{7}$
c. $\|2 - 3x\| + 5 = 7$ $2 - 3x + 5 = 7$ or $2 - 3x + 5 = -7$ $-3x + 7 = 7$ or $-3x + 7 = -7$ $-3x = 0$ or $-3x = -14$ $x = 0$ or $x = \frac{14}{3}$	d. $\|2 - 3x\| + 5 > 7$ $2 - 3x + 5 > -7$ or $2 - 3x + 5 > 7$ $-3x + 7 > 7$ or $-3x + 7 > -7$ $-3x > 0$ or $-3x > -14$ Algebraic Solution: $x > 0$ or $x > \frac{14}{3}$ Interval notation $(0, \infty) \cup \left(\frac{14}{3}, \infty\right)$
e. $\frac{3}{5}x - \frac{1}{5} = \frac{1}{3}x + 5$ $9x - 3 = 5x + 5$ $4x = 8 \rightarrow \quad x = 2$	f. $\frac{3}{5}x - \frac{1}{5} \geq \frac{1}{3}x + 5$ $9x - 3 \geq 5x + 5$ $4x \geq 8 \rightarrow x \geq 2$

Percentage Problems When the Original Quantity Is Unknown

📺 Percentage, Ratio and Proportions Problems (11 min)

http://www.youtube.com/watch?v=oLoRCRXTYv4

In module two we used "percentage of" as multiplication to compute percentage increases or decreases from a known reference quantity. When the original amount is not known, we label it with a variable name, e.g., x. Then we set up a linear equation that represents a given percentage decrease or increase. We use the tools above to solve these linear equations. We can also draw strip diagrams to help solve these problems.

Practice Examples:

1. The gender wage gap varies by occupation. Female waitresses on average earn 82% as much as male waiters. If a typical female waitress earns $12/hr in New York City, what does a typical male waiter earn in New York City? In other words what wage is $12/hr 82% of?

    We let x represent the typical male waiter salary. The $12/hr female salary is 82% of x.

    Thus $12 = 0.82x$ and $x = \frac{\$12}{0.82} \approx \$14.63$.

2. A car dealer marked the price of a new car down by 8% and the sale price was $18,000. What was the original price?

    A very common but wrong attempt at solving this problem is to add 8% of $18,000 back to the sale price. Since the original 8% discount was based on the larger non-sale price, adding 8% of the sale price back will not quite get us back to the original price.

    It is easy to set up an equation describing the 8% reduction if we let x represent the unknown original price. We simply start with x dollars and subtract 8% of x and the result must be equal to $18,000. This translates directly to the equation below.

    $x - 0.08x = 18,000$

    $0.92x = 18,000$

    $x = \dfrac{18000}{0.92} \approx \$19,565$

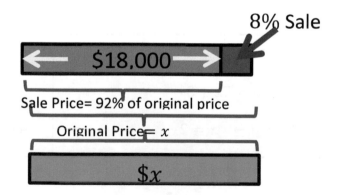

---

3. The pie chart below represents the ethnic breakdown of all UW-Colleges students. If the total number of non-white students is 1118 students, determine the total enrollment of the UW Colleges.

Ethnic Composition of UW Colleges Students

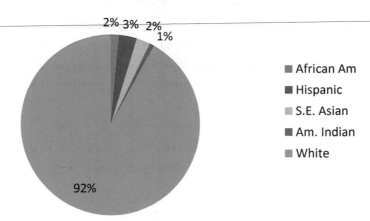

From the chart, we can see that these 1118 students represent 8% of the total student population. Algebraically if we assign x to represent the total number of UWC students, then we have $0.08x = 1118$ and $x = \frac{1118}{0.08} \approx 13{,}975$.

Ratio and Proportions

Mathematically, a **proportion** is an equality statement between two ratios.

Proportions show up in many applications from finding unknown lengths in similar geometric shapes to conversion between different units to computing rates and scaling of recipes or materials lists to larger or smaller batches. We will work through a series of examples to illustrate how to interpret written problems as an equality between two ratios.

1. Paul ran a Marathon (26.2 miles) in $3hr \ 7min$. At this rate, how long would it take Paul to run a 10k race which is 6.2mi?

   The problem statement "at this rate" means the ratio $\frac{distance}{time}$ remains the same for both races. If we let t represent the unknown time for the 10k race, the equivalent ratios for this proportion would be:

   $$\frac{26.2 \ mi}{187 \ min} = \frac{6.2 \ mi}{t \ min}$$

   $$\frac{26.2t \ mi}{187t \ min} = \frac{6.2 \times 187 \ mi}{187t \ min}$$

Solving this equation gives $t = \dfrac{6.2 \times 187}{26.2} \approx 44.3 \; min.$

2. A tall building casts a shadow of length 40 paces (100 feet) on a level city street. Also, the shadow of a six foot person is 2.5 feet long. Determine how tall the building is using the fact that the shadows and heights of the person and building form similar triangles where the ratio of corresponding sides is constant.

   The ratios can be set up in a variety of ways here. If we look at the height to shadow ratio, it must be the same for the person and the building. This leads to the proportion:

$$\frac{6 \; ft}{2.5 \; ft} = \frac{h \; ft}{100 \; ft}$$

This leads to $600 = 2.5h$ or $h = \dfrac{600}{2.5} = 240 \; ft.$

   We could also have solved this by adjusting the left ratio so the bottom is 100. Note that the 2.5 can be converted to 100 by multiplying by 4 and by 10 and converting the left ratio to the equivalent ratio

$$\frac{6}{2.5} = \frac{6 \times 4 \times 10}{2.5 \times 4 \times 10} = \frac{240}{100} = \frac{h}{100} \rightarrow h = 240.$$

3. A cookie recipe calls for 1.5 cups of flour and 7 oz. of almond paste and makes 2 dozen cookies. How much flour would be needed to make a huge batch of these cookies that utilizes a 90 oz. can of almond paste? Also how many cookies would this make?

   There are two ratios that should stay constant here. The ratio of flour to almond paste and the ratio of cookies to almond paste. We set up both proportions as below:
   Let $x = Number \; of \; cups \; of \; flour$, and $y = Number \; of \; cookies$

Flour:Almond Paste $\dfrac{1.5 \; cups}{7 \; oz} = \dfrac{x \; cups}{90 \; oz}$ and Cookie:Almond Paste $\dfrac{24 \; cookies}{7 \; oz} = \dfrac{y \; cookies}{90 \; oz}$

$$\frac{(1.5 \; cups)}{7 \; oz} \times 90 \; oz = x \; cups, \quad x \approx 19.3 \; cups \text{ of flour.}$$

$$\frac{24 \; cookies}{7 \; oz} \times 90 \; oz = y \; cookies, \quad y \approx 309 \; cookies.$$

Direct and Inverse Variation Relations
Lecture

🖥 Direct and Inverse Variation (5 min)

http://www.youtube.com/watch?v=sezsOC5fggo

Two common types of relationships between quantities are direct and inverse variation. In words, direct variation might look like "the volume of the balloon varies directly with the cube of the radius." This means the ratio of the $\frac{V}{r^3}$ is a constant k. Thus $\frac{V}{r^3} = k$ or $V = kr^3$. Another way that this might be expressed in words is "The volume of a balloon is proportional to the cube of the radius."

Terminology

<u>Direct variation</u> between quantities occurs when their ratio is a constant. In general "A *varies directly* with B" or "A is *directly proportional* to B" means that $A = kB$. The number k is called the constant of proportionality.

<u>Inverse variation</u> between two quantities occurs when the ratio of one quantity to the reciprocal of the other quantity is a constant. In other words, the product of the two quantities is a constant. In general "A *varies inversely* with B" or "A is *inversely proportional* to B" means $A = k\frac{1}{B}$. The number k is called the constant of proportionality.

For example "the number of miles a person drives per week varies inversely with the price of gasoline." This means that miles driven M varies with the inverse of the price of gas, $\frac{1}{g}$ or $M = k \cdot \frac{1}{g}$.

In a typical problem regarding variation, the type of variation is indicated by the language of the problem statement. The constant of variation, k, can then be determine when one pair of the variables is given. To do this the relation format is obtained, e.g., $M = k \cdot \frac{1}{g}$ and then k can be found by substituting in the given pair of the variables into the equation and solving for k. A further question might be to determine the value of one of the variables when another is known. For this, we use the now known value of k and the given variable to solve for the other variable.

Practice Examples:

1. The volume V of a balloon varies directly with the cube of the radius r. A balloon of radius 6 inches has a volume of 900 cubic inches. Find the relation between volume and radius and predict the volume of a balloon that is 24 inches in diameter.

   We have that $V = kr^3$. Also when $v = 900\ in^3, r = 6\ in.$ Substituting these set of data into the formula allows to determine the value of k.

   Thus $900 = k \cdot 6^3$ and $= \frac{900}{6^3} = 4.1\overline{6}$.

   Now we have the formula $V = 4.1\overline{6}\,r^3$

   For the balloon with diameter 24 in., $r = 12in$ and $V = 4.1\overline{6} \times 12^3 = 7200\ in^3$.

---

2. The number of miles, M, that Joe drives each week is inversely proportional to the price of gas, g. When the price was at \$3/gal, Joe drove 240 miles each week. Find the relationship between M and g. Predict how many miles Joe drives if the price of gas is \$5/gal.

We have that $M = k \cdot \frac{1}{g}$. Also, when $g = \frac{\$3}{gal}$, $M = 240 \, mi$. We first put these in to the relation to find k.

Thus $240 = k \cdot \frac{1}{3}$ and $k = 240 \cdot 3 = 720$

Now we have the formula $M = 720 \cdot \frac{1}{g}$.

When $g = 5$, $M = 720 \cdot \frac{1}{5} = 144 \, mi$.

Sometimes one quantity can vary with respect to two or more quantities in different ways. We call this **Joint Variation.** Several examples are: The volume V of a cone varies directly with the radius squared r^2 and directly with the height h. Thus $V = k \cdot r^2 \cdot h$. The volume V of a helium balloon varies directly with the temperature T and inversely with the pressure P: $V = k \cdot T \cdot \frac{1}{P}$. Again, the value of k can be determined from a given set of values of the variables.

3. The maximum load that a 2 inch wide plank can support varies directly with the square of the height of the plank and inversely with the length of the plank. A ten foot long 2" wide by 6" high plank can support 360 pounds. Write an equation that expresses how the maximum load L varies in terms of the height h and the length l of the beam. Use k for the constant of variation and note that the width, 2 inches, doesn't show up in the equation as it is constant. Also determine the maximum load for a 12 foot plank that is 10 inches high.

The formula for the maximum load is $L = k \cdot h^2 \cdot \frac{1}{l}$

To find k, substitute in $L = 360, h = 6 \, in, \, l = 10 \, ft$ and $360 = k \cdot 36 \cdot \frac{1}{10}$

Thus $360 \cdot 10 \div 36 = k$, $or \, k = 100$ and $L = 100 \frac{h^2}{l}$. Note that to use the formula, we must use the units on all of the variables that we used in finding k.

When $h = 10 \, in$, $and \, l = 12 \, ft$, $L = 100 \frac{12^2}{10} = 1440 \, lbs$.

Video Log 3.2b

1. Adam's salary is $55,000 a year and he earns 65% as much as his friend John. What is John's salary rounded to the nearest dollar?

2. Clare purchased a car for $23,400 that was on sale for 18% off. What was the presale price of the car?

3. The pie chart below shows the ethnic composition of entering students at the University of Michigan in 2005. If the total of the Hispanic and Asian students was 2457 students, determine the total number of incoming students at the University of Michigan in 2005. Round your answer to the nearest student.

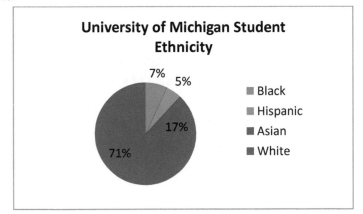

4. Joe can make 25 pizzas in a three hour shift. At this rate, how long would it take him to make 60 pizzas?

5. The polygons below are similar. Determine the length of the dashed side in the right polygon.

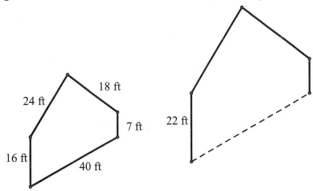

6. A recipe calls for 1 ¾ cups of flour, ½ c sugar and 1 stick of butter. It is critical that these ratios be adhered to in order for the cookies to turn out well. Paul was careless as he started and put in 2 cups of flour instead of the 1 ¾ c and had added the ½ c. sugar before realizing his error. Determine **how much** total sugar and **how much** total butter he should use to keep the ratios in line with the recipe.

---

7. The weight W of a Lake Michigan brown trout varies directly with the cube of its length l. A 25 inch fish weighs two pounds. Write an equation with a constant of variation k that expresses this variation and use the given data to determine the value of k. Also predict the weight of a 38 inch brown trout.

   Answer: Weight of 38 inch fish is about 7 pounds.

8. The energy intensity of sunlight I varies inversely with the square of the distance d from the sun. On earth which is $1.5 \cdot 10^{11} meters$ from the sun, the light intensity is $1300\frac{w}{m^2}$. (This means that on a piece of ground one meter by one meter, the solar energy comes in at about the same rate as the heat a hair dryer gives off.) Write an equation that expresses this inverse relation between I and d. Also estimate to the nearest tens, the solar energy intensity at Mars which is $2.3 \cdot 10^{11} m$ from the sun.

9. Write an equation that expresses the fact that P varies directly with T and inversely with V. Leave your constant of variation as k. Also determine the value of k when $T = 300$, $V = 25$, and $P = 15$.

10. Each problem has an error in it. Identify the error and determine the correct solution.

    a. Joe was making $35,000 and year and got a 5% raise at the end of 2008. Then the recession hit and his company cut everyone's salary by 5% in 2010. Thus Joe was back to making $35,000 a year.

    b. The price of a laptop was reduced by 20% and the sale price was $400. Thus the presale price was $400 + 0.20 \cdot \$400 = \$480$.

    c. The volume of a closed helium balloon varies directly as the absolute temperature and inversely with the pressure of the air surrounding the balloon. When the balloon is on the ground, the temperature is 300 degrees Kelvin and the pressure is 15 pounds per square inch and the volume is $27000\ ft^3$. Determine the volume of the balloon when it reaches 50,000 feet in the sky where the pressure is 2.5 pounds per square inch and the temperature is 220 degrees Kelvin.

    $$V = k \cdot T \cdot \frac{1}{P}, \quad \rightarrow \quad 27000 = k \cdot 300 \cdot \frac{1}{15} \quad \rightarrow \quad k = 1350. \text{ At 50,000 ft and 220 degrees K,}$$

    the volume is $V = k \cdot 220 \cdot \frac{1}{2.5} \quad \rightarrow \quad k = V \cdot \frac{2.5}{200}.$

3.3 Factoring and the Zero Property of Equality

Lecture

🖥 Zero Product Property (10 min)

http://www.youtube.com/watch?v=5zKug2bfT48

🖥 Examples (7 min)

http://www.youtube.com/watch?v=0FFGzy5Bw4s

Suppose $2 \times x = 0$. The only number that when doubled results in zero would have to be zero. This is true since two times any non-zero number will be farther away from zero on a number line than the number itself. However, if we had $2 \times x = 6$, then you would have no choice but to have $x = \frac{6}{2} = 3$. If you had **two** unknown numbers multiplying to give you a 6 then the two numbers have many choices, like 1×6, 2×3, $-\frac{5}{2} \times -\frac{12}{5}$, $\frac{7}{5} \times \frac{30}{7}$, ... infinitely many choices. If you had two numbers multiplying to give you zero however, you would need at least one of the numbers to be zero (otherwise, the product cannot be zero) .

Zero Product Property of Real Numbers: If $AB = 0$, then either $A = 0$ or $B = 0$.

In each example below we utilize the zero product property to find all solutions to equations that can be written as products of expressions set equal to zero. This is another important reason for factoring that was introduced in module two. We first use the additive and multiplicative properties of equality to take all the terms to one side of the equation, then factor the expression, and finally obtain solutions by setting each factor equal to zero and solving. Thus you will typically obtain as many solutions as there are factors with variables in them.

Sample Problems that use the Zero Product Property:

Solve the Equations Below.

1. $x(x + 5) = 0$

   We use the zero-product property to get

   $x = 0$ or $x + 5 = 0$

   $x = 0$ or $x + 5 - 5 = 0 - 5$

   Thus the solutions are $x = 0$, or $x = -5$.

2. $(3x - 5)(2x + 3) = 0$

   $3x - 5 = 0$ or $2x + 3 = 0$

   $3x = 5$ or $2x = -3$

   Thus the solutions are $x = \frac{5}{3}$, or $x = -\frac{3}{2}$.

3. $2\,x^2 + 3\,x - 5 = 0$
   We start by factoring the trinomial since it is already set equal to zero.

   $$2\,x^2 + 3\,x - 5 = 2\,x^2 + 5x - 2x - 5 = x(2x+5) - 1(2x+5) = (x-1)(2x+5)$$

   We have $(x-1)(2x+5) = 0$ or
   $x - 1 = 0$, or $2x + 5 = 0$
   $x = 1$, or $2x = -5$
   Thus the solutions are $x = 1$, or $x = -\dfrac{5}{2}$.

4. $4\,x^2 + 15\,x + 9 = 28$
   $4\,x^2 + 15\,x + 9 = 28$
   Can we write $(4x+3)(x+3) = 28$
   So $(4x+3) = 28$, or $(x+3) = 28$. **<u>NO!</u>**
   Infinite pairs of numbers multiply to give you 28
   like 2×14, 4×7, $\dfrac{4}{3} \times 21$, ...So we cannot be
   sure that each of the factors equal 28. We
   cannot be sure to account for all solutions of the
   equation.

   For My Eyes Only
   $4\,x^2 + 15\,x + 9$
   $= 4\,x^2 + 12\,x + 3x + 9$
   $= 4x(x+3) + 3(x+3)$
   $= (4x+3)(x+3)$

   We must have zero on one side of the equation,
   thus subtract 28 to get $4x^2 + 15x - 19 = 0$.
   Factoring we have:
   $$(x-1)(4x+19) = 0$$

   So: $x - 1 = 0$ $\quad or\ 4x + 19 = 0$
   Or $x = 1$ or $x = -\dfrac{19}{4}$.

   For My Eyes Only
   $4\,x^2 + 15\,x - 19$
   $= 4\,x^2 + 19\,x - 4x - 19$
   $= x(4x+19) - (4x+19)$
   $\qquad\qquad = (x-1)(4x+19)$

Note:The zero product property only works with zero on one side!

---

5. $\dfrac{3-x}{7-2x} = \dfrac{3x^2+7}{2x^2-9x+7} + \dfrac{x+1}{x-1}$

Note that $x \neq 1$, and $x \neq \dfrac{7}{2}$ as those numbers would cause division by zero.

Remember, make one fraction on each side with the same denominators so you can compare them by equating the numerators.

See the "For My Eyes Only" column for the factoring work.

$$\dfrac{(3-x)}{-1(2x-7)} = \dfrac{(3x^2+7)}{(2x-7)(x-1)} + \dfrac{(x+1)}{(x-1)}$$

$$\dfrac{(3-x)(-1)(x-1)}{-(2x-7)(-1)(x-1)} = \dfrac{(3x^2+7)}{(2x-7)(x-1)} + \dfrac{(x+1)(2x-7)}{(x-1)(2x-7)}$$

$$\dfrac{-(3-x)(x-1)}{(2x-7)(x-1)} = \dfrac{(3x^2+7)+(x+1)(2x-7)}{(2x-7)(x-1)}$$

$$\dfrac{x^2-4x+3}{(2x-7)(x-1)} = \dfrac{5x^2-5x}{(2x-7)(x-1)}$$

$0 = 4x^2 - x - 3$
$0 = (4x + 3)(x - 1)$
$4x + 3 = 0$ or $x - 1 = 0$
$4x = -3$ or $x = 1$
$x = -\dfrac{3}{4}$ or $x = 1$

Note that $x = 1$ is an extraneous solution since we knew from the outset that $x \neq 1$ and $x \neq \dfrac{7}{2}$.

Thus the solution is $x = -\dfrac{3}{4}$.

6. $3x^3 - 2x^2 - 5x = 0$

We factor and use the zero product property to get:

$x(3x^2 - 2x - 5) = 0$

Factoring further: $x(3x^2 - 5x + 3x - 5)$
$\qquad\qquad = x\big(x(3x - 5) + (3x - 5)\big)$
$\qquad\qquad = x(3x - 5)(x + 1) = 0$
$\qquad\qquad\qquad x = 0,$ or $3x - 5 = 0,$ or $x + 1 = 0$

Thus the solutions are $x = 0, x = \dfrac{5}{3},$ and $x = -1$.

Playing

What if the quadratic equation when set to zero does not factor, like $x^2 + 4x - 2 = 0$? We will later see how to handle these and in general how to solve any quadratic equation of the type $ax^2 + bx + c = 0$ for the variable x. We will draw upon our knowledge from module 2.

Tips to solve Equations and Inequalities

If you remember what undoes what operations, you can solve many kinds of equations. To solve an inequality you have at least a couple of methods to choose from. In the first method, you can solve it exactly like an equation keeping in mind that when you multiply or divide by a negative number, the direction of the inequality is reversed. A second method is to locate all the values of the variable where the two sides are equal or where either side is undefined or makes an abrupt change. In this course with polynomial and rational and absolute value inequalities, this amounts to locating x-values where the two sides are equal or where any denominator factor is zero. These x-values are called critical numbers. When plotted on a number line, they separate the real number line into intervals. On each interval between these points, the left side is either greater or less than the right side. To see which intervals make the original inequality true, we simply choose one test point from each interval and see if it makes the original inequality a true statement. If it does, that interval of points is included in the solution set. These words may make it seem like a complicated process but a few examples will show that it is easy to implement. The endpoint values of each interval will individually need to be checked to see whether they are included or are not part of the solution.

Examples using the critical number method for solving inequalities

1. Solve $x^2 - x > 6$.

First solve the equation $x^2 - x = 6$. Bring all terms to one side, and factor leading to $x^2 - x - 6 = 0$, or $(x - 3)(x + 2) = 0$.

The original inequality is equivalent to $(x - 3)(x + 2) > 0$.

The corresponding equation is true only at $x = 3$ and $x = -2$. Since our inequality is strictly greater than, the numbers $x = 3$ and $x = -2$ are not solutions to the given inequality. The critical numbers $x = 3$ and $x = -2$ separate the number line into three intervals. What is amazing to note is that for all numbers smaller than -2, the factors $x - 3$ and $x + 2$ will always be negative real numbers making their product positive. Similarly for all numbers greater than 3, both factors $x - 3$ and $x + 2$ are always positive real numbers making their product positive. That means for all real numbers less than -2, and the numbers greater than 3 we have $(x - 3)(x + 2) = x^2 - x - 6 > 0$ (or $x^2 - x > 6$). Another way to look at this process is to note that the factors $x - 3$ and $x + 2$ only switch sign at one of the critical numbers. Between critical numbers each factor stays either positive or negative. Since none of the factors switch sign in the interval between critical numbers, their product or quotient doesn't either, and if the inequality is true at any point in these intervals, it must be true for the whole interval. That is the reason why checking the validity of our inequality using a test point from each interval is enough.

So, plot the critical numbers $x = 3$ and $x = -2$ on a number line and we have three intervals to check: $(-\infty, -2), (-2, 3)$ and $(3, \infty)$. For test points we can substitute $x = -3$, $x = 0$, and $x = 4$ into the original inequality and check if the inequality is true as shown below.

Test Points	−3	0	4
Check	$(-3)^2 - (-3)$ $= 9 + 3 = 12 > 6$ which is True	$(0)^2 - (0)$ $= 0 > 6$ which is **False**	$(4)^2 - (4)$ $= 16 - 4 = 12 > 6$ which is True

The complete solution set is $(-\infty, -2) \cup (3, \infty)$.

Equations	Inequalities

2. $\dfrac{u-7}{u+1} + 1 = \dfrac{u+1}{u+4}$

2. $\dfrac{u-7}{u+1} + 1 \geq \dfrac{u+1}{u+4}$

We start by converting all terms to the LCD: $(u+1)(u+4)$. Note: x can't be -1 or -4.

$\dfrac{(u-7)(u+4)}{(u+1)(u+4)} + \dfrac{1((u+1)(u+4))}{(u+1)(u+4)}$

$= \dfrac{(u+1)(u+1)}{(u+4)(u+1)}$

Expanding the tops:

$\dfrac{(u^2 - 3u - 28) + (u^2 + 5u + 4)}{(u+1)(u+4)}$

$= \dfrac{(u^2 + 2u + 1)}{(u+4)(u+1)}$

Combine like terms and equate the tops.
$2u^2 + 2u - 24 = u^2 + 2u + 1$

Take to one side and factor:
$u^2 - 25 = 0$
$(u-5)(u+5) = 0$
And the solutions are $u = 5$ and

$u = -5$

We start by solving the equation as on the left to obtain that $x = 5$ and $x = -5$ are critical numbers. Note that both sides are equal at these x-values and hence these numbers are included in the solution intervals. The other critical numbers are when we have division by zero. Thus $x = -1$ and $x = -4$ are also critical numbers. These four critical numbers separate the real line into five intervals. We check each using test points as below in the original inequality.

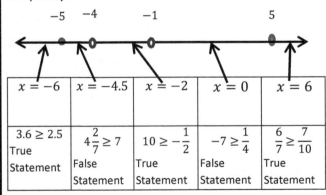

	$x = -6$	$x = -4.5$	$x = -2$	$x = 0$	$x = 6$
	$3.6 \geq 2.5$ True Statement	$4\frac{2}{7} \geq 7$ False Statement	$10 \geq -\frac{1}{2}$ True Statement	$-7 \geq \frac{1}{4}$ False Statement	$\frac{6}{7} \geq \frac{7}{10}$ True Statement

Solution: Algebraic:

$x \leq -5$ or $-4 < x < -1$ or $x \geq 5$
Interval Notation: $(-\infty, -5] \cup (-4, -1) \cup [5, \infty)$
Graphically:

Video Log 3.3a

1. Solve the equations and inequalities below:

Equations	Inequalities
a. $x^2 - 7x + 12 = 0$	g. $x^2 - 7x + 12 < 0$
b. $x^2 + 3x = 10$	h. $x^2 + 3x > 10$
c. $2x^2 + x - 6 = 0$	i. $2x^2 + x - 6 \geq 0$
d. $(3x + 1)(x - 2) = x^2 - 4x + 4$	j. $(3x + 1)(x - 2) \leq x^2 - 4x + 4$
e. $x^3 - 9x^2 + 20x = 0$	k. $x^3 - 9x^2 + 20x = 0$
f. $\dfrac{4}{x+2} + 1 = \dfrac{2}{x-1}$	l. $\dfrac{4}{x+2} + 1 \leq \dfrac{2}{x-1}$

Explain in your own words the similarities and dissimilarities between problems a & g, b & h, c & i, d & j, e & k, and f & l.

m. $\dfrac{5}{x^2-7x+6} = 3 + \dfrac{1}{x-6}$

n. $-\dfrac{3t}{t-2} = \dfrac{12}{t^2-6t+8}$

2. Below are some equations students have solved. Please read them carefully to see if their work is correct or incorrect. If incorrect, please explain what property or mathematical principles are misapplied and at what step and then find the solution.

   a. $x^2 - 25 = 7$

   $(x - 5)(x + 5) = 7$

   $x - 5 = 7 \ or \ x + 5 = 7$

   $x = 12 \ or \ x = 2.$

b. $\frac{3}{x-2} - \frac{5}{x+2} = 5$

$$\frac{3}{x-2} - \frac{5}{x+2} = 5 \quad (mult\ by\ (x-2)(x+2))$$

$$3x + 6 - 5x - 2 = 5x^2 - 20$$

$$5x^2 + 2x - 24 = 0$$

$$(x-2)(5x+12) = 0$$

$$x = 2\ or\ x = -\frac{12}{5}.$$

3.4 Radical and Power Equations
Lectures

⌨ Radical equations (9 min)

http://www.youtube.com/watch?v=qibBpu5vixk

We start with radical and power equations in which the variable appears within a radical or within an expression raised to a power. These will be of the type:

$$\sqrt[n]{expression} = (\# \ or \ expression) \qquad or \qquad (expression)^n = \#$$

We undo the radical as before, by raising both sides to the n power and undo the $n \ th$ power by taking the nth root of both sides.

Recall that raising both sides of an equation to an even power can introduce extra or extraneous solutions. If in the original equation the two sides are of the same size but of opposite sign for some x-value, that x-value will be a solution of the squared equation, but not of the original! **Thus we need to check for extraneous solutions when raising both sides to even powers.**

Also remember that when undoing an even power by taking even roots of both sides, there are always the positive and negative real even roots of a positive real number. So taking even roots leads to two equations to solve.

The examples below demonstrate these techniques and conditions.

Find all the real solutions to the following equations.

Radical Equations	Power Equations
1. $\sqrt{x} = 4$	2. $x^2 = 4$
Remember that in order for this equation to make sense, the restriction is that the quantity under the square root has to be non-negative, thus $x \geq 0$.	This example is similar to radical equation example number one, except here we will be undoing a square by taking square roots.
Remember that squares undo square roots, but when we raise both sides to an even power we need to check for extraneous solutions. $\left(\sqrt{x}\right)^2 = (4)^2$ $x = 16$ Checking: $\sqrt{16} = 4$✔ Solution: $x = 16$	Taking the square root of both sides and accounting for the even root: $\sqrt{x^2} = \pm\sqrt{4}$ or that $x = \pm\,2$ Checking:$(2)^2 = 4$✔ $and \ (-2)^2 = 4$✔ Solutions: $x = 2, \ or \ x = -2$

3. $\sqrt{x+3} = 4$

   Remember that in order for this equation to make sense, the restriction is that the quantity under the square root has to be non-negative or $x + 3 \geq 0$, or that $x \geq -3$.

   Again, check for extraneous solutions.

   $$\left(\sqrt{x+3}\right)^2 = (4)^2$$
   $$x + 3 = 16$$
   $$x = 16 - 3$$
   $$x = 13$$

   Checking: $\sqrt{13+3} = \sqrt{16} = 4$ ✓

   Solution: $x = 13$

4. $(x+3)^2 = 4$

   Similar to the above example we take the square root of both sides and get

   $$x + 3 = \pm\sqrt{4}$$
   $$x + 3 = \sqrt{4} \text{ or } x + 3 = -\sqrt{4}$$
   $$x = 2 - 3 \text{ or } x = -2 - 3$$
   $$x = -1 \text{ or } x = -5$$

   Checking: $(-1+3)^2 = 2^2 = 4$ ✓
   and $\quad\quad (-5+3)^2 = (-2)^2 = 4$ ✓

   Solutions: $x = -1$ or $x = -5$

5. $\quad \sqrt{1-2x} = -3$

   Remember that in order for this equation to make sense, the restriction is that the quantity under the square root has to be non-negative or that $1 - 2x \geq 0$, or $-2x \geq -1$ or $x \leq \frac{1}{2}$ (remember that dividing by a negative number necessitates changing the direction of the inequality sign).

   Note: Remember when we square both sides we need to check for extraneous solutions!

   $$\left(\sqrt{1-2x}\right)^2 = (-3)^2$$
   $$1 - 2x = 9$$
   $$-2x = 8 \text{ or } x = -4$$

   Checking: $\sqrt{1 - 2(-4)} = \sqrt{1+8} = \sqrt{9} = 3 \neq -3$, so

   Solution: **No solution.** Notice that $x = -4$ made the left side of the original equation equal to 3 and the right side equal to -3. This is obviously false, but became true when both sides were squared!

6. $\sqrt{5 - 3x} = 4$

   The restriction is that the quantity under the square root has to be non-negative or $5 - 3x \geq 0$, or that $-3x \geq -5$, or $x \leq \frac{5}{3}$.

   Remember squares undo square roots, but remember to check for extraneous solutions.

   $\left(\sqrt{5 - 3x}\right)^2 = (4)^2$

   $5 - 3x = 16 \text{ or } -3x = 16 - 5 \text{ or } -3x = 11$

   $x = -\frac{11}{3}$

   Checking:

   $$\sqrt{5 - 3 \times \left(-\frac{11}{3}\right)} = \sqrt{5 + 11} = \sqrt{16} = 4 = 4 \checkmark$$

   Solution: $x = -\frac{11}{3}$

7. $(1 - 2x)^2 = 3$

   "Undoing the square" means using square roots on both sides, keeping in mind the even root property.

   $1 - 2x = \pm\sqrt{3}$ so: $-2x = \sqrt{3} - 1 \text{ or } -2x = -\sqrt{3} - 1$

   $2x = -\sqrt{3} + 1 \text{ or } 2x = \sqrt{3} + 1$

   Solution: $x = -\frac{\sqrt{3}}{2} + \frac{1}{2}$, or $x = \frac{\sqrt{3}}{2} + \frac{1}{2}$

   Check: Please make sure you check your solutions.

8. $\sqrt{x} + 2 = 4$

   Remember that the quantity under the square root has to be non-negative or that $x \geq 0$. Remember that squares undo square roots, but we need to isolate the radical first. We first subtract the 2 from both sides before squaring, otherwise we would have to multiply the binomials $(\sqrt{x} + 2)(\sqrt{x} + 2)$ on the left which would expand to $x + 4\sqrt{x} + 4$. Note that this does not eliminate the radical. Thus we need to isolate radicals before raising both sides to the power equal to the radical index. Subtracting the 2, we can work with $\sqrt{x} = 4 - 2$ or $\sqrt{x} = 2$. Again, remember to check if you got any extraneous solutions.

   $\left(\sqrt{x}\right)^2 = (2)^2$

   $x = 4$

   Checking: $\sqrt{4} + 2 = 2 + 2 = 4 = 4 \checkmark$

   Solution: $x = 4$

9. $\sqrt{x+2} - x = -4$

Remember that the quantity under the square root has to be non-negative or that $x + 2 \geq 0$, or $x \geq -2$.

Remember that squares undo square roots, but we isolate the radical first. Add the x to the both sides before squaring. If we left the left side as is, squaring leads to $(\sqrt{x+2} - x)(\sqrt{x+2} - x)$ and we would still have a radical there after expanding this. Instead, we can work with $\sqrt{x+2} = x - 4$. When we square both sides, remember to check for extraneous solutions.

$$\left(\sqrt{x+2}\right)^2 = (x-4)^2$$

Remember that

$(x-4)^2 = (x-4)(x-4) = x^2 - 4x - 4x + 16 = x^2 - 8x + 16$

$x + 2 = x^2 - 8x + 16$

$0 = x^2 - 8x - x + 16 - 2$

$0 = x^2 - 9x + 14$

$0 = (x-7)(x-2)$

$x - 7 = 0$ or $x - 2 = 0$

$x = 7$ or $x = 2$

Checking

$x = 7$	$\sqrt{7+2} - 7 = \sqrt{9} - 7 = 3 - 7 = -4$ which is equal to the right side -4. ✔
$x = 2$	$\sqrt{2+2} - 2 = \sqrt{4} - 2 = 2 - 2 = 0 \neq -4$ Thus $x = 2$ is an extraneous solution

Solution: $x = 7$

10. $\sqrt{x+4} - \sqrt{2x+1} = -1$

Remember that the quantities under both square roots have to be non-negative, i.e., $x + 4 \geq 0$, and $2x + 1 \geq 0$; or $x \geq -4$ and $2x \geq -1$; or $x \geq -4$ and $x \geq -\frac{1}{2}$. The restriction therefore is that $x \geq -\frac{1}{2}$.

In this example with two radical terms, we first have to isolate one of the radicals before squaring to eliminate it. Thus we start by adding $\sqrt{2x+1}$ to each side.

$\sqrt{x+4} = \sqrt{2x+1} - 4$

Now square both sides to eliminate the radical on the left. Be <u>careful</u> when squaring the right side and note the possibility of extraneous roots!

$\left(\sqrt{x+4}\right)^2 = \left(\sqrt{2x+1} - 1\right)^2$

$x + 4 = 2x + 2 - 2\sqrt{2x+1}$

Use the same process over again and square both sides one more time after isolating the square root term on the right side.

$x - 2x + 4 - 2 = -2\sqrt{2x+1}$

Or $\quad -x + 2 = -2\sqrt{2x+1}$

For My Eyes Only

Use the distributive property of multiplication over subtraction to simplify the right hand side

$\left(\sqrt{2x+1} - 1\right)\left(\sqrt{2x+1} - 1\right)$

$= \left(\sqrt{2x+1}\right)^2 - \sqrt{2x+1} - \sqrt{2x+1} + 1$

$= 2x + 1 - 2\sqrt{2x+1} + 1$

$= 2x + 2 - 2\sqrt{2x+1}$

It is a bit nicer if we multiply both sides by -1.

$x - 2 = 2\sqrt{2x+1}$

Squaring both sides we get

$(x-2)^2 = \left(2\sqrt{2x+1}\right)^2$

$(x-2)(x-2) = (2)^2\left(\sqrt{2x+1}\right)^2$

$x^2 - 2x - 2x + 4 = 4(2x+1)$

$x^2 - 4x + 4 = 8x + 4$

$x^2 - 4x - 8x + 4 - 4 = 8x - 8x + 4 - 4$

$x^2 - 12x = 0 \quad$ or $\quad x(x-12) = 0$

$x = 0$, or $x - 12 = 0$, So the tentative solutions are $x = 0$, or $x = 12$

Checking: Checking these in the original equation $\sqrt{x+4} - \sqrt{2x+1} = -1$ we have:

$x = 12,$ | $\sqrt{12+4} - \sqrt{2(12)+1} = \sqrt{16} - \sqrt{25} = 4 - 5 = -1$
and the equation is true! $x = 12$ is a solution! ✔

$x = 0$ | $\sqrt{0+4} - \sqrt{2(0)+1} = \sqrt{4} - \sqrt{1} = 2 - 1 = 1 \neq -1$
$x = 0$ is an extraneous solution.

Thus the only solution to $\sqrt{x+4} - \sqrt{2x+1} = -1$ is $x = 12$.

11. $\sqrt{3x-5} - \sqrt{x+7} = 2$

Again, since we have two radical terms, we will first isolate one of them, square both sides, and then isolate the remaining radical term. Then square both sides again.

$\sqrt{3x-5} = \sqrt{x+7} + 2$, now squaring

$(\sqrt{3x-5})^2 = (\sqrt{x+7} + 2)(\sqrt{x+7} + 2)$

$3x - 5 = (\sqrt{x+7})^2 + 2\sqrt{x+7} + 2\sqrt{x+7} + 4$

$3x - 5 = (x+7) + 4\sqrt{x+7} + 4$

now isolating the $\sqrt{x+7}$

we obtain: $3x - 5 - x - 11 = 4\sqrt{x+7}$

$2x - 16 = 4\sqrt{x+7}$

We could square again now, but it is worth noting that we can divide both sides by 2 to simplify this a bit first. We then have

$(x-8) = 2\sqrt{x+7}$

$(x-8)^2 = 4(x+7)$

$x^2 - 16x + 64 = 4x + 28$

$x^2 - 20x + 36 = 0$

$(x-2)(x-18) = 0$

$x = 2 \ or \ x = 18$

We check both in the original equation $\sqrt{3x-5} - \sqrt{x+7} = 2$ since we could have extraneous answers from squaring both sides.

For My Eyes Only

$x^2 - 20x + 36$

$36x^2$

$x^2 - 2x - 18x + 36$

$= x(x-2) - 18(x-2)$

$= (x-18)(x-2)$

Checking: $x = 2$ ~~$x = 2$~~

$\sqrt{3(2)-5} - \sqrt{2+7} = \sqrt{6-5} - \sqrt{9} = 1 - 3 = -2 \neq 2,$

so $x = 2$ is an extraneous solution.

Solution: $x = 18$

$\sqrt{3(18)-5} - \sqrt{18+7} = \sqrt{54-5} - \sqrt{25} = \sqrt{49} - 5 = 7 - 5 = 2$

which is equal to the right side and thus ✔

$x = 18$ is the only solution to this problem.

1. Solve the following equations and check your solutions. If there are any extraneous solutions, please state so.

Radical Equations	Power Equations
a. $\sqrt{x} = 5$	l. $x^2 = 25$
b. $\sqrt{x} - 4 = 5$	m. $x^2 - 4 = 5$
c. $\sqrt{3x} = 5$	n. $9x^2 = 25$
d. $\sqrt{x-1} = 5$	o. $(x-1)^2 = 25$
e. $\sqrt{1-x} = 5$	p. $(1-x)^2 = 25$
f. $\sqrt{3x+1} = 5$	q. $(3x+1)^2 = 25$
g. $\sqrt{3x+1} - 1 = 4$	r. $(3x+1)^2 - 1 = 23$
h. $\sqrt[3]{2x} = 3$	s. $(2x)^3 = 27$
i. $\sqrt[3]{2x-1} = 3$	t. $(2x-1)^3 = 27$
j. $\sqrt[4]{4-x} = 3$	u. $(4-x)^4 = 81$
k. $\sqrt[3]{2+3x} = -1$	v. $(2+3x)^3 = -1$

Explain the similarities and differences between solving the two different kinds of equations in the problem above listed here a & l, b & m, c & n, d & o, e & p, f & q, g & r, h & s, l & t, j & u, and k & v.

2. Solve the following equations and check your solutions. If there are any extraneous solutions, please state so.

a. $\sqrt{3-x} = \sqrt{1+11x}$

b. $\sqrt{2+x} = \sqrt{3-x} + 1$

c. $\sqrt[5]{2x+1} = 2$

d. $\sqrt{t-2} = t - 8$

e. $\sqrt{3t-2} = t - 2$

f. $\sqrt{6-t} = \sqrt{2t+5}$

g. $\sqrt{x} - 4 = 5$

h. $x^3 = 15$

i. $(2x-7)^2 = 25$

j. $(1-x)^3 = 8$

k. $(11+3x)^2 = 5$

l. $(4+11x)^5 = 2$

m. $\frac{2}{3}x^2 = 5$

n. $2x^4 = 32$

3. Below are some equations students have solved. Please read them carefully to see if their work is correct or incorrect. If incorrect, please explain what property or mathematical principles are misapplied and at what step and then find the solution.

a. $\sqrt{3x - 3} = x + 5$

$$3x - 3 = x^2 + 25$$

$$x^2 - 3x + 28 = 0$$

$$(x - 7)(x + 4) = 0$$

$$x = 7 \ or \ x = -4.$$

b. $x^5 = 64$

$$x = \pm\sqrt[5]{64} = \pm\sqrt[5]{2^6} = \pm2\sqrt[5]{2}$$

c. $\sqrt[3]{x + 3} + 2 = 5$

$$x + 3 + 8 = 125$$

$$x = 114.$$

3.5 Quadratic Equations

Lectures

🖥 Quadratic Equations (15 min)

https://www.youtube.com/watch?v=29_SBzxChMw

Playing

We have seen how to solve quadratic equations that can be factored. We will next look at a series of examples (some of which don't factor) that we have been able to solve using square roots. We will look carefully at what makes these solvable and build from there.

Examples: Solving Quadratic Equations using the square root operation.

Find all solutions of the following quadratic equations.

Equations With Real Zeros	Equations with Complex Zeros
1. $x^2 = 4$ Square roots undo squares (remember even root property) $x = \pm\sqrt{4}$ $x = 2$, or $x = -2$	$x^2 = -4$ Square roots undo squares (remember even root property) $x = \pm\sqrt{-4}$ (recall $\sqrt{-1} = i$) $x = 2i$, or $x = -2i$
2. $x^2 = 5$ Square roots undo squares (remember even root property) $x = \pm\sqrt{5}$ $x = \sqrt{5}$, or $x = -\sqrt{5}$	$x^2 = -5$ Square roots undo squares (remember even root property) $x = \pm\sqrt{-5}$ $x = \sqrt{5}i$, or $x = -\sqrt{5}i$
3. $(x + 3)^2 = 5$ Square roots undo squares (remember even root property) $x + 3 = \pm\sqrt{5}$ $x = -3 + \sqrt{5}$, or $x = -3 - \sqrt{5}$	$(x + 3)^2 = -5$ Square roots undo squares (remember even root property) $x + 3 = \pm\sqrt{-5}$ $x = -3 + \sqrt{5}i$, or $x = -3 - \sqrt{5}i$
4. $4(x + 3)^2 = 5$ $(x + 3)^2 = \dfrac{5}{4}$ Square roots undo squares (remember even root property) $x + 3 = \pm\sqrt{\dfrac{5}{4}}$ $x = -3 + \dfrac{\sqrt{5}}{2}$, or $x = -3 - \dfrac{\sqrt{5}}{2}$	$4(x + 3)^2 = -5$ $(x + 3)^2 = -\dfrac{5}{4}$ Square roots undo squares (remember even root property) $x + 3 = \pm\sqrt{-\dfrac{5}{4}}$ $x = -3 + \dfrac{\sqrt{5}}{2}i$, or $x = -3 - \dfrac{\sqrt{5}}{2}i$

Completing the Square

In all the previous examples we undid squares by taking square roots. A question we may want to ask then is what makes a quadratic polynomial a perfect square. Also, can we modify any quadratic polynomial so it becomes a perfect square?

Examples: *(Assume all variables take on positive real values to make sense of the polynomials as areas of the rectangles shown)*

1. $x^2 + 6x$

   You can visualize the polynomial above as shown in figure 1 below. In order to change the rectangle into a perfect square using the pieces we have, we will have to move some of the 1 by x rectangular pieces to see what is needed for this polynomial to be part of a perfect square. Since x^2 already is a square, it would make sense to move the 1 by x rectangles. Since a square has the same length and width, it would make sense to take half of the 6 rectangles, turn them and put them under the blue square which would look as in figure 2. You can see that a corner square is missing. To complete the square then we need to add nine 1 by 1 squares as seen in figure 3. This process of adding 9 squares to the existing quadratic polynomial is called completing the square.

   $x^2 + 6x +$ ___ $= (x+?)^2$, we can see the process is to add $\left(\frac{6}{2}\right)^2 = 3^2 = 9$

   $x^2 + 6x + \left(\frac{6}{2}\right)^2 = x^2 + 6x + 9 = (x+3)^2$

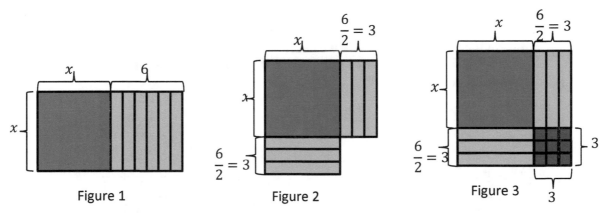

| Figure 1 | Figure 2 | Figure 3 |

   From the above diagram, we see that the 9 red squares needed to complete the square are obtained by taking half of the number of x pieces and squaring that, i.e., $\left(\frac{6}{2}\right)^2 = 9$.

2. $x^2 - 10x$

   $x^2 - 10x + \left(-\frac{10}{2}\right)^2 = x^2 - 10x + 25 = (x-5)^2$

3. $x^2 + 5x$

   $x^2 + 5x + \left(\frac{5}{2}\right)^2 = x^2 + 5x + \frac{25}{4} = \left(x + \frac{5}{2}\right)^2$

We can now use this new completing the square process to help us solve any quadratic equation. We can make all quadratic equations look like the examples 1-3 by making them perfect squares as shown below.

Examples

Find solutions to the quadratic equations below.

Equations With Real Zeros	Equations with Complex Zeros
1. $x^2 + 6x - 14 = 0$ We start by keeping just the x^2 and x terms on one side. $x^2 + 6x = 14$ Now, to complete the square on the left hand side we have to add $\left(\frac{6}{2}\right)^2 = 9$ to both sides giving us $x^2 + 6x + 9 = 14 + 9$ $(x+3)^2 = 23$ $x + 3 = \pm\sqrt{23}$ $x = -3 + \sqrt{23}, \text{ or } x = 3 - \sqrt{23}$ Solving an equation in this manner is called solving the equation using the completing the square method.	$x^2 + 6x + 14 = 0$ We get just the variable terms on one side. $$x^2 + 6x = -14$$ and then to complete the square on the left hand side we have to add $\left(\frac{6}{2}\right)^2 = 9$ to both sides giving us $$x^2 + 6x + 9 = -14 + 9$$ $$(x+3)^2 = -5$$ $$x + 3 = \pm\sqrt{-5}$$ $$x = -3 + \sqrt{5}i, \text{ or } x = -3 - \sqrt{5}i$$
2. $2x^2 - 10x - 10 = 0$ Completing the squares is easiest with the coefficient of the x^2 as 1. Rewriting the equation so that the coefficient of the square term is 1 and the constant term is on the right hand side we get $2x^2 - 10x = 10$ (divide both sides by 2) $x^2 - 5x = 5$ $$x^2 - 5x + \left(-\frac{5}{2}\right)^2 = 5 + \left(-\frac{5}{2}\right)^2$$ $$\left(x - \frac{5}{2}\right)^2 = 5 + \frac{25}{4}$$ $$x - \frac{5}{2} = \pm\sqrt{\frac{20}{4} + \frac{25}{4}}$$ $$x = \frac{5}{2} \pm \sqrt{\frac{45}{4}}$$ $$x = \frac{5}{2} \pm \frac{\sqrt{45}}{\sqrt{4}}$$ $$x = \frac{5}{2} \pm \frac{3\sqrt{5}}{2}$$ $$x = \frac{5}{2} + \frac{3\sqrt{5}}{2} \text{ or } x = \frac{5}{2} - \frac{3\sqrt{5}}{2}$$	$2x^2 - 10x + 15 = 0$ Rewriting the equation so that the coefficient of the square term is 1 and the constant term is on the right hand side we get $2x^2 - 10x = -15$ (divide both sides by 2) $$x^2 - 5x = -\frac{15}{2}$$ $$x^2 - 5x + \left(-\frac{5}{2}\right)^2 = -\frac{15}{2} + \left(-\frac{5}{2}\right)^2$$ $$\left(x - \frac{5}{2}\right)^2 = -\frac{15}{2} + \frac{25}{4}$$ $$x - \frac{5}{2} = \pm\sqrt{\frac{-30}{4} + \frac{25}{4}}$$ $$x = \frac{5}{2} \pm \sqrt{\frac{-5}{4}}$$ $$x = \frac{5}{2} \pm \frac{\sqrt{5}}{\sqrt{4}}i$$ $$x = \frac{5}{2} \pm \frac{\sqrt{5}}{2}i$$ $$x = \frac{5}{2} + \frac{\sqrt{5}}{2}i \text{ or } x = \frac{5}{2} - \frac{\sqrt{5}}{2}i$$

Quadratic Formula

Using the method of completing the square, we can solve any quadratic equation. Since the problem of solving quadratic equations comes up frequently and to save us some time later, we will generalize the completing the squares process to a generic quadratic equation $ax^2 + bx + c = 0$ to arrive at the "Quadratic Formula." We recommend knowing the process of completing the square as well as memorization of the quadratic formula. Sometimes completing the square is simpler.

A generic quadratic equation can be written as $ax^2 + bx + c = 0$, where $a \neq 0, and\ b$, and c are any real numbers. Applying the completing the square process we get

$ax^2 + bx + c = 0$

$ax^2 + bx = -c$ *(Get the variable terms alone on one side.)*

$x^2 + \dfrac{b}{a}x = -\dfrac{c}{a}$ *(Make the x^2 term have coefficient of 1.)*

$x^2 + \dfrac{b}{a}x + \left(\dfrac{b}{2a}\right)^2 = -\dfrac{c}{a} + \left(\dfrac{b}{2a}\right)^2$ *(Make the left side a perfect square by adding the square of half of the x-coefficient.)*

$\left(x + \dfrac{b}{2a}\right)^2 = -\dfrac{c}{a} + \dfrac{b^2}{4a^2}$

$\left(x + \dfrac{b}{2a}\right)^2 = -\dfrac{4a(c)}{4a(a)} + \dfrac{b^2}{4a^2}$ *(Get a common denominator on the right.)*

$\left(x + \dfrac{b}{2a}\right)^2 = \dfrac{-4ac + b^2}{4a^2}$

$x + \dfrac{b}{2a} = \pm\sqrt{\dfrac{b^2 - 4ac}{4a^2}}$ *(Take square root of both sides.)*

$x = -\dfrac{b}{2a} \pm \dfrac{\sqrt{b^2 - 4ac}}{\sqrt{4a^2}}$ *(Simplify the radical and combine the two terms.)*

Quadratic Formula: The solution set to the quadratic equation $ax^2 + bx + c = 0, a \neq 0$ and is given by

$$x = -\dfrac{b}{2a} \pm \dfrac{\sqrt{b^2-4ac}}{2a} = \dfrac{-b \pm \sqrt{b^2-4ac}}{2a}.$$

Note: *This means that the solutions to the quadratic equation $ax^2 + bx + c = 0$ are given by*

$$x = \dfrac{-b+\sqrt{b^2-4ac}}{2a}, \text{ or } x = \dfrac{-b-\sqrt{b^2-4ac}}{2a}.$$

Terminology

The radicand under the square root $b^2 - 4ac$ is called the <u>discriminant</u>.

Note: Depending on the discriminant's value we can identify what kinds of solutions we will get.
In fact:

1. If the discriminant $b^2 - 4ac > 0$, then the quadratic equation has two distinct real solutions.
2. If the discriminant $b^2 - 4ac = 0$, then the quadratic equation has one real solution.
3. If the discriminant $b^2 - 4ac < 0$, then the quadratic equation has two distinct complex solutions.

Examples

Find all solutions to the quadratic equations below.

1. $3x^2 - x + 3 = 0$

   Note that $a = 3, b = -1, c = 3$

   Using the quadratic formula we get

   $$x = \frac{-(-1) \pm \sqrt{(-1)^2 - 4(3)(3)}}{2(3)}$$

   $$x = \frac{1 \pm \sqrt{1 - 36}}{6}$$

   $$x = \frac{1 \pm \sqrt{-35}}{6} = \frac{1 \pm \sqrt{35}i}{6}$$

   $$x = \frac{1}{6} + \frac{\sqrt{35}}{6}i \text{ or } x = \frac{1}{6} - \frac{\sqrt{35}}{6}i$$

   Note that here $b^2 - 4ac < 0$.

2. $4x^2 - 20x + 25 = 0$

   $$x = \frac{-(-20) \pm \sqrt{(-20)^2 - 4(4)(25)}}{2(4)}$$

   $$x = \frac{20 \pm \sqrt{400 - 400}}{8}$$

   $$x = \frac{20 \pm 0}{8} = \frac{20}{8} = \frac{5}{2}$$

   Or by factoring:
   $4x^2 - 20x + 25 = 0$

   $4x^2 - 10x - 10x + 25 = 0$
   $2x(2x - 5) - 2x(2x - 5) = 0$
   $(2x - 5)^2 = 0$
   $2x - 5 = 0$
   $2x = 5 \text{ or } x = \frac{5}{2}$

   Note that here $b^2 - 4ac = (-20)^2 - 4 \cdot 4 \cdot 25 = 0$ and hence only one solution.

3. $4x^2 - x - 5 = 0$

Using the quadratic formula

$$x = \frac{-(-1) \pm \sqrt{(-1)^2 - 4(4)(-5)}}{2(4)} = \frac{1 \pm \sqrt{1 + 80}}{8}$$

$$x = \frac{1 \pm \sqrt{81}}{8} = \frac{1 \pm 9}{8}$$

$$x = \frac{1 + 9}{8} = \frac{10}{8} = \frac{5}{4} \quad or \quad x = \frac{1 - 9}{8} = \frac{-8}{8} = -1$$

Or by factoring:

$4x^2 - x - 5 = 0$

$4x^2 - 5x + 4x - 5 = 0$

$x(4x - 5) + 1(4x - 5) = 0$

$(x + 1)(4x - 5) = 0$

$x + 1 = 0$ or $4x - 5 = 0$

$x = -1$ or $4x = 5$

$x = -1$ or $x = \frac{5}{4}$

Note that here $b^2 - 4ac = (-1)^2 - 4 \cdot 4 \cdot (-5) = 81$ is positive, so two real solutions.

Video Log 3.5a

1. Complete the following squares and rewrite the resulting quadratic in the form $(x + a)^2$ or $(x - a)^2$.

   a. $x^2 + 8x$
   b. $x^2 - 12x$

   c. $x^2 + 18x$
   d. $x^2 - 2x$

2. Find all the solutions to the following quadratic equations.

   a. $3x^2 - 2x + 4 = 0$
   b. $5x^2 - 6x - 7 = 0$
   c. $x^2 - 4x + 3 = 0$
   d. $5x^2 - x + 4 = 0$

   e. $5x^2 - 2x + 7 = 0$
   f. $x^2 - x - 1 = 0$
   g. $9x^2 - 90x = -25$
   h. $2x(x - 4) + 3(x + 1) = 5(2x - 7) + 10$

3. Solve the following equations. If there are any extraneous solutions, please state so.

   a. $\dfrac{2x^2 + 2x - 10}{x^2 - 9} - \dfrac{x-2}{x-3} = \dfrac{-2}{x+3}$

   d. $\dfrac{3x+1}{2x-2} = \dfrac{x-1}{x-3}$

   b. $\dfrac{2x^2 - 5}{x^2 - 4} + \dfrac{6}{x+2} = \dfrac{4x-7}{x-2}$

   e. $\sqrt{x - 4} = x - 10$

   c. $\sqrt{2x^2 - 3x} = 3$

4. Below are some equations students have solved. Please read them carefully to see if their work is correct or incorrect. If incorrect, please explain what property or mathematical principles are misapplied and at what step and then find the solution.

   a. Solve $3x^2 - 5x + 7 = 0$.

   $a = 3, \ b = -5, \ c = 7 ,$

   $x = \dfrac{5 \pm \sqrt{-25 - 4 \cdot 3 \cdot 7}}{6} = \dfrac{5 \pm \sqrt{-109}}{6} = \dfrac{5 \pm i\sqrt{109}}{6} = \dfrac{5}{6} \pm \dfrac{\sqrt{109}}{6} i$

   b. Solve $5x^2 + 6x - 11 = 0$

   $a = 5, \ b = 6, \ c = -11 ,$

   $x = \dfrac{-6 \pm \sqrt{36 - 4 \cdot 5 \cdot (-11)}}{10} = \dfrac{-6 \pm \sqrt{256}}{10} = \dfrac{-3 \pm 16}{5}, \ x = \dfrac{13}{5} \ or \ x = -\dfrac{19}{5}$

Module 4: Applications and Graphing

Introduction

We have studied the many types of algebraic objects and how to manipulate and solve equations with them. In this module we focus on geometric representations and applications of some of the objects you have learned. We will work on understanding the meaning of solving equations and how to use algebra to model real-life scenarios. We also begin to study analytic geometry where algebraic equations and geometrical images provide alternative ways to view or analyze a problem. This is useful in understanding the many graphical displays of data in various fields of study and to understand what kinds of predictions are made from them. A less obvious, but equally important, motivation for our study of algebra is the development of reasoning skills and the ability to work with multistage problems. In our global economy, these skills are necessary to compete successfully.

4.1 Coordinate Plane Geometry

Lecture

💻 Cartesian Coordinate System

http://www.youtube.com/watch?v=QdqdISLovuM   (11 min)

Note that when we were working with real numbers in Module 1 we saw how to represent them on a number line. We saw that on a number line, before we can talk about where all the real numbers are located, we needed to have a reference point. When we pick zero as our reference point, it is called the **origin**. We saw that any real number could serve as our reference point. Once a reference point is selected, we then can visualize the remaining numbers relative to the reference point. On the number line you can move on the line left-right from the reference point (the space is one dimensional). Moving to the left of the reference point referred to as the negative direction, and to the right of the reference point as the positive direction.

We also saw that we can find the distance between any two real numbers by looking at the absolute value of their difference. So for example, the distance between the two real numbers -2 and 8 is given by $|-2 - 8| = |-10| = 10$, or $|8 - (-2)| = |10| = 10$.

Distance

Definition: The **distance** between any two points a and b on a number line is given by $|a - b| = \sqrt{(a - b)^2}$.

Midpoint

Definition: The **midpoint** of the two real numbers a and b is a point located exactly half way between them and is given by $\frac{a+b}{2}$.

Properties of absolute value

1. The distance between any two real numbers is greater than or equal to zero.
2. For any real number a, we have $|a - a| = |0| = 0$.
3. For any two real numbers a and b, we have $|a - b| = |b - a|$.
4. We also have that for any three real numbers a, b, and c,
   $$|a - b| \leq |a - c| + |c - b|$$
   This inequality is referred to as the triangle inequality. It is also clear from the geometry of three points on a line, that the distance from a to b is equal to the distance from a to b plus the distance from b to c exactly when c lies between a and b.

In mathematics, a metric space is a set of objects on which we define a metric or distance between objects. Essentially, the metric is a distance formula that defines how to compute distance between any two given members of the set. The metric must satisfy the 4 properties listed below for this to be a metric space. The field of mathematics that studies metric spaces is called topology.

Properties of a metric:

1. The distance between any two objects a and b must be non-negative.
2. The distance between the object a and a is zero.
3. The distance must be symmetric, which means that the distance between the objects a and b is the same as the distance between b and a.
4. The distance must satisfy the triangle inequality. Thus the distance between objects a and b is less than or equal to the sum of the distance between a and c and the distance between c and b. This means that the distance from object a to object b cannot be made shorter by going to an intermediate point c first. This is much like airline flights. The shortest plane ride from city a to city b would be a direct flight and the total distance will be as long or longer if there are two or more legs to the flight.

The set of real numbers, with the distance from a to b defined as $|b - a|$, forms a metric space.

Playing

In mathematics this structure of real numbers can be extended to higher dimensional spaces. We start at some reference point (which on maps on hiking trails are referred to by little stars and usually represent "you are here") and move left-right and up-down from there. We measure our left-right location (east-west on a map) by placing a real number axis horizontally on the plane and the up down location (north-south) by another perpendicular real number line. These horizontal and vertical lines are called axes and are labeled as the x-axis and y-axis respectively. The point of intersection of the two axes is called the origin or reference point.

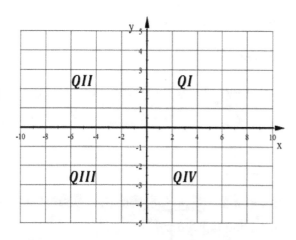

All points in this plane formed by the two perpendicular axes are labeled as (x, y), where the first coordinate tells you how much to move left or right from the origin and the second coordinate tells you how much to move up or down from the origin.

The coordinate axes divide the plane into four quadrants labeled I through IV as shown above.

Each location in the xy-plane has a unique value for its x-location and its y-location. The x-coordinate is sometimes referred to as the abscissa and the y-coordinate as the ordinate. We call these x and y values the coordinates of the point. The convention is that we list coordinates as an ordered pair or tuple with the x-coordinate first, followed with the y-coordinate. This "ordered pair" gives a concise way to describe locations in the plane. Thus the ordered pairs $(1, 2)$, $(-3, 1)$, $(-1, -2)$, $(2, -3)$, and $(0, 1)$ correspond to the points on the x, y-plane to the right.

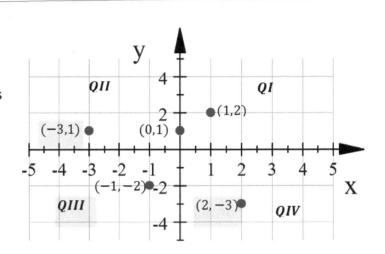

This system is used for a flat infinite plane, but a very similar system is used (in GPS units) to locate points on the surface of the earth using longitude and latitude coordinates to measure the east-west and north-south position. This is not the only way to locate points in a plane. Air traffic controllers often use the control tower as the origin, and then use the direction to the plane (measured in degrees from due north) and the distance between the plane and the tower to describe positions of airplanes in the sky near an airport. This is called a polar coordinate system which are developed more fully in an analytical trigonometry course.

Video Log 4.1a

1. Write the coordinates of each of the following points plotted below.

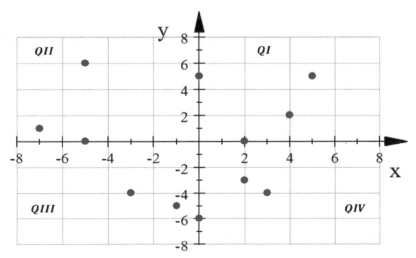

2. Plot each of the following groups of points on a separate rectangular coordinate system. Choose an appropriate scale on your axes for each group.

Group 1 $\quad\quad\quad (-2,1), (3,-1), (3,1), (2,-1), (-7,-7), (-5,-7), (-8,-1), (-7,3)$

Group 2 $\quad\quad (-.5,0.1), (0.3,-0.1), (0.3,1), (0.2,-0.1), (-0.7,-1.7), (-0.5,-1.7), (-0.8,-0.1),$

Group 3 $\quad\quad \left(\frac{2}{3},\frac{1}{4}\right), \left(-\frac{2}{3},\frac{-3}{4}\right), \left(0,\frac{4}{3}\right), \left(-\frac{5}{3},\frac{1}{4}\right), \left(\frac{5}{3},-\frac{1}{3}\right)$

Group 4 $\quad\quad\quad (-20,400), (300,-100), (500,100), (200,-150), (-700,-700),$

Group 5 $\quad\quad\quad (20000,400), (30000,100), (50000,100), (20000,150), (70000,700)$

Midpoint of a line segment and distance between two points in the x, y-plane

Lecture

🖥 Midpoint Formula

http://www.youtube.com/watch?v=kRivyxLD_IM **(3 min)**

Sometimes mathematicians need to work with more than one point and need to distinguish the x-coordinates and the y-coordinates of two or more points. A clever way of labeling uses subscripts on each coordinate to distinguish between point (1), point (2) etc. The first point can be labeled as (x_1, y_1), the second point as (x_2, y_2), the third point as (x_3, y_3), and so on, where x_1 refers to the x-coordinate of the first point, x_2 refers to the x-coordinate of the second point, y_1 refers to the y-coordinate of the first point, y_2 refers to the y-coordinate of the second point, and so on.

Using subscripts, we can work with many different points and still understand the difference between the x-coordinates and the y-coordinates.

Definition: Given two points (x_1, y_1), and (x_2, y_2) in the coordinate plane, the point that lies exactly halfway between them on the line segment connecting these two points is called their midpoint and is given by $\left(\frac{x_1+x_2}{2}, \frac{y_1+y_2}{2}\right)$. Notice this is consistent with the midpoint of the real numbers x_1 and x_2, and the real numbers y_1 and y_2.

The midpoint of the line segment from $(3,5)$ to $(7,3)$ is $\left(\frac{3+7}{2}, \frac{5+3}{2}\right) = (5,4)$. Another way to get to the midpoint is by traveling exactly half-way from one point to the other. To do this we would start at one of the points say (x_1, y_1) and move horizontally half of the x-difference $(x_2 - x_1)$ and then move vertically half of the y-distance $(y_2 - y_1)$. In this way we'd end up at

$$\left(x_1 + \frac{1}{2}(x_2 - x_1), \; y_1 + \frac{1}{2}(y_2 - y_1)\right).$$

If we distribute through, we see that e.g., for x we get: $x_1 + \frac{1}{2}x_2 - \frac{1}{2}x_1 = \frac{1}{2}x_1 + \frac{1}{2}x_2 = \frac{x_1+x_2}{2}$.

This is the same as what we got by thinking of the midpoint as the average of each of the coordinates of the endpoints. See the graph.

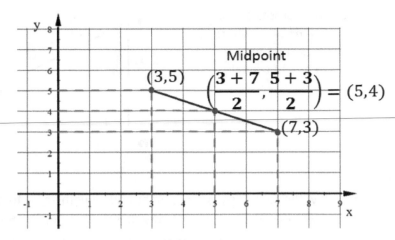

Practice examples

Find the midpoint of the line segment with given endpoints.

1. $(3, 5)$ and $(7, 2)$
2. $(12, 72)$ and $(-45, 37)$

Solutions

1. The midpoint is at $\left(\frac{3+7}{2}, \frac{5+2}{2}\right) = (5, 3.5)$.
2. The midpoint is at $\left(\frac{12-45}{2}, \frac{72+37}{2}\right) = (-16.5, 54.5)$.

Distance between two points in the coordinate plane

Lecture

🖥 Pythagorean Theorem and Distance Formula

http://www.youtube.com/watch?v=KrLZuOhus4U **(10min)**

The shortest distance between any two points in the plane is the length of the line segment between them. In order to compute distances in the plane, we review an ancient result about right triangles called the Pythagorean Theorem.

Pythagorean Theorem: In any right triangle, the square of the length of the hypotenuse is equal to the sum of the squares of the two legs of the triangle.

There are many different proofs of this theorem that says $a^2 + b^2 = c^2$ where $a, b,$ & c are the two legs and the hypotenuse lengths of a right triangle respectively.

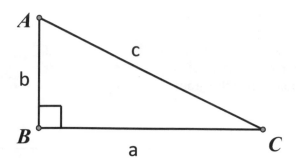

In the first image below the central square region has side length equal to c, the hypotenuse, and hence its area is c^2. We can rearrange the triangles in the first image to make the second image below. The total area remains the same and thus the two squares in the second image must be equal in area to the one large central square in the first. The squares in the second image have areas a^2 and b^2 and hence it is true that $c^2 = a^2 + b^2$.

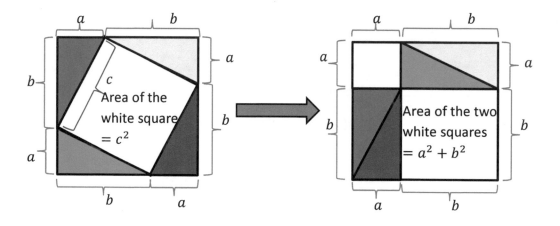

If we are given two points (x_1, y_1) and (x_2, y_2) in the coordinate plane, we can form a right triangle by moving vertically from the first point (x_1, y_1) to a point directly right or left of the second point and then move horizontally to get to the second point. Since the horizontal and vertical movements are in perpendicular directions, they form the legs of a right triangle where the hypotenuse (d) is the direct distance from the start to the end point.

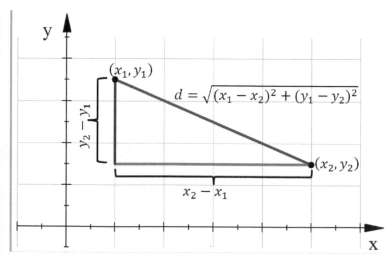

We recommend that when finding distances between points, it is better to think of the triangle relationship between its hypotenuse and its legs rather than simply memorizing the distance formula. It is better to think your way out when stuck on a problem, rather than just remembering a formula. The horizontal movement is the difference between the two x-values, i.e., $(x_2 - x_1)$ and the vertical leg is $(y_2 - y_1)$ and hence $d^2 = (x_2 - x_1)^2 + (y_2 - y_1)^2$ or $d = \sqrt{(x_2 - x_1)^2 + (y_2 - y_1)^2}$ using the Pythagorean Theorem . See the visual representation above.

Practice examples

Find the distance between the given points.

1. $(-3, 1)$ and $(5, 3)$
2. $(3.5, 7.8)$ and $(5.2, -3.4)$

Solutions

1. The x-difference is 8 units and the y-difference is 2 units and thus $d = \sqrt{64 + 4} = \sqrt{68} = \sqrt{4 \times 17} = 2\sqrt{17}$.
2. The x-difference is $5.2 - 3.5 = 1.7$ units and the y-difference is $-3.4 - 7.8 = -11.2$ units and thus $d = \sqrt{1.7^2 + (-11.2)^2} = \sqrt{128.33} =$ the exact distance between the two given points. We can also use a calculator to get the approximate value of $\sqrt{128.33}$ to be about 11.3 .

Video Log 4.1b

Find the distance between and the midpoint of the points below.

1. $(-3.5, 2)$ and $(-6, -20)$

2. $(0, -18)$ and $(-12, 0)$

3. $(4, -7)$ and $(-4, -2)$

4. $(-5, -13)$ and $(-5, 13)$

5. $\left(\frac{5}{2}, \frac{2}{5}\right)$ and $\left(-\frac{6}{5}, -\frac{11}{2}\right)$

Playing

This real plane (or sometimes we refer to it as the coordinate plane) is the set of all points (x, y) where x and y are any real numbers. The real plane along with the distance function as defined above forms a metric space of 2 dimensions. We can extend this definition to higher dimensional spaces.

For example, 3 dimensional space can be written as collection of all points (x, y, z) where x, y, and z are any real numbers. We show how to visualize the point (3,5,2) in the figure to the right. The space is divided into 8 parts called octants. One octant is where all the coordinates are positive. Try to locate the octant where x and y are negative and z is positive. The 3 axes called the x-axis, y-axis, and z-axis are perpendicular lines that intersect at the origin given by the coordinates $(0, 0, 0)$. We can describe locations in our 3-dimensional world using coordinate triples in this manner.

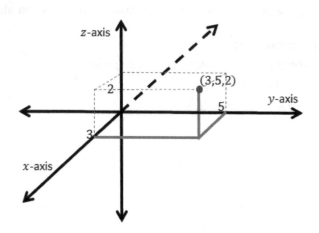

The distance between two points $(x_1, \ y_1, \ z_1)$ and $(x_2, \ y_2, \ z_2)$ is obtained via the Pythagorean Theorem as: $d = \sqrt{(x_2 - x_1)^2 + (y_2 - y_1)^2 + (z_2 - z_1)^2}$. This space also forms a metric space with this distance function.

We can keep on extending this coordinate system to 4 and higher dimensions. In general the collections of all points $(a_1, a_2, a_3, a_4, \dots, a_n)$ where all the entries $a_1, a_2, a_3, a_4, \dots, a_n$ are real numbers is called an n-dimensional space. The distance between two points $(a_1, a_2, a_3, a_4, \dots, a_n)$ and $(b_1, b_2, b_3, b_4, \dots, b_n)$ is given by $= \sqrt{(b_1 - a_1)^2 + (b_2 - a_2)^2 + \dots + (b_n - a_n)^2}$. With this distance function this space also forms a metric space.

4.2 Graphing Solutions to Equations in Two Variables

Lecture

🖥 Plotting solutions to equations in x and y.
   http://www.youtube.com/watch?v=MEs1zAr--bc   (11 min)

When we had an equation or inequality in just one variable we plotted the solution(s) on a number line in Module 3. With equations in two variables x & y, a solution to the equation requires both an x and a y value. Thus we can consider solutions to an equation or inequality in two variables as a point or set of points in and x, y-plane. Usually there are infinitely many ordered pairs (x, y) that make an equation or an inequality in the variables, x and y, true. If we were to plot all the solution points of an equation in two variables in the coordinate plane they usually will form some type of a curve in the plane. If we were to plot all the solution points of an inequality in two variables in the coordinate plane, they form a region bounded by some type of a curve in the plane.

We will investigate equations and inequalities that represent lines, circles, a few other types of curves, and specific regions bounded by these curves. This idea of describing geometric curves with algebraic equations is called **analytic geometry**.

Playing

Let us play with some equations to see what kind of curves we get. Since we do not yet have a sense of how things will look, we start by plotting lots of points that make an equation in x and y true. Then we often see there is a pattern to the points along or on some side of a curve in the plane.

Examples
Determine if the points below are solutions to the given equations or inequalities.
1. Let $y = x - 1$. Are the points $(-2,1)$, $(2,1)$, $(-5,0)$, and $(0,-1)$ solutions to this equation?
2. Let $y > 2x - 1$. Are the points $(-2,1)$, $(2,3)$, $(-5,0)$, and $(4,-1)$ solutions to this inequality?

Solutions

1. Are the points $(-2,1)$, $(2,1)$, $(-5,0)$, and $(0,-1)$ solutions of the equation $y = x - 1$?
    $(-2, 1)$ is not a solution since when $x = -2$, the right side is $(-2) - 1 = -3$ while the left side is $y = 1$. Since $1 \neq -3$, the equation is false at $(x, y) = (-2,1)$.

    $(2, 1)$ is a solution, since when $x = 2$, the right side is $(2) - 1 = 1$ which is equal to the left side $y = 1$. Thus the point $(2, 1)$ is a solution of the equation $y = x - 1$.

    $(-5,0)$ is not a solution, since when $x = -5$, the right side is $(-5) - 1 = -6$ and this is not equal to the left side $y = 0$.

    $(0,-1)$ is a solution, since when $x = 0$, the right side is $(0) - 1 = -1$ and this is equal to the left side $y = -1$.

2. Are the points $(-2,1), (2,3), (-5,0),$ and $(4,-1)$ solutions of the inequality $y > 2x - 1$?

$(-2,1)$ is a solution, since when $x = -2$, the right side is $2(-2) - 1 = -4 - 1 = -5$ which is smaller than the left side of $y = 1$ thus making the inequality a true statement.

$(2,3)$ is not a solution, since when $x = 2$, the right side is $2(2) - 1 = 3$ and this is not smaller than the left side of $y = 3$.

$(-5,0)$ is a solution, since when $x = -5$, the right side is $2(-5) - 1 = -10 - 1 = -11$ and the left side $y = 0$ is greater than -11.

$(4,-1)$ is not a solution, since when $x = 4$, the right side is $2(4) - 1 = 8 - 1 = 7$ and this is not less than the left side value of $y = -1$.

Additional examples

1. *Determine the missing coordinates below if you wanted these points to be solutions to the equation* $y = 1 - 2x$.
   a. $(2, ?)$ b. $(?, -1)$ c. $(0, ?)$ d. $(?, 0)$ e. $(-5, ?)$

2. Determine the missing coordinates below if you wanted these points to be solutions to the inequality $y > 1 - 2x$.
   a. $(2, ?)$ b. $(?, -1)$ c. $(0, ?)$

Solutions:

1. *Determine the value of (?) so that each point below is a solution to the equation* $y = 1 - 2x$.
   a. $(2, ?)$ b. $(?, -1)$ c. $(0, ?)$ d. $(?, 0)$ e. $(-5, ?)$

   a. $x = 2$, so we have $y = 1 - 2(2) = 1 - 4 = -3$, so the coordinates are $(2, -3)$.
   b. $y = -1$, so we have $-1 = 1 - 2x$ or $-2 = -2x$, or $\frac{-2}{-2} = x = 1$, so the coordinates are $(1, -1)$.
   c. $x = 0$, so we have $y = 1 - 2(0) = 1$, so the coordinates are $(0,1)$.
      a. The solution(s) of an equation that have the x-coordinate zero are called the y-intercepts, as those points lie on the y-axis.
   d. $y = 0$, so we have $0 = 1 - 2x$, or $-1 = -2x$, or $\frac{-1}{-2} = \frac{1}{2} = x$, so the coordinates are $\left(\frac{1}{2}, 0\right)$.
      a. The solutions of an equation that have the y-coordinate zero lie on the x-axis and are called the x-intercepts.
   e. $x = -5$, so we have $y = 1 - 2(-5) = 1 + 10 = 11$ so the coordinates are $(-5, 11)$.

2. Determine the values of (?) so that each point below is a solution to the inequality $y > 1 - 2x$.

    a. $(2, ?)$ *b.* $(?, -1)$ *c.* $(0, ?)$

    a. $x = 2$, so we the right side is $1 - 2(2) = 1 - 4 = -3$ and thus the solution points when $x = 2$ must have $y > -3$. Thus: $(2, -2), (2, 0), (2, 10.3), \ldots$ are all solution points. Basically, when we pick $x = 2$, any y-coodinate that satisfies $y > -3$ would work. Thus all points vertically above the point $(2, -3)$ are solutions.

    b. $y = -1$, so we must have $-1 > 1 - 2x$. Solving for x, we see that $-2 > -2x$, or $\frac{-2}{-2} < x$, or $1 < x$, so the coordinates are $(2, -1), (1.1, -1), \ldots$ Basically, when we pick $y = -1$, any x-coodinate that satisfies $x > 1$ would work. So, from the point $(1, -1)$ any point to the right where $x > 1$ is a solution.

    c. $x = 0$, so we have the right side is $1 - 2(0) = 1$, and we must have $y > 1$. Thus the points $(0, 1.1), (0, 2), (0, 3), \ldots$ are solutions. Basically, when we pick $x = 0$, any y-coodinate that satisfies $y > 1$ would work. So there are infinitely many solution points on the y-axis above $y = 1$.

Graphical Representation of Equations and Inequalities

Graphing Equations and Inequalities in Two Variables

    http://www.youtube.com/watch?v=IHCGlPoewJc (9 mins)

Solutions to equations and inequalities in two variables made up of objects we studied in Module 1 can be plotted in the x, y-coordinate plane. The combined plot of all solution points to an equation is called the graph of the equation. In order to understand this relationship, let us look at graphs of a few equations and then inequalities.

To understand graphs of complicated equations, we will need to develop more mathematical tools which continue in College Algebra, Calculus and beyond. However, we can often get a sense of the shape of the graph of an equation by finding and plotting a small set of solution points.

We will start with simple equations and plot a set of solution points and observe any pattern that emerges.

Graphing Equations and Inequalities In Two Variables

Examples:

1. $y = x$

   To plot a few points if we pick an x-value, the y-value will be determined by the equation $y = x$.

x	$y = x$
-3	-3
-2	-2
-1	-1
0	0
1	1
2	2
3	3

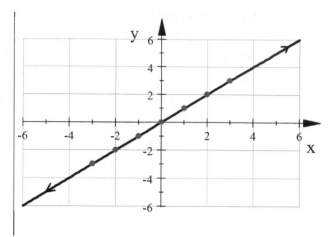

This graph appears to be a straight line. The point where a line cuts the x-axis is called the **x-intercept**, and where it cuts the y-axis is called the **y-intercept.** In this case the x-intercept and the y-intercept are both the origin (0,0).

Connection: You learned equation solving in Module 3. In this context solving the equation when $x = 0$ corresponds to finding the y-intercept, and solving when $y = 0$ corresponds to find the x-intercept.

Extension: Just as you solved different types of inequalities in Module 3, we can plot inequalities the same way.

$y \leq x$ can be plotted using the equation $y = x$ as shown above and an extension of our second method, where we make use of test points to find the solution set for the inequality (just as we did when we worked with inequalities in one variable in Module 3). The line $y = x$ gives us all the points that satisfy the equality; to get the inequality, since the plane is divided into two distinct regions (above the line, and below the line), we have to figure out which region would satisfy the inequality.

You can see that all coordinates on and under the line satisfy the inequality

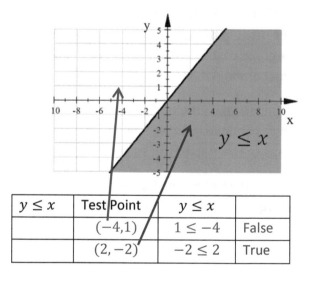

$y \leq x$	Test Point	$y \leq x$	
	$(-4,1)$	$1 \leq -4$	False
	$(2,-2)$	$-2 \leq 2$	True

2. $y = x + 2$

   To plot a few points, if we pick an x-value, the y-value will be determined by the equation $y = x + 2$.

x	$y = x + 2$
-2	0
-1	1
0	2
1	3
2	4
3	5

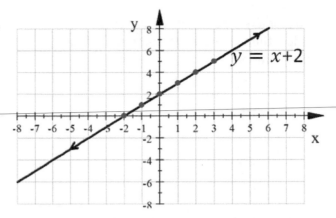

The point where the line cuts the x-axis is called the **x-intercept**, and where it cuts the y-axis is called the **y-intercept**. In this case the x-intercept is $(-2, 0)$ and the y-intercept is $(0, 2)$.

Connection: You learned equation solving in Module 3. In this context setting $y = 0$ and then solving the equation $0 = x + 2$, giving us $x = -2$, corresponds to finding the x-intercept. Also setting $x = 0$ and solving $y = 0 + 2$, giving $y = 2$, corresponds to finding the y-intercept.

The inequality $y > x + 2$ can be plotted using the graph of the equation $y = x + 2$ as shown above and checking test points. The line $y = x + 2$ gives us all the points that satisfy the equality, and since we have the 'strictly greater than' sign in the inequality, we have to use a dotted line indicating that points on the line are not included in the solution set. Now testing points from the region above and the region below the line will indicate which region is the solution of the inequality. This is typical of solutions of inequalities in two variables in that they often consist of points on one side of the curve of the equation obtained by replacing the inequality with equality.

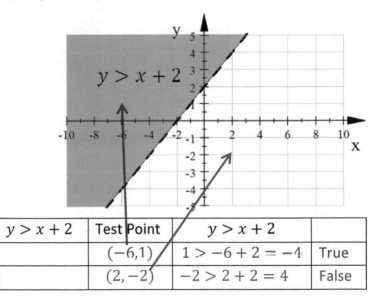

$y > x + 2$	Test Point	$y > x + 2$	
	$(-6, 1)$	$1 > -6 + 2 = -4$	True
	$(2, -2)$	$-2 > 2 + 2 = 4$	False

3. $y = x^2$

To plot a few points, if we pick an x-value, the y-value will be determined by the equation $y = x^2$.

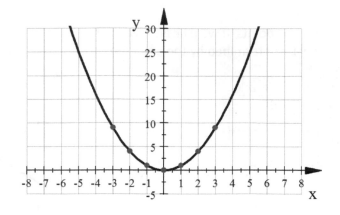

x	$y = x^2$
-3	9
-2	4
-1	1
0	0
1	1
2	4
3	9

In this case the x-intercept and the **y-intercept** is the origin (0,0).

The inequality $y < x^2$ can be plotted using the equation $y = x^2$ as shown above and test points. The curve $y = x^2$ gives us all the points that satisfy the equality. Since we have the 'strictly less than sign' in the inequality, we don't include the curve of $y = x^2$, and use a dotted line to indicate this. This curve divides the plane into two distinct regions - above the curve, and below the curve. We have to figure out which region satisfies the inequality. You can see that all coordinates under the curve satisfy the inequality.

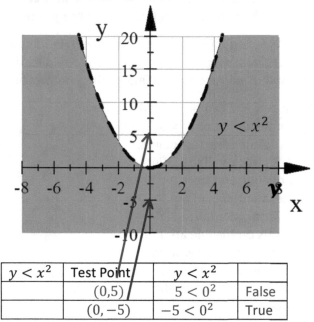

$y < x^2$	Test Point	$y < x^2$	
	$(0,5)$	$5 < 0^2$	False
	$(0,-5)$	$-5 < 0^2$	True

Side Note: Notice that if you were to plot $y = x^2 + 2$, the graph would be very similar to that of $y = x^2$ except it would be shifted 2 up. See the graph to the right. You can also check that by plotting points yourself.

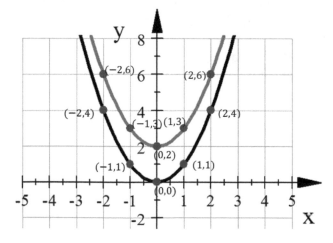

4. $y^2 = x$

To plot the graph, we can create a set of points as we did for $y = x^2$. Note that these two equations are similar but with the x, y roles reversed. Mathematicians try to take advantage of things like this. We have already graphed the equation $y = x^2$ and so to graph this equation we just plot the original points with the x and y coordinates interchanged.

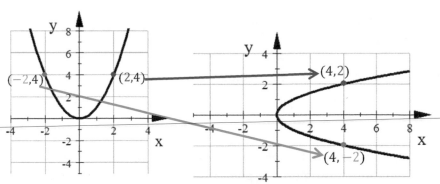

For example, the points $(2,4)$, and $(-2,4)$ that belonged to the graph of $y = x^2$ with their coordinates interchanged become $(4,2)$, and $(4,-2)$ as solutions to $y^2 = x$. The effect on the whole graph is to pick up the original graph and reflect it across the 45 degree diagonal of the line $y = x$.

If you wanted to plot the inequality, $y^2 < x$, then the test point method shows us that the solution set is described as in the graph to the right.

$y^2 < x$	Test Point	$y^2 < x$	
	$(0,6)$	$6^2 < 0$	False
	$(5,0)$	$0^2 < 5$	True

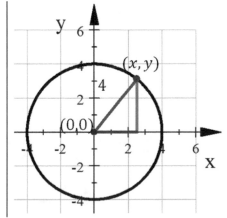

5. $y = |x|$, you can play with this example to verify that the graph is as shown to the right.

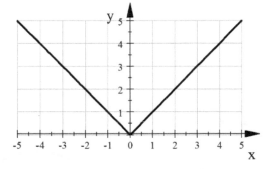

6. $x^2 + y^2 = 4^2$ or $x^2 + y^2 = 16$

To plot this equation you can do the table of x and y values or you can put on your mathematician hat and see if we can graph it without doing the table of values using what we know so far. Another way to write the above equation is that
$(x-0)^2 + (y-0)^2 = 4^2$ and it should remind you that it looks like we are looking at all points (x,y) that are at distance of 4 from $(0,0)$.

Thus this appears to be the graph of a circle centered at the origin of radius 4. We develop the algebraic representations of circles next.

Equations of Circles

Lecture

🖥 Equations of Circles

http://www.youtube.com/watch?v=fzNXmoCHRCk **(10 min)**

Next, we seek to find an algebraic equation to describe the set of points on a generic circle with radius R and center at some given point (h, k). By definition, these points (x, y) that represent a circle must be distance R units away from the point (h, k). Can we write down an equation in x and y that must be true only for the points on this circle?

Hint: The distance formula between two points (x_1, y_1), and (x_2, y_2) is given by
$$d^2 = (x_2 - x_1)^2 + (y_2 - y_1)^2 \text{ or}$$
$$d = \sqrt{(x_2 - x_1)^2 + (y_2 - y_1)^2} \ .$$

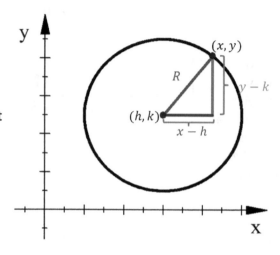

As in example 6 on the previous page the circle centered at $(0,0)$ with radius of 4, when a point (x, y) is on the circle we must have:
$$4 = \sqrt{(x - 0)^2 + (y - 9)^2}.$$

In general then, if (x, y) is to be R units away from the center (h, k), then, the equation
$$R = \sqrt{(x - h)^2 + (y - k)^2} \text{ must be true.}$$
Squaring both sides we get:
$$R^2 = (x - h)^2 + (y - k)^2$$

So the graph of the equation
$(x - 2)^2 + (y + 1)^2 = 3^2$ would be a circle
with radius of 3 and center of $(2, -1)$ since
$(x - 2)^2 + (y + 1)^2 = 3^2$ can be written as
$(x - 2)^2 + (y - (-1))^2 = 3^2$

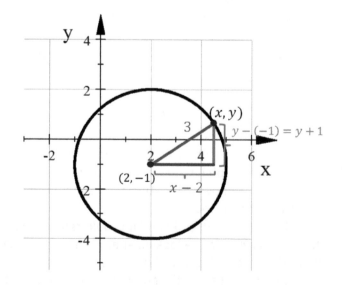

To determine the solutions to $x^2 + y^2 \leq 4$, we plot the equation and use test points again. Check for yourself that the solution to this inequality would be all points on and inside the circle.

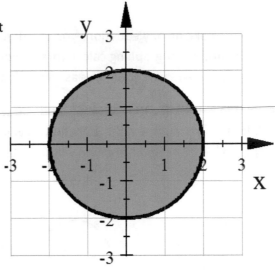

Equation of a Circle in Standard Form

In general an equation of a circle in the form $(x - h)^2 + (y - k)^2 = R^2$, where the center is at (h, k) and the radius is R is said to be in **standard form**.

Examples

1. An equation for the circle centered at $(3, 5)$ with radius 2 is $(x - 3)^2 + (y - 5)^2 = 2^2$.

2. The circle of radius 5 centered at $(-3, 7)$ is represented by
   $\left(x - (-3)\right)^2 + (y - 7)^2 = 5^2$ or $(x + 3)^2 + (y - 7)^2 = 25$.

3. The equation $(x - 6)^2 + (y + 3)^2 = 49$ represents a circle centered at $(6, -3)$ of radius 7.

4. The equation for the circle graphed to the right is obtained by reading off the center as $(3, -2)$ and radius as $r = 3$ from the graph. Thus the equation is $(x - 3)^2 + (y + 2)^2 = 9$

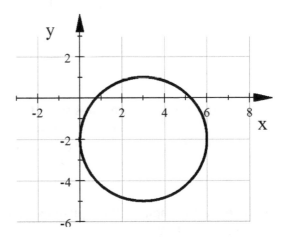

There are many different kinds of curves and regions in the plane that arise from the infinite number of different kinds of equations and inequalities one can write down using the variables x and y. (Note: x and y are variables representing real numbers here.) In fact an equation or an inequality in any two variables will represent a curve or a region in the plane. The coordinate axes labels are based on the variable names you use.

Playing

We recommend you make up any equations you can think of and use graphing utilities like Microsoft Word Mathematics Add-In, or graphing calculators, or you can go to the website www.wolframalpha.com and plot equations as shown in the examples below.

1. Type "plot $(x^2 + y^2 - x)^2 = x^2 + y^2$ and you will see the graph on the left.
2. Type "plot $t = s^3 - 6s^2 + 4s + 12$" and you will see the graph in the middle.
3. Type "plot $p^3 - q^3 = 8pq$" and you will see you will see the graph on the right.

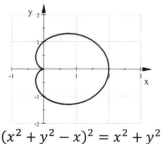
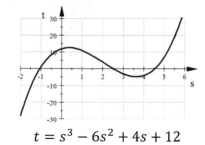
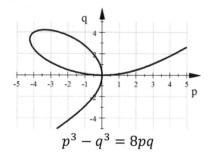

$$(x^2 + y^2 - x)^2 = x^2 + y^2 \qquad t = s^3 - 6s^2 + 4s + 12 \qquad p^3 - q^3 = 8pq$$

Plotting graphs of equations, and writing equations of given graphs of curves and surfaces you see around you, is how geometry and algebra are connected to each other. This connection is crucial to much of our technological advancement such as computer controlled robots and machines, auto piloting of planes, and weather modeling.

Video Log 4.2a

1. Determine if the points $(2, 2)$, $(0, -2)$, and $(2,4)$ are solution points to each of the equations or inequalities below.
   A. $y = 3x - 2$
   B. $y = 4x^2 - 2$
   C. $y \leq 4 - x$

2. Find the missing coordinates so that the point becomes a solution to the given equation or inequality.
   A. $(2, y)$ is a solution to $3x - 1 = y$
   B. $(x, -1)$ is a solution to $2x - 5 \leq y$
   C. $(0, y)$ is a solution to $4 - 2x = y$

3. Sketch the graphs of the equations below by plotting points (the (x, y) coordinates) using the x-values of $-2, -1, 0, 1, 2$.
   A. $y = -2x + 3$
   B. $y = x^2 - 3$

4. Sketch the graphs of the inequalities below. **Hint:** First plot the relevant equations using information from problem number 3, and then use appropriate test points to graph the solutions to the inequalities.
   A. $y \leq -2x + 3$
   B. $y > x^2 - 3$

---

5. Plot the graphs of the circles described by the equations below.
   A. $x^2 + y^2 = 36$
   B. $(x - 3)^2 + (y - 4)^2 = 25$
   C. $(x + 2)^2 + (y - 1)^2 = 9$

6. Sketch graphs and write equations that represent each circle described below.
   A. The center is at $(2, 7)$ and the radius is $r = 9$.
   B. Two endpoints of a diameter are the points $(1, 2)$ and $(5, 4)$.

7.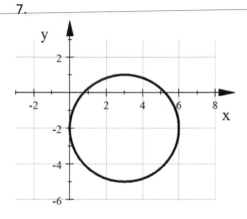

8. Use Wolfram Alpha to determine which holiday, early in the year, the graph of the equation $(x^2 + y^2 + y)^2 = x^2 + y^2$ is associated with.

4.3 Graphs of Linear Equations In Two Variables

In this section we will explore all aspects of lines. We will investigate questions like:

1. What information do we need about a line to get its equation?
2. What kinds of equations generate graphs of lines?
3. What information about a line can be found from its equation?

Horizontal and Vertical Lines

Lecture

💻 Horizontal and Vertical lines and their equations

http://www.youtube.com/watch?v=IamhB_5youg **(6 min)**

Start with the following questions.

1. How many distinct lines can you draw given the condition that the line has to pass through the point (3,2)?

   Let us start with graphing lines going through the point (3,2). You can see there are infinitely many lines we can draw going through this point since we can draw one line and then keep rotating it about this fixed point.

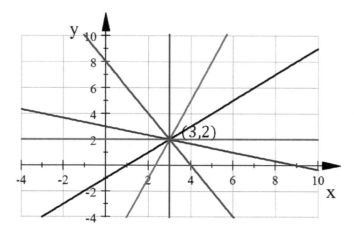

2. How many distinct lines can you draw given the condition that the line has to pass through the points (3,2) and (5,4)?

   You can see that two points determine a unique line. No other distinct line can pass through these two points.

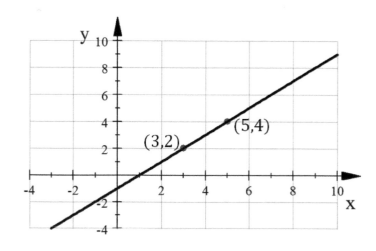

Playing

So now that given two points there is only one line that can go through them. Consider the two vertical lines in the graph to the right. Looking at each line, the thing in common on that line is that the x-coordinate is the same for all points on the line and the y-coodinate is what changes. Each line shows many points on the line. See if you can come up with an equation of each line. Don't peek ahead but really spend time to see if you can come up with the equations. It really comes down to the fact that the x-coordinate is e.g. 4 for the line on the lt.

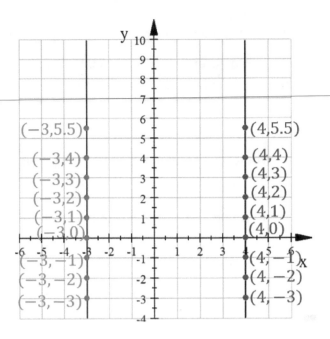

Answers:

The equation of the lines in the previous graph would be written as $x = 4$ and $x = -3$ respectively.

In general then a good way to represent these **vertical lines** algebraically where the x-coordinates are fixed and y-coordinate can be any real number is $\underline{\textbf{\textit{x} = \textit{a.}}}$

Examples

1. $x = \frac{1}{2}$ would represent a vertical line passing through $\left(\frac{1}{2}, 0\right)$.
2. $x = -300$ would represent a vertical line passing through $(-300, 0)$.

Looking at the two lines in the graph to the right, we can see that the points on each horizontal line have one thing in common and that is that the y-coordinate is fixed, and the x-coodinate is what changes. Each line shows many points on the line. See if you can come up with an equation that describes each of these lines.

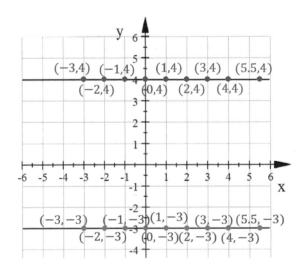

Answers:

The equation of the lines in the previous graph would be written as $y = 4$ and $y = -3$ respectively.

In general then a good way to represent these **horizontal lines** algebraically where the y-coordinates are fixed and x-coordinate can be any real number is **$y = a.$**

Examples

So the lines

1. $y = \frac{1}{2}$ would represent a horizontal line passing through $\left(0, \frac{1}{2}\right)$.

2. $y = -300$ would represent a horizontal line passing through $(10, -300)$.

3. An equation of a horizontal line passing through the point $(300, -40)$ would be given by $y = -40$.

4. An equation of a vertical line passing through the point $(300, -40)$ would be given by $x = 300$

3.   4.

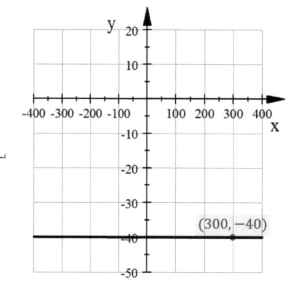

(300, −40)

1. Find an equation for each of the horizontal and vertical lines graphed below.

    a.

    b.

    c.

    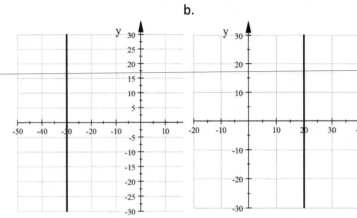

    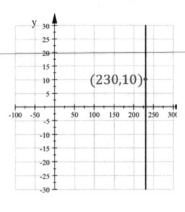

    (230,10)

    d.

    e.

    f.

    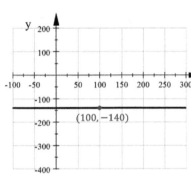

    (100, −140)

    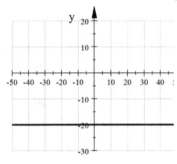

    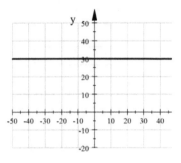

2. Given the two points on each horizontal or vertical line, find the equation of each line.

    a. $(-3, 6), (-3, -6)$

    b. $(-5, 6), (-6, 6)$

    c. $\left(-100, \frac{3}{4}\right), \left(-100, -\frac{60}{213}\right)$

    d. $(-30.49, 0), (412.98, 0)$

    e. $(0, -30.49), (0, 412.98)$

    f. $\left(\frac{30}{41}, -10\right), \left(\frac{30}{41}, -\frac{60}{213}\right)$

3. Sketch the graphs of the lines below.

    a. $y = -\frac{5}{4}$

    b. $x = -30.6$

    c. $x = 7$

    d. $y = -5$

    e. $x = 0$

    f. $x = \sqrt{3}$

    g. $y = 3^{-2}$

    h. $y = 50 + \sqrt{2}$

    i. $x = \frac{\pi}{2}$

4. Find equation of a vertical and a horizontal line passing through the points below.

    a. $(30, 6)$

    b. $(-5, 6)$

    c. $(-54.6, 0)$

    d. $\left(\frac{3}{4}, -10\right)$

    e. $\left(0, \frac{5\pi}{3}\right)$

    f. $(-30.49, 43.7)$

Slope of Lines
Lecture

💻 Slopes of lines

http://www.youtube.com/watch?v=hbrLS3ifskQ (13 min)

Now that we know how vertical and horizontal lines behave let us look at the line $y = x$ and see what information is hidden in this equation.

We already saw that the graph of equation $y = x$ was given plotting a few points.

x	$y = x$
-3	-3
-2	-2
-1	-1
0	0
1	1
2	2
3	3

As you can see from the graph no matter what point you pick the ratio of the vertical distance to the horizontal distance travelled from one point on the graph to another is the same.

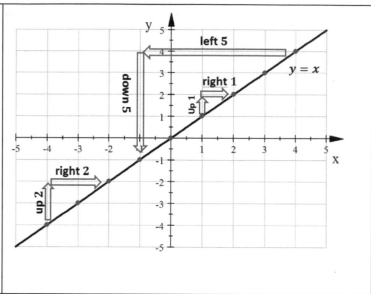

In this case it is one up (rise) and one to the right (run) or two up and two the right, or you can think of it as going the same amount up as right. This ratio of rise over run is called the slope of the line. The slope of the line remains the same no matter what two points on the line you pick. In this case you can see the slope is one. So just like two points determine a unique line, a point and the slope determines a unique line.   This is so since using the rise/run ratio we can start from one given point and obtain a second point by moving horizontally by the run and then vertically by the rise.

Slope of a Line

Note: We define the slope of a line to be the ratio of change in the y-coordinate divided by the change in the x-coordinate between any two points on a non-vertical line.   We use the letter m to denote the slope. With vertical lines the slope is undefined because the x-coordinate change is zero and dividing by zero is undefined! Remember when we say "no slope" (no real number is associated to it), this is different than saying a line has zero slope (since zero is real number). In fact, the slope of a horizontal line is zero.

Playing

What do you think an equation of a line is passing through the point (0,0) and slope of $2 = \frac{2}{1}$.

| See the graph to the right.... You can see that starting at (0,0) we can move up 2 units and then right 1 unit we land on the line and it gives us the second point on our line which will be at (1,2), moving it again in the same pattern will give us the point (2,4), moving again using the slope we will be at the point (3,6) and so on. You can see that the pattern seems evident that the y-coordinate is always two times more than the x-coordinate. If we had to write the equation of this line algebraically it would be $y = 2x$. | 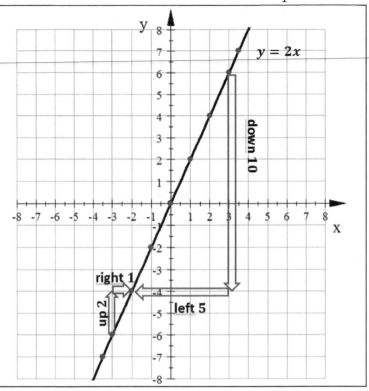 |

So it seems that for any line passing through the origin, slope of the line will be the x-coefficient, i.e., $y = mx$.

We will look at several lines below so you can see this pattern.

$$m = \frac{3}{2} \quad \rightarrow \quad y = \frac{3}{2}x$$

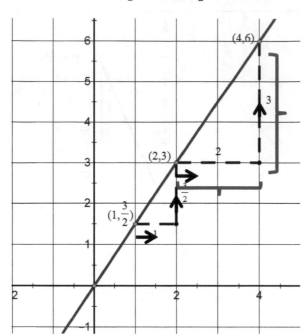

$$m = \frac{2}{1} \quad \rightarrow \quad y = 2x$$

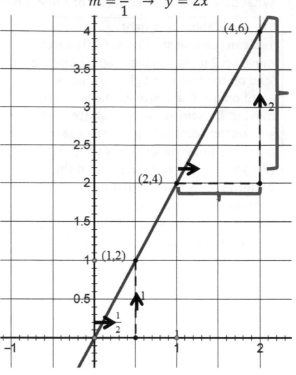

$$m = -\frac{1}{2} \quad \rightarrow \quad y = -\frac{1}{2}x$$

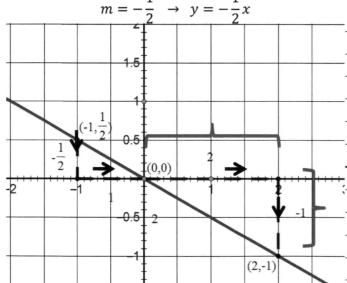
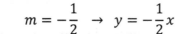

$$m = -\frac{5}{4} \quad \rightarrow \quad y = -\frac{5}{4}x$$

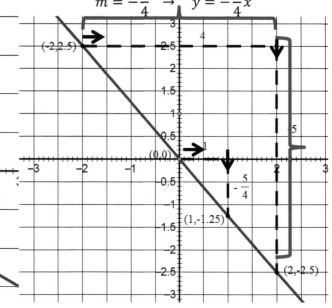

If we plot lines with negative reciprocal slope as shown below, you will notice that the angle between them is 90°. Two lines are said to be perpendicular, when they intersect each other at a right angle, or 90°.

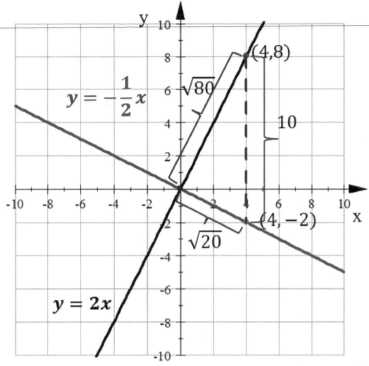

One way to be sure we have right angle between lines is to look at the triangle formed by the points $(0,0)$, $(4,8)$, and $(4,-2)$ and show that it is a right angled triangle using the Pythagorean Theorem. See below.

Distance between $(0,0)$, $(4,8)$ is given by $\sqrt{4^2 + 8^2} = \sqrt{16 + 64} = \sqrt{80}$, distance between $(0,0)$, $(4,-2)$ is given by $\sqrt{4^2 + (-2)^2} = \sqrt{16 + 4} = \sqrt{20}$, and distance between $(4,8)$ and $(4,-2)$ is given by $\sqrt{0^2 + (10)^2} = \sqrt{100} = 10$

So now we see that $\left(\sqrt{80}\right)^2 + \left(\sqrt{20}\right)^2 = 10^2$ or $80 + 20 = 100$. The sides of the triangle with vertices of $(0,0)$, $(4,8)$, and $(4,-2)$ satisfy Pythagorean Theorem and therefore must form a right triangle.

This implies that the two lines $y = 2x$ and $y = -\frac{1}{2}x$ form a right angle with each other. You can verify for yourself that this happens anytime we have lines $y = mx$ and $y = -\frac{1}{m}x$ for a non-zero real number m.

> *Note: Lines that have slopes that are negative reciprocals of each other in the examples we looked at are perpendicular to each other.*

1. Sketch the graphs of the lines below. Plot the lines in parts a., & b., and c. & d. on the same rectangular coordinates provided.

a. $y = 3x$	b. $y = -\frac{1}{3}x$

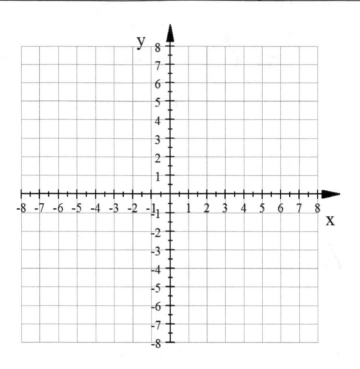

c. $y = \frac{2}{3}x$	d. $y = -\frac{3}{2}x$

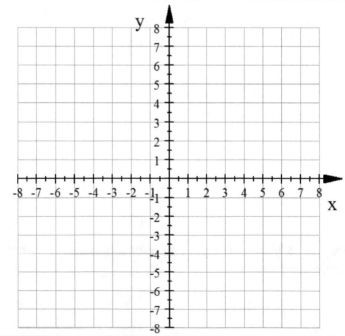

What conclusions can you draw from plotting graphs a & b, and c & d together.

2. Plot the graphs of the lines below.

a. $x = 5$ b. $y = 5$ c. $y = 5x$ d. $x = 5y$	e. $y = \dfrac{5}{3}x$ f. $y = -\dfrac{5}{3}x$ g. $y = 7y$ h. $y = -7x$	i. $x = \dfrac{2}{3}y$ j. $x = -\dfrac{2}{3}y$ k. $x = \dfrac{2}{3}y$ l. $x = -\dfrac{3}{2}y$

3. List all pairs of lines 2a through 2l that are perpendicular to each other.

4. Find the equations of the lines whose graphs are given below passing through the origin (0,0).

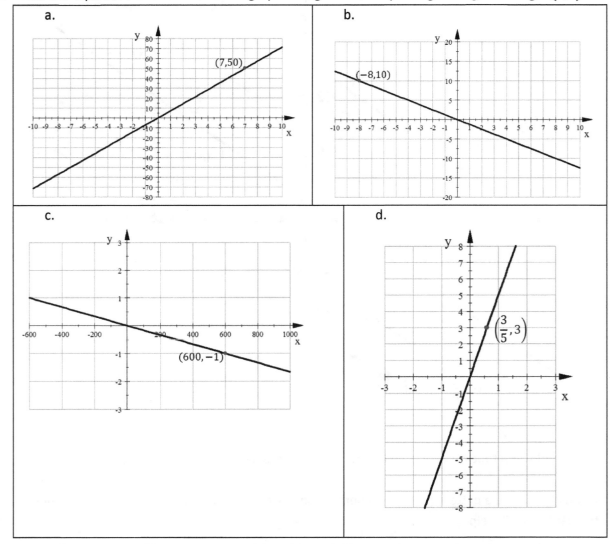

5. Find the equation of the lines that are perpendicular to lines in parts 4a through 4d.

Slope Intercept Form of a Line

Lecture

🖥 Lines

http://www.youtube.com/watch?v=l2TPmIzfkLo   **(6 min)**

Now lets us look at lines and see what happens to their equations if we moved the entire line up or down a certain number of units. See graph below and see if you can determine the relationship between the graph of $y = 2x$ line and the other lines.

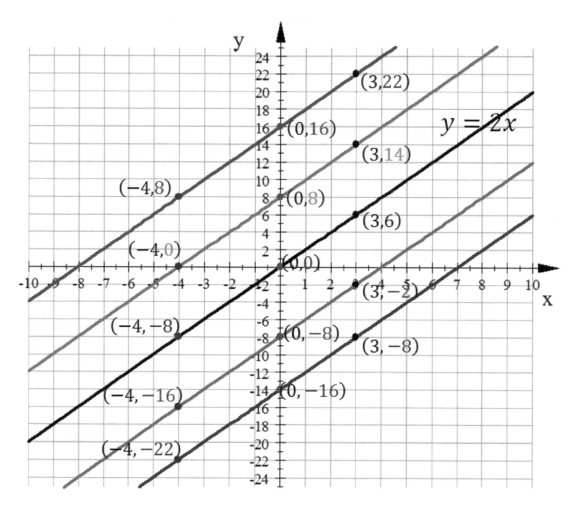

Spend some time on your own before looking at the next page.

If you did not see a pattern graphically perhaps seeing all the points on the lines as listed below in the tabular form will help.

x	y
−4	−22
0	−16
3	−8

x	y
−4	−16
0	−8
3	−2

x	y = 2x
−4	−8
0	0
3	6

x	y
−4	0
0	8
3	14

x	y
−4	8
0	16
3	22

As you can see from the tables: In the green line the y-coordinate is 8 more than the original **black line** making the equation of the line $y = 2x + 8$, and similarly the **pink line** will be $y = 2x + 16$, the **aqua line** will be $y = 2x - 8$, and the **purple line** would be given by $y = 2x - 16$.

Notice that the when $x = 0$ in each equation we get the y-intercept of the corresponding line.

In general this pattern holds not just for lines but for the graph of any function $y = f(x)$. When you lift the graph of a function, k units in the vertical direction the new equation for that graph would be given by $y = f(x) + k$. If $k < 0$ then the graph is shifted down, otherwise it will shift up.

The equation $y = mx + b$ represents equation of a line that has slope of m and y-intercept of b. The $y = mx + b$ form is called the **slope intercept form** of a line (the name is self-explanatory).

Given that you know how to solve equations look what happens if we solve the equation $ax + by = c$ where a, b, c are real numbers, with $b \neq 0$. If we solve it, we get $y = -\frac{a}{b}x + \frac{c}{b}$ showing that this equation represents a line with slope of $-\frac{a}{b}$ and y-intercept of $\frac{c}{b}$.

Any equation of the form $ax + by = c$ has a graph that is a line. This is called the standard form for line equations. **Meaning of slope**

Examples

1. Consider an equation that describes total cost y for purchasing x units of some quantity. E.g., if flour costs $\frac{\$0.50}{lb}$ then purchasing x lbs would cost $y = \frac{\$0.50}{lb} \times x$ lbs, $y = 0.5x$, or $y = \frac{1}{2}x$. You know that this equation represents a line with slope of $\frac{1}{2}$ =costs \$1 for every 2 lbs of flour. The y-intercept of this line is zero and see the graph of the line on the right. $y = \frac{\$0.50}{lb} \times$ x lbs, $y = 0.5x$, or $y = \frac{1}{2}x$. You know that this equation represents a line with slope of $\frac{1}{2}$ =costs \$1 for every 2 lbs of flour.

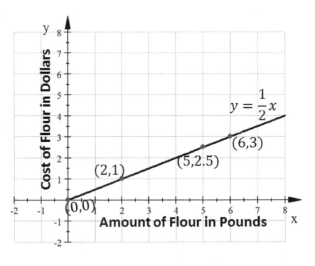

The y-intercept of this line is zero and see the graph of the line above. You can see since we do not buy negative pounds of flour we will not make use of the graph for values of x smaller than zero. The graph allows you to read of the cost of flour you may which to purchase. See if the points on the graph make sense to you...

2. If one buys Bing cherries (type of cherries very high in antioxidants that are grown in Wisconsin and a few other North Pacific States in the U.S.), they might cost $\frac{\$3}{lb}$ and the cost for x pounds would be given by $y = 3x$. You can see that that the y-coordinate increases by 3 units for every one unit increase in x. Both of these lines are plotted on the right.

When we plot both lines on the graph below you can compare the cost of flour and the cost of Bing cherries. The Bing cherries cost more than the flour per pound reflected in its steeper rise.

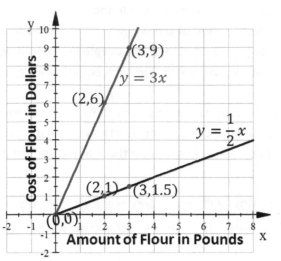

There are several ways to compute the slope. On a graph, the change in y-coordinate is called the "rise" between the points, and the change in the x-coordinate the "run". With this vocabulary, the slope is obtained as the ratio of rise over run.

Slope: To compute the ratio of the rise over the run between any two known points on the line say (x_1, y_1) and (x_2, y_2) we need to compute slope$= m = \frac{rise}{run} = \frac{y_2 - y_1}{x_2 - x_1}$. It does not matter which points you call (x_1, y_1) and (x_2, y_2). Just make sure you subtract in the same order for both coordinates.

Examples

1. For the line $y = 3x$ if we use the points (1,3) and (3,9), the slope is computed as $m = \frac{rise}{run} = \frac{9-3}{3-1} = \frac{6}{2} = 3$ which is also the same as $\frac{3-9}{1-3} = \frac{-6}{-2} = 3$. We could also have used the points (0, 0) and (1, 3) and obtained $m = \frac{3-0}{1-0} = \frac{3}{1} = 3$.

2. For the graph of $y = 0.5x$, we could use the points (1, 0.5) and (3, 1.5) and thus $m = \frac{(1.5-0.5)}{(3-1)} = \frac{1}{2}$.

   The above two lines both had positive slope since the rise and the run have the same sign as x increased (in other words when you move left to right on the graph of the line the graph rises up). A negative slope means that the rise and the run had opposite signs, (in other words when you move left to right on the graph of the line the graph falls down).

3. $y = -\frac{5}{9}x$ if we use the two points (0, 0) and $\left(1, -\frac{5}{9}\right)$, we get its slope$= \frac{-\frac{5}{9}-0}{1-0} = -\frac{5}{9}$.

Note: *If you write the equation as $y = mx + b$ format, then the slope is given by coefficient of the x term. Any equation in two variables that has degree one is called a linear equation and its graph is a line.*

4. $2x + 3y = 6$ if we want slope here we can solve the linear equation for y which gives us $3y = -2x + 6$ or $y = \frac{-2}{3}x + \frac{6}{3}$ or $y = -\frac{2}{3}x + 2$. The slope here is $-\frac{2}{3}$

5. $-\frac{2}{3}x + \frac{1}{2}y = 1$ To compute the slope here, we can solve the linear equation for y which gives us $\frac{1}{2}y = \frac{2}{3}x + 1$ or $y = \frac{2}{1}\left(\frac{2}{3}x\right) + \frac{2}{1}(1)$, or $y = \frac{4}{3}x + 2$. The slope here is $\frac{4}{3}$.

Video Log 4.3c

1. Are the points a, b, and c on the line $3x - 4y = 12$? Explain your answer.
    a. $(-3,5)$
    b. $\left(\frac{5}{3}, -\frac{7}{4}\right)$
    c. $\left(-\frac{1}{3}, \frac{3}{4}\right)$

2. Sketch the graphs of the lines below.
    a. $y = 3 - x$ d. $3y + 4x = 2$ g. $x = 4 - 2y$
    b. $y = 2x - 2$ e. $2x - 3y = 6$ h. $x = 4$
    c. $3x - 4y = 12$ f. $x = 3y - 2$ i. $y = -3$

3. If an equation of a line is given by $y = mx + b$, then $m =$slope and $b = y$-intercept. State the meaning of m and b.

Parallel and Perpendicular Lines

Two lines are said to be perpendicular, as talked about before, if they intersect each other at a right angle, or $90°$. Two lines in a plane are said to be parallel if they never intersect. We saw before that the slopes of perpendicular lines were negative reciprocals of each other in the examples we looked at. If you looked at examples of parallel lines we would see they must have the same rise over run ratio meaning that the slopes must be the same. Both of these slope relations can be observed through many examples. However, in mathematics examples of a pattern only provide an insight into a general rule of law. We need to prove these claims that parallel lines have the same slope and that perpendicular line slopes are negative reciprocals. We present a graphical proof for both.

To prove that parallel lines have the same slope look at the parallel lines labeled below.

The two triangles $\triangle AEF$ and $\triangle ADB$ are similar. The horizontal transversal $\overleftrightarrow{AF}$ forms the same angle at B with the first line as it does at F with the second line and thus the two right triangles are similar.

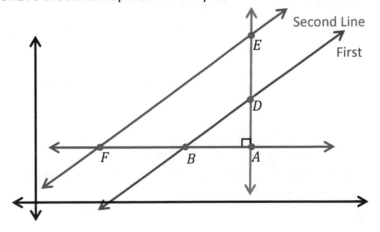

See the triangles pulled out so you can see them to the right. The two lines $\overleftrightarrow{FE}$ and $\overleftrightarrow{BD}$ being parallel implies that the corresponding angles $\angle AFE$, $\angle ABD$ and the angles $\angle FEA$, $\angle BDA$ are congruent, or have equal measures. The two triangles are similar, which means that the ratio of the lengths of the corresponding sides are equal.

Thus the slope $m = \dfrac{\text{rise}}{\text{run}} = \dfrac{l(\overline{AE})}{l(\overline{AF})} = \dfrac{l(\overline{AD})}{l(\overline{AB})}$ *of parallel lines are the same.*

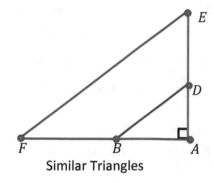

Similar Triangles

To prove that the slopes of perpendicular lines have negative reciprocal slopes, consider the perpendicular lines $\overleftrightarrow{AC}$, $\overleftrightarrow{AE}$. If you consider the triangle $\triangle ABC$, then the slope of line 1 is given by $\frac{b}{a}$. The slope of line 2 is obtained by rotating $\triangle ABC$ 90^0 and $m_\perp$ is negative, and $m_\perp = -\frac{a}{b}$.

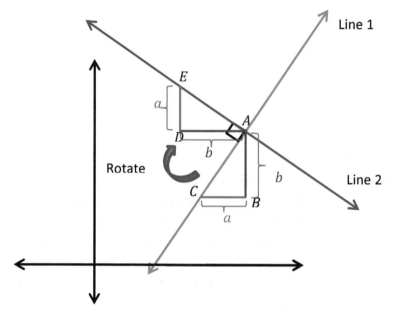

Note: *The product of the slopes of two perpendicular lines is $\frac{b}{a} \times -\frac{a}{b} = -1$. Or equivalently that slopes of perpendicular lines are negative reciprocals of each other.*

Examples

1. Determine if the lines in each example are perpendicular, or parallel to each other, or neither.
    a. $y = \frac{3}{2}x$, and $y = -\frac{2}{3}x$
    b. $3y - 6x = 5$, and $y = 2x + 1$
    c. $3x + y = 1$, and $3x + 2y = 4$
    d. Line that goes through the points $(1,3), (4,-1)$ and the line through the points $(-1,0), (3,3)$.
2. Graph each equation below
    a. $y = \frac{3}{4}x - 2$
    b. $3y + 4x = 12$.

---

3. Find the equation of the lines below.

a.

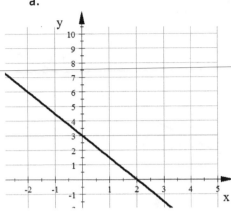

b.

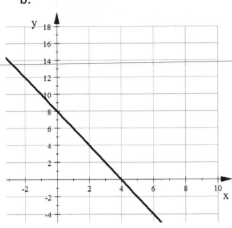

Solutions

1.

a. The product of the two slopes is $\frac{3}{2} \times -\frac{2}{3} = \frac{-6}{6} = -1$ so the lines are perpendicular.

b. Slope of the line $3y - 6x = 5$ can be found by rewriting it in the slope-ntercept form which would be $3y = 6x + 5$, or $y = \frac{6}{3}x + \frac{5}{3}$, or $y = 2x + \frac{5}{3}$, giving us the slope to be 2. The other line $y = 2x + 1$ has slope 2 also and therefore the two given lines are parallel.

c. The slope of the line $3x + y = 1$ can be found by rewriting it in the form $y = -3x + 1$ giving us that the slope is -3. The slope of the line $3x + 2y = 4$ also can be found by rewriting it as $2y = -3x + 4$, or $y = -\frac{3}{2}x + \frac{4}{2}$ or $y = -\frac{3}{2}x + 2$ giving the slope of that line as $-\frac{3}{2}$ making the line neither parallel nor perpendicular to the second line.

d. The slope of the line going through $(1, 3)$ and $(4, -1)$ is $\frac{-1-3}{4-1} = -\frac{4}{3}$ and the slope of the line passing through $(-1, 0)$ and $(3, 3)$ is $\frac{3-0}{3-(-1)} = \frac{3}{4}$. The two slopes of the two lines are negative reciprocals therefore they are perpendicular.

2. Graph each equation below

a. $y = \frac{3}{4}x - 2$

We know the slope is $\frac{3}{4}$ which means we go up 3 and right 4 and on the line starting at the y-intercept -2. Or we could also start any point on the line, say $(4, 1)$ as shown in the plot to the right.

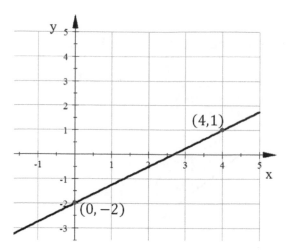

b. $3y + 4x = 12$.

We can either find any two points that work or we could solve for y and use the slope and intercept. Two points that are easy to determine are the x and y-intercepts. To find x-intercept set $y = 0$ original equation and solve for x, $3(0) + 4x = 12$, or $4x = 12$, giving us $x = 3$. To find y-intercept we set $x = 0$ in the original equation and solve for y, $3y + 4(0) = 12$, or $3y = 12$, giving us $y = 4$. This gives two points and we can connect them with a line as shown in the graph to the right.

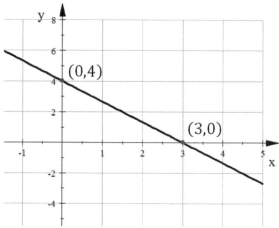

Alternatively, we could solve the original equation for y to get $3y = -4x + 12$, or $y = -\frac{4}{3}x + 4$. This says the y-intercept is at 4 and slope is $-\frac{4}{3}$, we move 3 right and 4 down from there to stay on the line.

3. **Find equations of the lines.**

   a. We can see from the graph that the y-intercept of the line is 3 and that the x-intercept is 2 which means that the point $(2,0)$ is on the line. So our equation would look like $y = mx + b$ where $b = 3$ so we have $y = mx + 3$ using our coordinate $(2,0)$ we get $0 = m(2) + 3$ or $0 = 2m + 3$, or $-3 = 2m$ or that $m = -\frac{3}{2}$. Therefore the equation of the line is $y = -\frac{3}{2}x + 3$.

   b. From the graph, two points on the line are $(4,0)$, and $(8, -8)$.
   So the slope is $\frac{-8-0}{8-4} = \frac{-8}{4} = -2$. To find the equation of the line we use one of the points and the slope intercept form of the line giving us $y = -2x + b$ or that $0 = -2(4) + b$ or that $0 = -8 + b$ giving us $b = 8$. Therefore the equation of the line is $y = -2x + 8$.

Point Slope form for the Equation of a line

Lecture

🖥 Slope-intercept and point-slope forms of equations of lines

http://www.youtube.com/watch?v=Mqh-1mGnuU0 (15 min)

The equation of a line that has the slope m and passes through a given point (x_1, y_1) in the **point-slope form** is given by $y = y_1 + m(x - x_1)$.

This says that we start with $x = x_1$ and $y = y_1$. If we move over one unit to the right of x_1, or let $x = x_1 + 1$, then $y = y_1 + m(x_1 + 1 - x_1) = y_1 + m$. Thus y increased by m amount from y_1 with the increase of one unit in x. This confirms that the slope, being the ratio of the rise over run, of this line is indeed m.

Another interpretation of the point-slope form $y = m(x - x_1) + y_1$ is that it is a modification of the line $y = mx$ which goes through the origin. The form $y = m(x - x_1) + y_1$ is a shift x_1 units to the right and y_1 units up of the line $y = mx$. You can also note that this form of line can be thought of as coming from knowing the slope of the line say m, and a point on the line say (x_1, y_1). We know that any point on the line (x, y) would only belong to this line if the slope between (x, y) and (x_1, y_1) is given by $\frac{y - y_1}{x - x_1} = m$. Multiply both sides by $(x - x_1)$ to get $y - y_1 = m(x - x_1)$. Solving the equation for y, we get $y = m(x - x_1) + y_1$.

Note that when $x_1 = 0$ $((0, y_1)$ which is the y-intercept) is the given point our equation would like $y = mx + y_1$

The equation of a line that has the slope m and y-intercept of b in the **slope-intercept form** is given by $y = mx + b$.

Examples

1. Find equations of the lines with the given information.
   a. The line has slope $-\frac{2}{5}$, and goes through the point $(3, 2)$.
   b. The line has slope -0.0035, and goes through the point $(-35, -243)$.
   c. The line passes through $(3, 5)$ and $(-2, 1)$.
   d. The line passes through the point $(2, -3)$ and is perpendicular to the line $3x + 5y = 10$.
   e. The line passes through the point $(2, -3)$ and is parallel to the line $3x + 5y = 10$.

Solutions

   a. The equation of the line is $y = -\frac{2}{5}(x - 3) + 2$.
   b. The equation of the line is $y = -0.0035(x + 35) - 243$.
   c. The slope $m = \frac{1 - 5}{-2 - 3} = \frac{-4}{-5} = \frac{4}{5}$. We can use point-slope form and write down an equation as $y = 5 + \frac{4}{5}(x - 3)$. We can leave the equation in this form or simplify to write in the slope-

intercept form to get $y = 5 + \frac{4}{5}x - \frac{12}{5}$, or $y = \frac{4}{5}x + \frac{13}{5}$. Alternatively, we could have started by looking at the slope-intercept form to begin with. With $m = \frac{4}{5}$ we'd have $y = \frac{4}{5}x + b$. We can determine the value of b because we know the equation must be true at both given points, so we substitute either one in. Using the point $(3, 5)$, we get $5 = \frac{4}{5} \cdot 3 + b$, or $5 - \frac{12}{5} = b$, or $b = \frac{13}{5}$. Therefore the equation of the line would could be written as $y = \frac{4}{5}x + \frac{13}{5}$.

d. Since the line we seek is perpendicular to $3x + 5y = 10$, its slope will be the negative reciprocal of the slope of $3x + 5y = 10$. To find the slope of the original line we can rewrite the equation of the line as $y = mx + b$. So we get $5y = -3x + 10$, or $y = -\frac{3}{5}x + 2$. The slope of this line is $-\frac{3}{5}$, and therefore the slope of the line perpendicular to this line would be $\frac{5}{3}$. Since the line goes through the point $(2, -3)$, its equation in the point-slope form is $y = \frac{5}{3}(x - 2) - 3$.

e. Since the line we seek is parallel to $3x + 5y = 10$, its slope will be the same as the slope of $3x + 5y = 10$. We already found this to be $-\frac{3}{5}$, and therefore the slope of the line parallel to it would also be $-\frac{3}{5}$. Since the line goes through the point $(2, -3)$, its equation in the point-slope form is $y = -\frac{3}{5}(x - 2) - 3$.

Review of Graphing Linear Inequalities

As we saw earlier, we can graph solutions to linear inequalities by plotting either a solid or dotted line depending on the inequality sign, and then choosing test points to determine the solution set. Another way to determine the correct side to shade is to solve for y in the inequality so that y is isolated on the left side of the inequality. You then

1. Shade the region above the line if the inequality wants the y to be greater than, or greater than or equal to the right hand side.

    OR

2. Shade the region below the line if the inequality wants the y to be less than, or less than or equal to the right hand side.

Examples: Sketch the graph of the following inequalities

a. $y \geq 2x + 3$

b. $y < -\frac{3}{5}x + 4$

Solution

a. $y \geq 2x + 3$		
Test Point	**Inequality**	**Truth Value**
$(0, -2)$	$-2 \geq 2(0) + 3$ or $-2 \geq 3$	False

b. $y < -\frac{3}{5}x + 4$		
Test Point	**Inequality**	**Truth Value**
$(10, 4)$	$4 < -\frac{3}{5}(10) + 4$ $4 < -2$	False

Lecture

🖥 Summary of Lines and Linear Equations and Inequalities in Two Variables

http://www.youtube.com/watch?v=wq8NG65DZtE (2 min)

Summary of lines and linear equations:
➤ A point (x_1, y_1) belongs to the line $y = mx + b$ if and only if $y_1 = mx_1 + b$ is a true statement.
➤ Two points determine a unique line. (That means to graph a line you need to find two points on that line.)
➤ A point on the line and the slope of the line also determine a unique line.
➤ To find points on the line $y = mx + b$ you can pick any value for x, say $x = x_1$, then substitute that value into the equation of the line and solve for y. So that would give us that the $y_1 = mx_1 + b$ or that the point $(x_1, mx_1 + b)$ is a point on the line $y = mx + b$.
➤ Equation of a line in the slope intercept form is given by $y = mx + b$, where m =slope, $b = y$-intercept.
➤ Equation of a line in the point slope form is given by $y = m(x - x_1) + y_1$ where m =slope, (x_1, y_1)point on the line.
➤ Equation of a line in the standard form is given by $Ax + By = C$.
➤ Slope of a line passing through points $(x_1, y_1), (x_2, y_2)$ is given by $\frac{y_2 - y_1}{x_2 - x_1}$ as long as $x_2 \neq x_1$.
➤ Slope represents the rate of change of the y-value per one unit increase in x.
➤ Equation of a vertical line passing through the point (a, b) is given by $x = a$.
➤ Equation of a horizontal line passing through the point (a, b) is given by $y = b$

Video Log 4.3d

1. Find the coordinates of two points that are on the line, and of two points that are not on each line below.

   a. $\frac{4}{5}x - \frac{2}{7}y = 11$

   b. $-3(y - 2) + x = 5$

   c. $-\frac{3}{2}(x - 4) + 1 = y$

   d. $4x - 7y = 5$

   e. $y = 3(x - 2) + 1$

   f. $x = 4$

2. Find the slope, x-intercept and y-intercept of each line below.

a. $y = 4$	i. $x = 4$
b. $y = 3x$	j. $x = 3y$
c. $y = 3x + 2$	k. $x = 3y + 2$
d. $y = -2x + 5$	l. $x = -2y + 5$
e. $y = -\frac{2}{5}x - \frac{10}{3}$	m. $x = -\frac{2}{5}y - \frac{10}{3}$
f. $3y - 2x = 7$	n. $3x - 2y = 7$
g. $-\frac{3}{8}x + \frac{4}{5}y = 11$	o. $-\frac{3}{8}y + \frac{4}{5}x = 11$
h. $y = -2(x - 1) + 5$	p. $x = -2(y - 1) + 5$

   Explain the similarities and differences between the lines a & i, b & j, c & k, d & l, e & m, f & n, g & o, and h & p.

   Use your observations to describe how one can extract slope, y-intercept, and x-intercept of a line without first having to rewrite the equation of the line in slope-intercept form.

3. Sketch the graphs of the equations and inequalities below.

Equation	Inequality
a. $y = 3 - x$	a. $y \geq 3 - x$
b. $x = 3 - y$	b. $x \geq 3 - y$
c. $y = 2x - 2$	c. $y < 2x - 2$
d. $x = 2y - 2$	d. $x < 2y - 2$
e. $2x - 3y = 6$	e. $2x - 3y \leq 6$
f. $2y - 3x = 6$	f. $2y - 3x \leq 6$
g. $3x = y - 4$	g. $3x > y - 4$
h. $3y = x - 4$	h. $3y > x - 4$
i. $y = -2(x - 1) + 5$	i. $y > -2(x - 1) + 5$
j. $x = -2(y - 1) + 5$	j. $x > -2(y - 1) + 5$
k. $x = -\frac{2}{5}y - \frac{10}{3}$	k. $x \leq -\frac{2}{5}y - \frac{10}{3}$

   Explain the similarities and differences between graphing the solutions of the correspondingly numbered equations and inequalities. In other words compare the solutions you graphed for equation a & inequality a, equation b & inequality b, equation c & inequality c, and so on....

4. Find the equations of the lines below.

a.

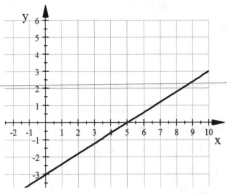

b.

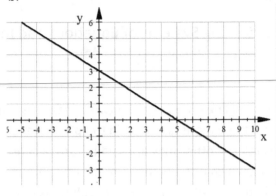

c.

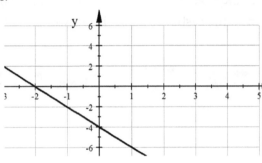

d.

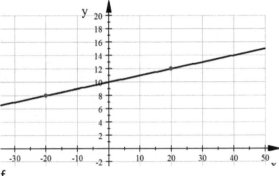

e.

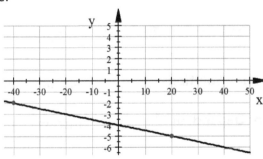

f.

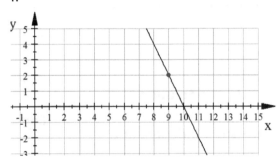

g. Passing through the point (-1,-4) and (2,7).

h. Passing through the point (2,-3) with a slope of $-\frac{2}{3}$.

i. Passing through the point (-2,-5) and parallel to the line $y = 3x + 4$.

j. Passing through the point (-2,-5) and perpendicular to the line $y = -\frac{2}{3}x - \frac{11}{5}$.

k. Passing through the point (-2,-5) and having an x-intercept of $(\frac{4}{5}, 0)$.

l. Passing through the point $(\frac{3}{4}, -\frac{1}{5})$ and perpendicular to the line $2y + 3x = 0$.

m. Passing through the points $(-5, -9)$ and (3,8).

n. Passing through (-3, 4) and perpendicular to the line $2y - 3x = 6$.

o. Find the equation of a line passing through the point $(-5,1)$ and parallel to the line $2y = 3x - 4$.

p. Having slope of -3 and x-intercept of 4.

q. Having slope of -3 and y-intercept of -5.

Solving Systems of Linear Equations and Inequalities in Two Variables
Lecture

🖥 Solving Systems of Equations and Inequalities
http://www.youtube.com/watch?v=Ek8oBqJ2E_4 **(14 min)**

A system of linear equations in two variables is a set of two or more linear equations. A solution to a system of equations is a point in the plane that satisfies all the equations in the system. If two lines intersect each other they are said to form a consistent independent system of equations with a unique solution, which is the point of intersection. If the two graphs lie on top of each other, i.e, are the same line, then all points on the line are solutions to the system of equations. Such a system of equations is called a consistent dependent system of equations with infinitely many solutions. If the graphs of the two lines are parallel to each other but are separate lines, the system is inconsistent with no solution. Graphically, the three scenarios are depicted below.

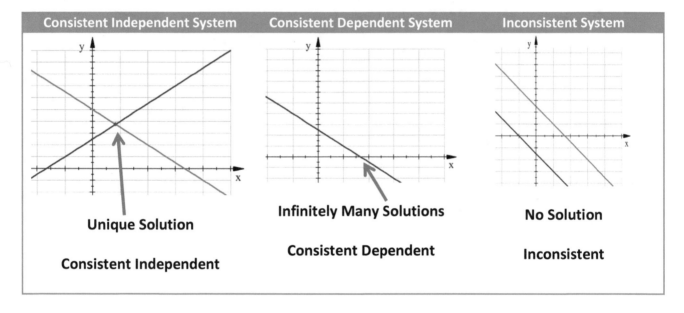

Methods for Solving Systems of Equations and Inequalities

To solve a system of equations and inequalities the **graphical method** of solving a system is to plot the graphs of all the equations or inequalities in the system on the same coordinate system and then from the graph locate the solution as the point or set of points that are on all of the graphs. Depending on the graph though you may at times only be able to get an **approximate value** of the x and y coordinates of the solution or the point(s) that satisfies all the equations, or inequalities in the system.

There are two other analytical methods for finding exact values to systems of equations that work directly with the equations.

In the **substitution method,** you solve one of the equations for either the x or y and substitute this value into the other equation making it then an equation in one variable. This will allow you to solve the new equation in one variable. Then replace that value in one of the original equations to find the other coordinate.

In a third method called the **elimination method,** you align the equations one above the other so that the $x's$, and the $y's$ are lined up. Then you multiply one of both of the equations by the required constants so that when you add the two equations one of the variables drops out. Thus we multiply each equation in such a way so that the coefficients on either the x or y variable are exact opposites. We then solved for the one variable that remains and substitute this back into one of the original equations to find the remaining variable.

We will illustrate all three methods in the examples that follow.

Graphical Method

Steps to find solutions using the graphical method for a system of equations and inequalities in two variables are below. We will focus on linear systems of two equations in two variables but the method can be extended to non-linear systems of equations and inequalities and to systems with more than two variables.

System of Equations	System of Inequalities
Step 1 Graph each of the lines in the system of equations. Step 2 Determine using your graphs the points of intersection and draw conclusions as shown below.	Step 1 Replace the inequality sign with equality for all the equations in your system of inequalities and then graph each of these lines. Step 2 If the original inequality is a strict inequality (e.g., $<$, or $>$), the points on the line are not part of the solution set. Therefore you will draw the line a dotted line. Otherwise (i.e., your inequality is a not a strict inequality, e.g., $\leq$, or $\geq$) all points on the line are part of the solution set and you will draw a solid line. Step 3 So shade the appropriate solution set for each of the inequalities in your system.

Points of Intersection	Conclusion
One	That point you see is the unique solution to the system.
None. (Lines are parallel to each other)	No Solution
Both lines overlap each other (have same slope and y-intercept	Infinitely many solutions. All points on the line you see are your solutions.

To shade region or to determine the solution set for each of the inequalities you will begin by testing a point not on the line. So first find a point (a, b) not on the line. Then plug in $x = a$, and $y = b$ in the inequality. If the result is a true statement, then all the points from the same region that the point (a, b) is from form your solution set. Otherwise all points on the other side of the line form your solution set.

Step 4 The intersection of all the solution sets in your system will determine the final solution set for your system of inequalities.

Examples

1. Solve the systems of equations and inequalities below using the graphical method.

System of Equations	System of Inequalities

a. $\begin{cases} 3x - 2y = 4 \\ x + y = 3 \end{cases}$

a. $\begin{cases} 3x - 2y < 4 \\ x + y > 3 \end{cases}$

Step 1 Graph the two lines $3x - 2y = 4$ and $x + y = 3$

Step 2 Both lines will be drawn as dotted lines since we have a strict inequality.

Step 3 The test point table shows what the solution set is.

Step 4

Step 1 Graph the two lines.

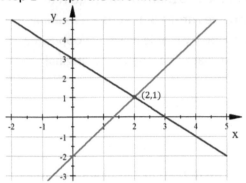

Step 2 From the graph we can see that the point (2,1) is the unique solution.

Test Point	$3x - 2y < 4$	$x + y > 3$
$(0,0)$	$3(0) - 2(0) < 4$ $0 < 4$	$0 + 0 > 3$ $0 > 3$
Truth Value	True	False
	Solution Set	Solution Set

b. $\begin{cases} x + y = 3 \\ y = 2x + 3 \end{cases}$

Step 1 Graph the two lines.

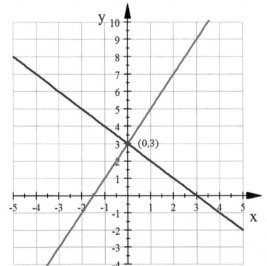

Step 2 From the graph we can see that the point (0,3) is the unique solution.

b. $\begin{cases} x + y \le 3 \\ y \ge 2x + 3 \end{cases}$

Test Point	$x + y \le 3$	$y \ge 2x + 3$
$(0,0)$	$0 + 0 \le 3$ $0 \le 3$	$0 + 0 > 3$ $0 > 3$
Truth Value	True	False
	Solution Set	Solution Set

We will look at the same two problems as above and use the substitution and the elimination methods.

Substitution method

In this method, you solve one of your equations for one of the variables and substitute this value of the variable in the other equation. This gives you an equation in one variable which you can solve. Once solved, use this value of the second variable into any of the equations to get value of the first variable. Below are some examples to demonstrate this method.

Examples

1. $\begin{cases} 3x - 2y = 4 \\ x + y = 3 \end{cases}$

   Solving the second equation for y we get $y = -x + 3$, substitute this value of y into the first equation giving us $3x - 2(-x + 3) = 4$ or $3x + 2x - 6 = 4$ or $5x = 10$ giving us $x = 2$. We can use this value of x into the equation $y = -x + 3 = -(2) + 3 = 1$ or the solution to this system of equation is $(x = 2, y = 1)$.

2. $\begin{cases} x + y = 3 \\ y = 2x + 3 \end{cases}$

   The second equation is already solved for $y = 2x + 3$ substituting this value into the first equation we get $x + (2x + 3) = 3$ solve this equation for x and we get $3x + 3 = 3$, $3x = 0$, $x = 0$. Using this value of x into the equation $y = 2x + 3 = 2(0) + 3 = 3$ we get our solution to be $(x = 0, y = 3)$

3. $\begin{cases} 3x - y = 4 \\ 6x - 2y = 3 \end{cases}$

   Solving the first equation for y we get $3x - 4 = y$, using this value in the second equation we get $6x - 2(3x - 4) = 3$, $6x - 6x + 8 = 3$ or $8 = 3$ which is a false statement therefore leading us to conclude there is no solution to this system of equation. In fact you can see that the lines are parallel to each other.

4. $\begin{cases} 7x + 5y = 1 \\ 2x + 5y = 3 \end{cases}$

   Solving the first equation for y we get $5y = -7x + 1$ or $= \frac{-7x+1}{5}$. Substituting this value of y into the second equation we get $2x + 5\left(\frac{-7x+1}{5}\right) = 3$, or $2x - 7x + 1 = 3$, or $-5x = 2$, or $x = -\frac{2}{5}$. Use this value of x to find value the of y. We get

$$y = \frac{-7x+1}{5} = \frac{-7\left(-\frac{2}{5}\right)+1}{5} = \frac{\frac{14}{5}+1}{5} = \frac{\frac{14}{5}+\frac{5}{5}}{5} = \frac{\frac{19}{5}}{\frac{5}{1}} = \frac{19}{5} \times \frac{1}{5} = \frac{19}{25}$$

The solution to this system of equation is $\left(-\frac{2}{5}, \frac{19}{25}\right)$

Elimination method

Another method frequently used in solving systems of equations is the elimination method. Here, align the like variables in the two equations above each other, then multiply one or both equations by a constant so that the coefficients on either the x or y variables are exact opposites in the two equations.

Then when you add the resulting equations that variable is eliminated and solving this equation will give you the value of the remaining variable. Put this value of the variable into any of the original equations to get the value of the second variable. Below are some examples to demonstrate this method.

Examples

1. $\begin{cases} 3x - 2y = 4 \\ x + y = 3 \end{cases}$

   The equations are already aligned so now you can choose to multiply the second equation by 2 and then add the resulting equations as shown below.

   $\begin{cases} 3x - 2y = 4 \\ (2)x + (2)y = (2)3 \end{cases}$ or $\begin{cases} 3x - 2y = 4 \\ 2x + 2y = 6 \end{cases}$

   Adding the two new equation we get $5x = 10$ or $x = 2$, and then substituting this value in the second original equation we get $2 + y = 3$ or $y = 1$. The solution to our system of equations is then given by $(2,1)$.

2. $\begin{cases} x + y = 3 \\ y = 2x + 3 \end{cases}$

   Rewriting the second equation so that the variables are aligned we get

   $\begin{cases} x + y = 3 \\ -2x + y = 3 \end{cases}$

   multiply the second equation by -1 and then add the two equations.

   $\begin{cases} x + y = 3 \\ (-1)(-2x) + (-1)y = (-1)3 \end{cases}$ or $\begin{cases} x + y = 3 \\ 2x - y = -3 \end{cases}$

   Adding the two new equations we get $3x = 0$ or $x = 0$, and then using the first equation we get $0 + y = 3$ or $y = 3$. The solution to the system of equation is $(0,3)$.

3. $\begin{cases} 3x - 7y = 4 \\ 2x + 5y = 3 \end{cases}$

   The equations are already aligned. Multiply the first equation by 2 and the second one by -3 and we get

   $\begin{cases} (2)3x - (2)7y = (2)4 \\ (-3)2x + (-3)5y = (-3)3 \end{cases}$ or $\begin{cases} 6x - 14y = 8 \\ -6x - 15y = -9 \end{cases}$

   Adding the two new equations we get $-29y = -1$ or $y = \frac{1}{29}$. To get x, substitute this value of y into the first equation giving us $3x - 7\left(\frac{1}{29}\right) = 4$ or $3x = 4 + \frac{7}{29}$ or $3x = \frac{4 \times 29}{1 \times 29} + \frac{7}{29}$, or $3x = \frac{123}{29}$ or $x = \frac{\frac{123}{29}}{3} = \frac{123}{87} = \frac{41}{29}$. So the solution is $\left(\frac{41}{29}, \frac{1}{29}\right)$.

4. $\begin{cases} x + y = -2 \\ 3x + 3y = -6 \end{cases}$

   Multiply the first equation by -3 and we get $\begin{cases} -3x - 3y = 6 \\ 3x + 3y = -6 \end{cases}$ adding the two equations we get

   $0 = 0$ which is always a true statement for any values of x and y. There are infinitely many solutions and they are all the points belonging to the line $x + y = -2$. This is a consistent dependent system.

1. Solve the systems of equations below. Use any method you think is suitable.

   a. $\begin{cases} 5x - 2y = 6 \\ 5x + 3y = 2 \end{cases}$

   d. $\begin{cases} 7x = 2y + 6 \\ 5x + 11y = 2 \end{cases}$

   g. $\begin{cases} x - y = 6 \\ 5x + 9y = 2 \end{cases}$

   b. $\begin{cases} x - 2y = 6 \\ 5x + 7y = 2 \end{cases}$

   e. $\begin{cases} x = 2y + 6 \\ 3x + 2y = 10 \end{cases}$

   h. $\begin{cases} y = x - 6 \\ 2x + 3y = 2 \end{cases}$

   c. $\begin{cases} x + y = -2 \\ x - y = 2 \end{cases}$

   f. $\begin{cases} 2x - 3y = 6 \\ 6y + 12 = -4x \end{cases}$

2. Sketch the graphs of the solution sets to the systems of inequalities below.

   a. $\begin{cases} 5x - 2y > 6 \\ 5x + 3y \leq 2 \end{cases}$

   d. $\begin{cases} 7x \leq 2y + 6 \\ 5x + 11y > 2 \end{cases}$

   g. $\begin{cases} x - y \leq 6 \\ 5x + 9y > 2 \end{cases}$

   b. $\begin{cases} x - 2y < 6 \\ 5x + 7y < 2 \end{cases}$

   e. $\begin{cases} x < 2y + 6 \\ 3x + 2y \leq 10 \end{cases}$

   h. $\begin{cases} y < x - 6 \\ 2x + 3y \geq 2 \end{cases}$

   c. $\begin{cases} x + y \geq -2 \\ x - y \geq 2 \end{cases}$

   f. $\begin{cases} 2x - 3y > 6 \\ 6y + 12 > -4x \end{cases}$

Students often ask or wonder how they are ever going to use the knowledge they have learned outside of the class. We will try to connect most of the topics you have learned in the four modules so far to problems from a variety of other disciplines. One of the biggest reasons for students to not notice where mathematics is applied outside of the classroom is the context in which these problems appear. If you pay attention, you might notice the mathematical problem solving techniques you learned being applied in other disciplines, especially since we are calling mathematics the queen of all sciences.

Most often the applied problems are referred to as "Word Problems." Students often cringe when they hear these words. If this has happened to you, then just try and keep an open mind through this process and you will see that once you learn how to read and interpret the words, these problems are no different in their difficulty level than the ones you already saw. Some of the problem types might seem like repeats but it is necessary to repeat these so you can see the different methods you can apply to solve them.

4.4 Interpreting Graphs and Linear Models

In this section we will learn to read information from given graphs and also work with applied situations where a linear model describes how two quantities are related to each other. Linear models are often used to predict short-term values in many business and science applications. Sometimes the slope-intercept form $y = mx + b$ of a line is appropriate when we are working with x-values near to the y-axis. However, in many situations, it is not practical or useful to work near the y-intercept. For example if x represents the year and $2002 \le x \le 2025$, we won't be using the part of the graph anywhere near the y-axis at $x = 0$. In these settings the point-slope form of a linear equation is more useful.

Interpreting Graphs

Next we look at interpreting information presented graphically and how to "read" information from a graph.

Lectures

🖥 Applications of lines and graphs Reading Graphs (7 min)
http://www.youtube.com/watch?v=plhuVnNFYxc

We start with interpreting graphs of data that we might typically see in reading a news article or textbook.

Example

1. Suppose that the graph below shows profit function for a company for 25 years since 1987, where $t = 0$ represents the year 1987, and P represents the profit in millions of dollars.

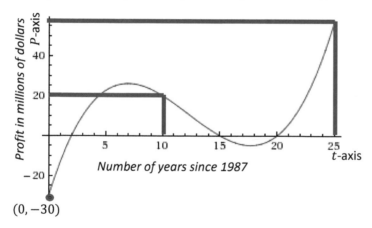

a. In the year 1987, what was the profit in millions of dollars?
b. What was the profit in millions of dollars in 1997?
c. What was the profit in millions of dollars in 2012?
d. In what year/s was the profit of the company more than 20 million dollars?
e. For what years did the company have negative profit? What does this mean?

Solution

a. The profit was −30 million dollars or the company had a loss of 30 million dollars.
b. The profit was about 20 million dollars in 1997.
c. The profit was over 55 million dollars in 2012.
d.

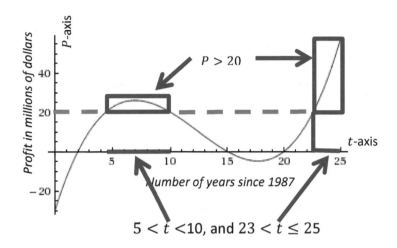

The profit was more than 20 million dollars between the years 1992 and 1997, and between the years 2010 and 2012.

e.

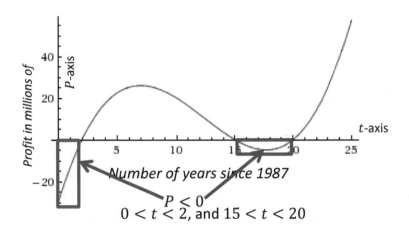

The company has negative profit in the years 1987-1989, and also from 2002 to 2007. Negative profits means the company lost money.

2. Consider the graph of the average high and low temperature for Milwaukee, WI, over a year. To see what information can be "read" off of the graph, please answer the questions below. Note that this graph is actually the plot of two functions that have month of year as the input and the outputs are the average high and low temperatures for that month.

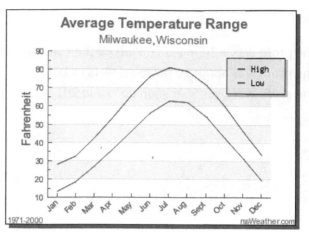

a. What is the hottest month of the year, how hot?

b. What is the coolest month of the year and how cold?

c. Which months have an average high temperature below 40 degrees?

d. Write a linear equation that represents this linear trend from the month of March to June.

e. Does it appear that the high and low temperature difference is greater in January than in July?

f. What differences might you expect in this graph for Panama City (near the equator) and Lima, Peru?

Solution

a. From the graph we see that July appears to be the hottest month where the average high is about 81 and average low is about 62 degrees.

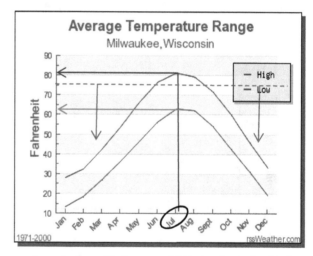

b. What is the coolest month of the year and how cold? Again, from the graph, it appears that January is the coolest month with an average high/low of 29 and 14 degrees Fahrenheit.

c. Which months have an average high temperature below 40 degrees? We look at the high temperature graph and see that it lies below the horizontal line at 40 degrees only for December, January and February.

d. The high temperature graph is nearly linear from month 3 (March) at 42 deg. to month 6 (June) at 76 deg. Write a linear equation that represents this linear trend. We compute the slope as $m = \frac{76°F - 42°F}{6\,mon - 3\,mon} = 11\frac{1}{3}\frac{deg}{mon}$. Then use point-slope with the point (3, 42) to obtain $= 42°F + 11\frac{1}{3}\frac{°F}{mon}(x - 3\,mon)$.

e. Does it appear that the high and low temperature difference is greater in January than in July? In January the high and low are at 28 and 13 degrees for an average warming of 15 degrees during a day. In July the high and low are at 81 and 62 degrees for an average warming of 19 degrees during a day.

f. What differences might you expect in this graph for the Panama City (near the equator) and Lima, Peru? For Panama City, the climate is tropical and has little variation over the course of a year and hence the plot would be much flatter. For Lima in the southern hemisphere, the seasons are reversed relative to Milwaukee and hence the warmest and coolest months would be January and July respectively.

Video Log 4.4a

1. The graph below represents height of a plant over a 10 week period.

    a. In week 4 what is the plant height in centimeters?

    b. In what week was the plant height about 15 cm?

    c. What is the maximum expected plant height reached by this plant?

    d. In what weeks was the height of the plant between 10 and 15 cms?

    e. What was the range of the plant height for days between week 6 and week 10?

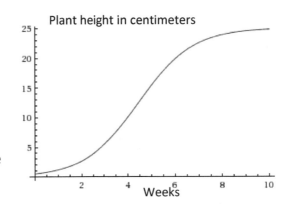

2. The graph to the right indicates the use of corn for animal feed, food export and for ethanol fuel production in the U.S.

    a. Estimate the total millions of tons of corn use in the years 1990, 1995, 2000, 2005 and 2010.

    b. What is the trend for the total corn production over this 20 year period?

    c. Can you explain the steep drop in corn exports from 2007 to 2012?

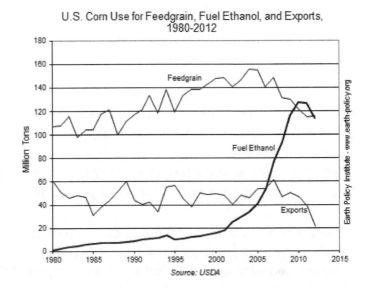

3. The graph below shows the revenue from selling a commodity in millions of dollars with respect to the selling price in dollars of the commodity.
   a. What is revenue when the price is set at 10$/unit?
   b. What should the unit price be set at to maximize the revenue?
   c. What unit price(s) of the commodity will generate $800,000,000 in revenue?
   d. What unit price range which will generate more than $800,000,000 in revenue?

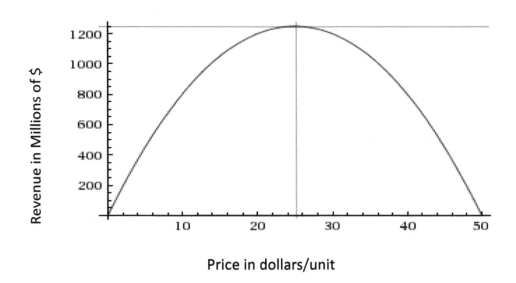

Price in dollars/unit

Linear Models
Lecture

🖥 Linear Models (11 min)

http://www.youtube.com/watch?v=8DXMehKa6_w

Examples
1. Consider a linear relation model for the population of Wisconsin. In 1990 and 2000 Wisconsin's population was 4,891,769 and 5,363,675 respectively.
   a. Determine the linear relation between time and Wisconsin's population.
   b. Can you predict what the population of Wisconsin will be in the current year? (You can check how close your prediction is to the actual prediction at http://www.census.gov/population/)

2. Suppose the cost of a base-model Honda-Civic in 2002 at $16,000 and in 2012 at $19,000.
   a. Use a linear model to predict the price of this model car for years in between and beyond.
   b. Use your model to predict the price of the car in year 2017.

3. Biologists have observed that the rate of a cricket's chirping is approximated well by a linear equation with the temperature as a variable. During two nights at Wausau, WI, when the temperature was 64 and 71 degrees Fahrenheit, the local crickets chirped at 92 and 122 chirps per minute.

   a. Use a linear model to predict the relationship between the number of chirps per minute, and the temperature outside measured in Fahrenheit.

   b. Use your model to predict the number of chirps per minute when it is 80 degrees Fahrenheit outside.

   c. Use your model to predict the degrees Fahrenheit outside if the rate of chirps is 150 chirps per minute.

Please try these problems on your own before peeking on the next page...

Solutions:

1.

   a. Let $x =$ the year, and $y =$ the population of Wisconsin in the year x. To find an equation of this line, we first find the slope $m = \dfrac{rise}{run} = \dfrac{5363675 - 4891769}{10} = \dfrac{235953}{5}$ which is about $\dfrac{47191\ people}{1yr}$ which states the rate of increase in population y per one year increase in x. Here it is not very useful to determine what y would be at year $x = 0$. It is better to use perhaps 2000 as the reference point. If we do this, then the population at year x is given by $y = 5,363,675 + 47,191(x - 2000)$. What the second term says is that the population will grow 47,191 people for each year that x is larger than 2000. The equation of a line written in this form $y = y_1 + m(x - x_1)$ is called point slope form.

   b. If we wanted to estimate the population of Wisconsin in the year 2030, we would substitute $x = 2030$ into the equation of the line in part a). So using our equation we predict that there will $y = 5363675 + 47191(2030 - 1990) = 7251315$ people in the year 2030. You should use caution when using something like this to predict that far away from the given data as many times there are additional factors that could affect outcomes.

2.

   a. Let x be the year and y the dollar cost of the car. We are given two points $(2002, \$16,000)$ and $(2012, \$19,000)$. The rise is $\$3,000$ for a run of 10 years and thus the slope is $\$300$ per year. Using our point-slope equation is given by $y = 19,000 + 300(x - 2012)$.

   b. Using the model in part a), we have that the 2017 price prediction for this base-model civic would be $\$19,000 + 300(5) = \$21,500$.

3.

   a. We can find a linear relation between temperature and cricket chirps per minute by considering the above data as two points $(temp, chirps\ per\ min)$ $(64, 92)\ and\ (71, 122)$. The slope is $= \dfrac{122-92}{71-64} = \dfrac{30}{7} = \dfrac{30\ chirps}{7F}$. This says the chirp rate increases ~4 chirps per min for each one degree increase in the temperature. We can use the point-slope form to get an equation for this relationship as $C = 122 + \dfrac{30}{7}(T - 71)$.

b. Using the model in part a) we can either predict the chirp rate at various temperatures or estimate the temperature when the chirp rate is observed. Thus this relation would predict that at 80°F, the chirp rate would be $C = 122 + \frac{30}{7}(80 - 71) \approx 161 chirps$.

c. Also if we count 150 chirps per minute, we'd have $150 = 122 + \frac{30}{7}(T - 71)$ or $28 = \frac{30}{7}(T - 71)$, or $28 \cdot \left(\frac{7}{30}\right) = T - 71$, or $28 \cdot \left(\frac{7}{30}\right) + 71 = T$, or $T \approx 77.5°F$. It is about 77.5 degrees Fahrenheit outside.

Video Log 4.4b

1. A plant growth formula is given by the linear equation $y = \frac{5}{3}t + 4$, where y =height in inches and t=number of weeks. What is the height of the plant in the 3rd week and at how many weeks will the plant be 19 inches tall?

2. Let the amount of water in a leaking bucket be given by $A = 8 - 0.25t$, where A =amount of water in bucket in liters and t = time in minutes after it began leaking.
   a. How much water is in the bucket after 5 minutes?
   b. How much water was in the bucket at the beginning just when it started leaking?
   c. When will the bucket be completely empty?
   d. What is the t-intercept and the A-intercept? What is the significance of these intercepts?
   e. What is the slope of this line? What is the physical significance of the slope?

3. Suppose Anna has a phone card and the amount of money left on the card is given by $B = 37.30 - 0.02x$ where B =balance of money left on Anu's card after x minutes of call.
   a. What is the rate Anna is paying per minute on her phone card?
   b. How much money is on Anna's card after talking to her sister for 2 hours and 5 minutes?
   c. What is the physical significance of the slope?
   d. What is the maximum number of minutes Anna can talk using her card? How many hours is it?

4. Linda's parents loaned her 12,345 dollars interest free for her college tuition and books. Linda promised to pay her parents back 80 dollars a week until the loan is completely paid off. How long will it take Linda to pay her parents back? Write an equation that will allow Linda a quick overview of how much money she owes her parents x weeks after she began paying on the loan.

5. In 2000 the population of India was 1014 million people. In 2010 its population was 1170 million people (almost four times as many people as in the U.S.).
   a. Find a linear equation that fits the above data where y is India's population in millions in the year x.
   b. Use the equation in (a) to predict India's population in 2025.
   c. Explain the meaning of the slope of the line in (a).

6. Suppose that the growth of a plant is charted as shown below.

   a. Determine what height the plant will be at week 9.

   b. If you assume a linear growth rate, what is the relationship between time t in days and the height h of the plant measured in inches?

   c. At how many days will the plant reach a height of 2 feet?

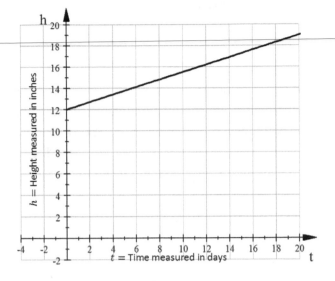

Applications

Lecture

🖥 Applications (8 min)

http://www.youtube.com/watch?v=idPmgnUD-X0

Next we look at fairly simple modeling where we assume a linear relationship between two varying quantities. Typically we have a set of data points that can be plotted in a plane graph. If the points on the graph seem closely aligned along a line, a linear "fit" to the data will provide a useful model for the relationship between the variables. A spread-sheet such as Excel, a graphing calculator or an on-line program such as Wolfram Alpha (www.worlframalpha.com) can be used to obtain a "best fit" linear equation when all the data don't lie exactly on a line. You can usually do nearly as well by simply plotting the data points and visually drawing what looks like the best linear fit to the data. Then simply choose two points from that line and find its equation.

Examples

1. The height of corn plants is a nearly linear function of time for the two-week period after the corn reaches 20 inches in height. We are given the data of the growth in inches days after the corn reached 20 inches.

day	Height (in)
0	20
2	25
4	29
6	33
8	38
10	44

a. Plot the data by hand on a graph or using an Excel data sheet, where you can then highlight the data cells including the headings and then click on insert a scatter plot to get the first plot below. You can also click somewhere near the data points, you will be given the option of adding a trend line with options to include its equation as shown in the second plot.

b. Find the equation of the line that best describes the data.

c. Can you use the equation of the line to predict what the height of the corn would be 13 days after it reached 20 inches.

Solution

a.

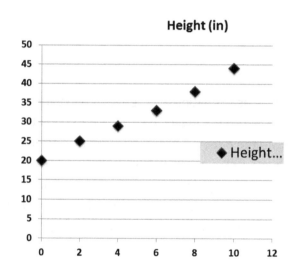
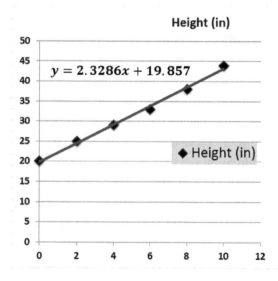

b. For this data, we'd do pretty well by visually seeing that a decent linear fit would go through the points at (0, 20) and (8, 38). Then we could use slope-intercept to obtain the equation. Thus $m = \frac{38-20}{8-0} = \frac{18}{2.25x8} = 2.25\frac{in}{day}$. Then we have $y = 20 + 2.25(x - 0)$, $y = 2.25x + 20$ which is very close to the best fit line $y = 2.5286x + 19.857$.

c. We can now use either linear model to estimate the plants' height 13 days after it was 20 inches tall. We simply plug in $x = 13$ to get $y = 2.25(13) + 20 \approx 49\ inches.$

The supply and demand concept of the marketplace says that, as the price of an item increases, the amount that people will buy decreases. We will assume a linear relation with x being the number of units sold and y being the per unit price. Only two data points are needed to obtain this relationship. Once this demand relationship is obtained, revenue and projected profit can also be arrived at if the cost of producing the items is also known.

2. A Boy Scout club sells hot dogs at a local ball club during the summer. They can purchase the hotdogs and buns and supplies for $0.40 per hot dog. They played around with pricing a bit to try to maximize their profit. For several weeks they charged $2.50 per hot dog and on average sold 300 hot dogs each night. They then raised the price to $3.00 per hot dog and the nightly sales dropped off to 220 per night.
   a. Find the linear demand relationship where x is the number sold and y the selling price. (In other words equation of the line that goes through the two points (300, $2.50) and (220, $3.00).)
   b. Find the revenue relationship using the fact that revenue is price per hotdog times the number of hotdogs sold.
   c. Find the profit function using the fact that profit is revenue minus the cost.
   d. Use a graphing calculator or Excel, or www.wolframalpha.com , or make a table of points to plot the profit function output with number of hotdogs sold per night (x) as the input. Use x-values ranging from 0 to 400.
   e. From your graph in d.) estimate the maximum profit and how many hot dogs should they sell per night in order to maximize their profit? Also, use (a.) to obtain the price they should charge per hot dog.

Solution

   a. To find the linear demand relationship where x is the number sold and y the selling price, we use the two points (300, 2.50) and (220, 3.00). The slope is then $= \dfrac{3.00-2.50}{220-300} = \dfrac{0.5}{-80} = -\dfrac{\$1}{160\ hot\ dogs}$. Note that this says to increase sales by 160 hot dogs, the price needs to be dropped $1. Next, we can use point-slope to obtain $y = 2.50 - \dfrac{1}{160}(x-300)$ or expanding we have $price = y = -\dfrac{1}{160}x + 4.375$.
   b. To find the revenue function where y is the revenue in dollars from selling x hotdogs we have that the revenue is equal to the number sold times the selling price. From part a), the selling price needed to sell x hotdogs is equal to $unit\ price = -\dfrac{1}{160}x + 4.375$, therefore the revenue is given by $R = x\left(-\dfrac{1}{160}x + 4.375\right) = -\dfrac{1}{160}x^2 + 4.375x$. Note that this is not a linear relation; It is called a quadratic relationship between x and R.
   c. Using the revenue from (b.) and the cost information to determine the net earnings from selling x hotdogs, we get that the net earnings is equal to revenue minus costs. It is stated that the cost is $0.40 per hotdog, so for x hotdogs, the club will need to pay $C(x) = 0.4x$ to buy their

supplies. This leaves the net earnings to be $R - C = -\frac{1}{160}x^2 + 4.375x - 0.4x$ or Profit $P = -\frac{1}{160}x^2 + 3.975x$.

d. Plot the net earnings $P = -\frac{1}{160}x^2 + 3.975x$ and determine how many hotdogs they should sell per game to maximize their revenue. Since this is not a line, we should plot a series of points to get a sense of the graph. One can use a graphing calculator or Excel or Wolfram Alpha to plot it as well.

e. From the plot, the maximum earnings occurs very near to (300, $630). To plot this in Excel, you can enter a column of x values and then type in the formula for the first entry in the y-column as shown.
    To obtain the y-values down the column, click and drag the lower corner of the first y-cell down. When adding the trend line, choose a second degree polynomial. Finally, the selling price should be the price to sell 300 hotdogs or $2.50

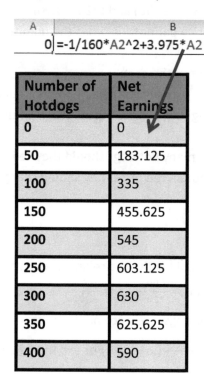

A	B
0	=-1/160*A2^2+3.975*A2

Number of Hotdogs	Net Earnings
0	0
50	183.125
100	335
150	455.625
200	545
250	603.125
300	630
350	625.625
400	590

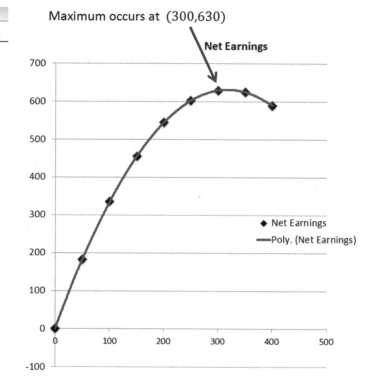

Maximum occurs at (300,630)

Video Log 4.4c

1. The graph below is of the Wisconsin population over the past twenty five years.
   a. Draw a line that seems to fit this population trend.
   b. Estimate from your line in (a) when the population will reach 6 six million.
   c. Select two points from your line in (a) (approximately) to determine the slope of the line and interpret the meaning of this slope.
   d. Find an equation of the line using the slope from (c) and one of the points selected.
   e. From your equation determine when the population will reach 6,000,000 and compare with your answer in (b)

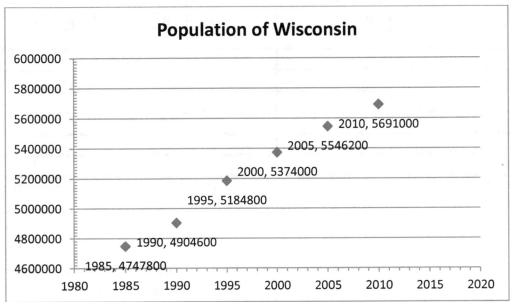

2. A campus club sells cupcakes each Monday as a fundraiser. They play around with pricing to see how the demand for cupcakes depends on the selling price. When they charge $0.65 per cupcake, they notice that on average they sell 125 cupcakes each Monday, but when the price was set at a $0.75 per cupcake, they sold 75 cupcakes each Monday. They purchase their cupcakes in bulk from a local bakery for $0.25 each.
   a. Find a linear demand relation $y = p(x) = mx + b$ that fits the data given, i.e. $(125, 0.65), (75, 0.75)$ where x is the number of cupcakes that will sell and y is the selling price.
   b. Find the revenue function $y = R(x) = x \cdot p(x)$, that gives the total revenue from selling x cupcakes.
   c. Give the cost function $y = C(x)$ that gives the total cost for buying x cupcakes from the local bakery.
   d. Use b and c to state the net profit function $y = P(x)$ obtained each week when x cupcakes are sold.
   e. Plot the profit function at http://www.wolframalpha.com/examples/PlottingAndGraphics.html for sales between 0 and 180 cupcakes per week and estimate the number of cupcakes to sell to make the profit as large as possible.

3. A local fundraising event for student scholarships involves volunteer chefs who provide a variety of food samples for an evening event that charges admission. The organizing committee wants to optimize revenue and has data from two years on total number of tickets sold and the ticket price. In the first year when the ticket price was $30 per person, 360 tickets were sold. The next year, the price was $40, and 280 tickets were sold.

   a. Plot the information above where the x-coordinate represents total number of tickets sold and the y-coordinate the price per ticket.

   b. Assuming there is a linear relation between x and y, find the equation $y = mx + b$.

   c. Use your equation in (b) to fill in the missing values in the table below.

Number of Tickets	Price per Ticket	Total Revenue in Dollars = Number of Tickets × Price per Ticket
	$50	
240		
280	$40	$280 \times 40 = 11200$
	$35	
360	$30	$360 \times 30 = 10800$
	$25	
440		

   d. Plot the set of points in (c.) as (total number of tickets, total revenue) and from your plot estimate what number of tickets that will generate the maximum revenue. Also use your equation from (b.) to determine what the ticket price should be to sell this number of tickets.

4. Two cell phones offer the rates below for one year of service. Touchphone charges $60 plus 7 cents a minute for all calls. BT&U charges $80 a year plus 5 cents a minute for calls.

   a. Find linear equations for each provider $y = mx + b$ where y is the total cost for a year of service and x is the number of minutes of calls.

   $touchphone(x) =$ _____ , $BT\&U(x) =$ _____

   b. Plot both lines and determine for how many minutes a year the Touchphone plan is cheaper.

4.5 Other Applications
Lecture

🖥 Applications (14 min)

http://www.youtube.com/watch?v=WXLZKrZUnKQ

We will start with some generic tips on how to read the problems, interpret what is being asked of you, how to organize or sort out the given information so as to readily generate a mathematics equation to solve.

In most applications, the problems are not given in a mathematical formulation. A major task is to "mathematize" the problem. Below are some tips that will aid you in this process:

1. Read the problem so you understand what is being asked.

2. Draw a rough sketch if that helps.

3. Assign variables or use given variables for all the quantities involved in the problem. Below are some guidelines you can use to assign variables.

   A. Look for words like "How much", "How far", "How long", "Find", "When",…

   B. Use letters for variables that make sense to you

   C. Sometimes the problem tells you what variables to use and then make sure you use the given variables paying careful attention to whether they are capital or small letters.

4. When using known formulas to solve a problem, organize information in a chart form.

5. Sometimes you will have to translate words into mathematical expressions as we did in Module 1. Below are just a few examples to review the terminology, you might have to go back to module 1 to see more details.

   Recall words like

   A. "Is" might translate mathematically to "=."

   B. "Sum" might translate mathematically to addition "+."

   C. "Product" or "Of" might translate mathematically to multiplication "×."

   D. "Square" might translate mathematically to second power of the quantity involved " ^{2}."

   E. "Twice" might translate to two times a quantity

6. Substitute any known quantities into the formulas.

7. When working with equations and inequalities, solve for the unknown variable.

8. Keep track of units throughout your work and be sure your final answer has the appropriate units.

9. Check your answer and estimate or consider the reasonableness of your answer.

---

10. Write your final answer in a sentence that fits the question being asked with the appropriate units.

At times you also might have to

1. Make some assumptions (e.g., that two quantities are related linearly);
2. Assign variables to represent quantities that change;
3. Come up with one or more equations relating the variables.
4. Use the tools of algebra to solve the equation or system of equations or to graph the equation to explain visually what is going on.

There are more advanced areas of mathematics such as calculus, abstract algebra, and graph theory that basically were developed, and are being further developed, to model more and more complicated problems. Many applications require an ability to translate a real life situation into a graphical representation of the data gathered, or some mathematical expression, or equations, or inequalities. Sometimes the data collected does not represent a mathematical expression or equation/inequality until a process called curve fitting is used and then that equation is used to predict values for the near future. The process of taking situations and representing them mathematically is called mathematical modeling. The result of this process is called a mathematical model of the situation.

Examples

1. A recipe calls for 1 ¾ cups of flour, ½ c sugar and 1 stick of butter as shown below.

Original recipe= $1\frac{3}{4}$ C of flour $+\frac{1}{2}$ C of sugar + 1 stick of butter

Another way to visualize the same thing would be to have same number parts of flour, sugar and butter.

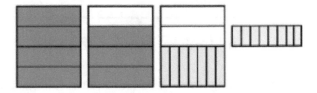

Original recipe= $\frac{7}{4}$ C of flour $+\frac{7}{14}$ C of sugar $+\frac{7}{7}$ stick of butter

Problem Statement: Paul put in 2 cups of flour instead of the 1 ¾ c and had added the sugar before realizing his error. Paul has added an additional part of flour so we need to add additional part of sugar and butter as shown below.

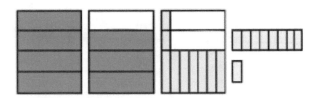

To the 2 c of flour and ½ c of sugar, add $\frac{1}{7}\left(\frac{1}{2}\right)=\frac{1}{14}$ C of sugar + $1\frac{1}{7}$ stick of butter

Method 2: We can solve this using ratios since the ratio of what is needed to what the recipe called for will be the same for all ingredients.   Thus

For sugar:

$$\frac{2}{1\frac{3}{4}}=\frac{sugar\ total\ c}{\frac{1}{2}c}$$

$\rightarrow \frac{8}{7}=\frac{x\ c\ sugar}{\frac{1}{2}} \rightarrow \frac{4}{7}=x\ c\ sugar\ total.$ This is also $\frac{8}{14}c$ which is $\frac{1}{14}c$ extra beyond the $\frac{1}{2}c$ called for.

And for Butter: $\frac{2}{1\frac{3}{4}}=\frac{8}{7}=\frac{x\ sticks\ butter}{1\ stick} \rightarrow$ we need $\frac{8}{7}$ sticks of butter.

2. The tank on Karl's truck went from $\frac{1}{3}$ full to ½ full when he added 4 gallons of gas. Use this information to determine how many gallons the tank holds when full.

Method 1: A strip diagram of the tank can be used to solve the problem. It is clear that the space between $\frac{1}{3}$ and $\frac{1}{2}$ of a tank corresponds to 4 gallons. Recall representing both $\frac{1}{3}$ and $\frac{1}{2}$ in one strip diagram require we divide the tank into 6 equal pieces. We can now see that 4 gallons corresponds to $\frac{1}{6}$ of the whole tank. Thus the full tank capacity is $6 \times 4 = 24\ gallons$.

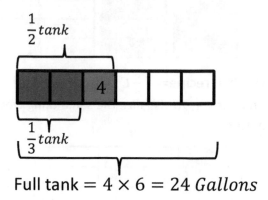

Full tank $= 4 \times 6 = 24\ Gallons$

Method 2: Let $x =$ The full capacity of the tank. Then going from $\frac{1}{3}x$ to $\frac{1}{2}x$ requires four gallons of gas can be written as:

$$\frac{1}{3}x + 4 = \frac{1}{2}x$$

$$4 = \frac{1}{2}x - \frac{1}{3}x.$$

$$4 = \frac{3}{6}x - \frac{2}{6}x$$

$$4 = \frac{1}{6}x$$

$$4 \times \frac{6}{1} = x$$

$$24 = x$$

The tank's full capacity is $24\ gallons$.

3. Jenn started school with $800 on her meal debit card and each time she used the card for a meal, $4.50 was deducted from the card balance. Two months into the semester, she noticed her card balance was $71. How many meals did Jenn charge to her card by this time?

We can let N = The number of meals purchased.

The debit card dropping from $800 down $4.50 for each meal and ending up at $71 translates to the equation:

$800 - 4.5N = 71$, solving for N, we get

$800 - 71 = 4.5N$

$729 = 4.5N$

$162 = N.$

Jenn purchased 162 meals.

4. A rectangular shaped piece of property has a perimeter of 1.5 miles. If the width of the property is $\frac{1}{4} mile$, determine the area of the property.

It is always useful to draw a diagram for geometry related problems.
Let l = The unknown length of the property.
The perimeter around the edge of the property is 1.5 mi and the short ends are each ¼ mile. Note that perimeter of a rectangle is the sum of the length of all the sides giving us the equation. This problem can be solved just by looking at the diagram and realizing that the two short sides amount to ½ mile and thus the other mile of perimeter must be for the two long sides which must each be ½ mile.
Algebraically, with the perimeter of a rectangle $P = 2l + 2w$.
$2l + 2 \times \frac{1}{4} = 1.5$, solving for l, we get

$2l + 0.5 = 1.5$

$2l = 1.5 - 0.5$

$2l = 1$

$l = \frac{1}{2} mi$

Thus the area of the property is

$A = l \times w = \frac{1}{2} mi \times \frac{1}{4} mi = \frac{1}{8} mi^2$

The area of the property is $\frac{1}{8} mi^2$.

5. Consider the situation where you need to mix yellow, blue and red paints in the ratio of 3:2:4 to obtain a certain shade of paint. You've decided to make a batch with half of the above numbers of cups. Thus the plan is to use 1.5, 1 and 2 cups of yellow, blue and red paint. By accident, however, you started by putting in 2.5 cups of yellow, but did not notice this until the 1 cup of blue and 2 cups of red had been mixed in. You could start over, or just add an appropriate amount of blue and red to obtain the correct shade. **How much** more of the blue and red should be added?

Consider the situation where you need to mix yellow, blue and red paints in the ratio of 3:2:4 to obtain a certain shade of paint.

You've decided to make a batch with half of the above numbers of cups. Thus the plan is to use 1.5, 1 and 2 cups of yellow, blue and red paint.

By accident, however, you started by putting in 2.5 cups of yellow, but did not notice this until the 1 cup of blue and 2 cups of red had been mixed in. You could start over, or just add an appropriate amount of blue and red to obtain the correct shade. By making equal divisions of the original paint, we can see that each cup of yellow corresponds to 2/3 cups of blue and 4/3 cups of red.

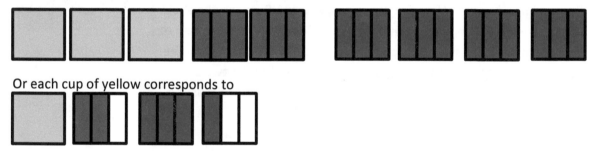

Or each cup of yellow corresponds to

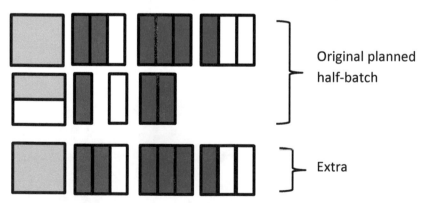

That would mean to make the correct shade, since we had already added one extra cup of yellow, we still need to add the 2/3 cup of blue and the 4/3 cup of red.

Original planned half-batch

Extra

Lecture

⬛ Applications (7 min)

http://www.youtube.com/watch?v=dsbrQ54So38

6. Find two consecutive integers whose sum is 49.

Method 1:

Since consecutive integers are 1 unit from each other, if x =the first number, then $x + 1$ =the second number. Their sum is 49, translates to $x + x + 1 = 49$. Solving for x, we get

$2x + 1 = 49$

$2x = 48$

$x = \dfrac{48}{2} = 24$

The two integers whose sum is 49 are 24 and 25.

Method 2:

Let $x =$ the first number, and

$y =$ the second number.

$\begin{cases} x + y = 49 \\ y = x + 1 \end{cases}$ using substitution method we get

$x + (x + 1) = 49$

$2x + 1 = 49$

$2x = 48$

$x = \dfrac{48}{2} = 24$

The two integers whose sum is 49 are 24 and 25.

7. Amy needed 17 volunteers for her church fundraiser last year. This year her church predicted that Amy will need 25 volunteers for the same fund raiser. How many more volunteers does Amy need to recruit this year compared to last year?

Method 1:

Amy will need $25 - 17 = 8$ extra volunteers.

The second method will come in handy when the problems get more complicated so it might be good to start doing the problems in this systematic manner.

Method 2:

Let $V =$ Number of extra volunteers Amy needs to recruit this year.

$25 =$ Number of volunteers needed this year.

$17 =$ Number of volunteers needed last year.

The equation that connects the given information is $25 = 17 + V$.

Solving for V, we get $V = 25 - 17 = 8$.

Amy will need 8 extra volunteers this year.

8. A school bus can hold maximum of 72 kids. If there are 353 kids that are to be taken on field trip to Chicago's Science and Industry Museum, how many buses will be needed?

    Let $B =$ Number of buses needed to transport 353 kids.

    $353 = 72B$, solving for B, we get $B = \frac{353}{72} \approx 4.9$. Since the number busses has to be a whole number, the school will need to arrange for 5 school buses.

9. **How much** of a tip should be left at a restaurant for a $45 bill?

    Method 1

    The problem can be clarified with a strip diagram or even a mental image of one. We must be clear about what the whole is and show the percentage change up or down from that whole. The diagram below shows how to compute the tip for a $45 bill assuming that you are paying a 15% tip on your bill. In the strip diagram below lets us break $45 into ten equal parts and the second piece break in halves. This will allow you to represent 15% clearly.

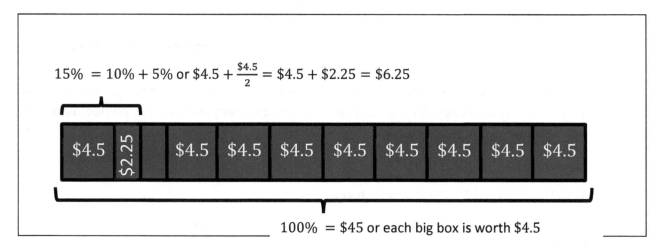

$$15\% = 10\% + 5\% \text{ or } \$4.5 + \frac{\$4.5}{2} = \$4.5 + \$2.25 = \$6.25$$

$100\% = \$45$ or each big box is worth $4.5

    Method 2

    Let $T =$ amount of tip left at a restaurant for a $45 bill.

    Assuming you pay 15% tip on the bill we have $T = 0.15 \times \$45 = \$6.75$.

    You might want to leave a tip of $6.75 on the table.

    Although the first method seems more tedious, visulazing a problem is very useful and even to get an approximate answer this way will help avoid wrong answers due to mis-entering numbers on a calculator.

10. A shoe store is advertising a 35% off sale and you have been planning to buy an $80 pair of shoes at that store. Determine **what** the sale price of the shoes will be.

Method 1

The percentage markdown is based on the original $80 price which would represent the whole. We can think of $35\% = 25\% + 5\% + 5\%$. The diagram below shows how the sale price is arrived at.

Whole 100% = $80, 25% of $80=$\frac{1}{4} \times 80$ = $20, 5% of $80 = $4

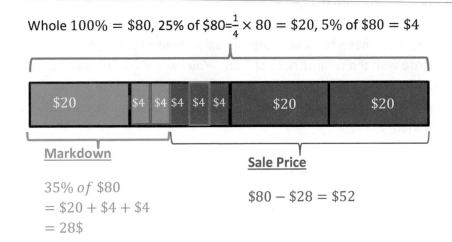

Markdown

$35\% \ of \ \$80$
$= \$20 + \$4 + \$4$
$= 28\$$

Sale Price

$\$80 - \$28 = \$52$

The sale price of the show is $52.

Method 2

Let $x =$ sale price of the shoes.

Then we have $Sale \ price = Original \ Price - Discount$

$x = \$80 - 0.35(\$80)$ or $x = \$80 - \$28 = \$52$

The sale price of the shoe will be $52.

11. Last year Amy made $45,000 and this year she made $48,300. What is the percentage increase in her salary?

Let $p =$ percentage increase in Amy's salary. Note that the reference amount that the percentage increase is computed from is Amy's salary from last year.

$45000 + 45000p = 48300$, solving for p we get

$45000p = 48300 - 45000$

$45000p = 3300$

$p = \dfrac{3300}{45000} = \dfrac{11}{150} \approx 0.073$

Amy salary increased by 7.3%.

Or more directly, the $\% \ increase = \dfrac{increase \ amount}{reference \ amount} = \dfrac{3,300}{45,000} \approx 0.073 = 7.3\% \ increase.$

Video Log 4.5a

1. A recipe calls for $1\frac{1}{3}$ cups of flour, ½ c sugar and 1 stick of butter. It is critical that these proportions be adhered to in order for the cookies to turn out well. Ari was careless as he started and put in 2 cups of flour instead of the $1\frac{1}{3}$ cups and had added the sugar before realizing his error. Determine how much additional sugar and how much total butter he should add to keep the proportions in line with the recipe.

2. Consider the situation where you need to make a large volume of punch using pineapple juice, passion fruit juice and sprite with the volume ratio of 2:3:2. You have already mixed together 3 gallons of pineapple juice and 4 gallons of passion fruit juice and 2 gallons of sprite. Determine the minimum amount of two of the ingredients that you should add to keep the correct volume ratio of the three ingredients.

3. The sum of three consecutive even integers is 96. What are the three numbers?

4. Kim's Prepaid phone card started with a $90 balance and each minute of call time costs 12 cents. Determine how many minutes of calls she had made when her balance had decreased to $39.

5. A rectangular swimming pool is 10 meters longer than twice its width. Determine the dimensions of the pool if the perimeter of the pool is 140 meters.

6. Jim's salary increased from $45,359 to $48,234 from 2012 to 2013.
    a. What was the dollar value of the increase?
    b. What percentage did Jim's salary increase by?
    c. What percent smaller was his salary in 2012 compared to 2013?

7. A new school server hard drive has a capacity of 16,000 gigabytes and needs to provide storage space for 134 staff members. Determine how many gigabytes of server space is available for each staff member.

8. John earns $64,000 a year and pays 27% of his salary in income tax. How much income tax does he pay?

9. A pair of $120 shoes was marked down 45%. What was the sale price? Use a diagram to show your answer.

🖥 Applications (11 min)

http://www.youtube.com/watch?v=CZQu8Q3maEk

Mixture Problems:

The examples below are all of a similar type, they can all be classified as mixture problems. Mixture Problems involve creating a mixture by combining two or more components and requiring that the value of the components is equal to the value of the mixture. Here the **"value"** may be: The interest earned on each component of an investment; Or the amount of some solution component such as acid, antifreeze, or alcohol; Or the dollar-value of each component. With two-component mixture problems, there are two unknowns, x & y being the amount of each of the two components. There are also two equations: One that the total sum of the two components must be equal to that of the mixture; The other equation states that the sum of the **value** of each of the components must be equal to the value of the mixture.

Examples:

1. Anita works at two jobs for 50 hours a week, one in the math lab at a pay rate of $8/hr and the other at a nursing home at a rate of $9.50/hr. In a week where she earned a total of $460, how many hours did she work at each job?

   Solution: Let
   M =Number of hours worked in the math lab, and
   N = Number of hours worked in the nursing home

   Organize the given information in a chart to help set up the equation.

	Math Job	Nursing Home Job	Total
Pay Rate	$8/hr	$9.50/hr	
Numbers of Hours	M	N	$M + N = 50$
Amount of Money Made	$8M$	$9.50N$	$8M + \$9.50N = \$460$

   This leads to the system of equations below.

   $$\begin{cases} M + N = 50 \\ 8M + 9.50N = 460 \end{cases}$$

   We can solve this system of equations using either the substitution or the elimination method. We will use the elimination method. Multiply the first equation by -8 to get
   $$\begin{cases} -8M - 8N = -400 \\ 8M + 9.50N = 460 \end{cases}$$ adding the two equations we get

   $1.5N = 60$ or $N = \frac{60}{1.5} = 40$
   Substituting this value in the first equation we get $M + 40 = 50$, or $M = 10$.

   Anita worked 10 hours at her math lab job and 40 hours at her nursing home job.

2. A theater sold 550 tickets. Some were discounted and sold for $6 each with the remaining tickets sold for full price of $8 a ticket. If the total revenue from ticket sales was $4050, how many of each type of ticket was sold?

Solution: We have a mixture of discounted and regular tickets. Let:
$D =$ the Number of discounted tickets sold, and
$F =$ the Number of full price tickets sold.

Organize the given information in a chart to help set up the equation.

	Discounted Tickets	Full Price Tickets	Total
Price Per ticket	$6/ticket	$8/ticket	
Numbers of Tickets	D	F	$D + F = 550$
Amount of money from tickets	$6D	$8F	$6D + $8F = $4050

This leads to the system of equations below.

$$\begin{cases} D + F = 550 \\ 6D + 8F = 4050 \end{cases}$$

We can solve this system of equations using either the substitution or the elimination method. We will use the elimination method. Multiply the first equation by -6 to get

$$\begin{cases} -6D - 6F = -3300 \\ 6D + 8F = 4050 \end{cases}$$ adding the two equations we get

$2F = 750$ or F$= \frac{750}{2} = 375$
Substituting this value in the first equation we get
$D + 375 = 550$, or D$= 550 - 375 = 175$.

The theater sold 175 discounted tickets and 375 full price tickets.

3. The campus union wants to make a vanilla hazelnut blend of coffee beans worth $5.75 per pound. The Vanilla flavored coffee beans cost $4 a pound and the hazelnut $11 a pound. How many pounds of each should be mixed to make 20 pounds of the blend?

Solution: Let
$V =$ Number of pounds of vanilla flavored beans, and
$H =$ Number of pounds of hazelnut flavored beans

Organize the given information in a chart to help set up the equation.

	Vanilla Flavored	Hazel Nut Flavored Beans	Total

	Beans		
Price Per Pound	$4/lb	$11/lb	$5.75/lb
Number of Pounds	V	H	$V + H = 20$
Cost	$\$4V$	$\$11H$	$\$4V + \$11H = \$5.75 \times 20$

This leads to the system of equations below.

$$\begin{cases} V + H = 20 \\ 4V + 11H = 115 \end{cases}$$

We can solve this system of equations using either the substitution or the elimination method. We will use the elimination method. Multiply the first equation by -4 to get
$$\begin{cases} -4V - 4H = -80 \\ 4V + 11H = 115 \end{cases}$$ adding the two equations we get
$7H = 35$ or $H = \dfrac{35}{7} = 5.$
Substituting this value in the first equation we get
$V + 5 = 20$, or $V = 20 - 5 = 15.$

The campus union should mix 15 pounds of vanilla flavored beans and 5 pounds of hazelnut flavored beans.

As you can see the above example follow similar pattern and the next couple of examples can be solved in this manner but you might get more of a sense of what is happening if you do the problem visually. We will present both visual solutions and algebraic methods as we did above so you can compare the two methods.

4. Suppose that a truck's radiator is filled with 10 liters of 30% antifreeze solution. **How much** of the fluid must be drained and then replaced with pure antifreeze to get a 44% antifreeze solution?

Method 1 : Drain and replace 2 liters of solution with pure antifreeze to get 10 liters of 44% antifreeze solution.

You can see below that for each liter you drain, you make a net gain only 0.7 liters of new antifreeze. Thus draining one liter yields $(3 + 0.7)$ liters of antifreeze, making the new solution 37% antifreeze solution. So 2 draining 2 liters yields a net gain of 1.4 liters of antifreeze so that we have 4.4 liters of antifreeze or 44% of the antifreeze solution.

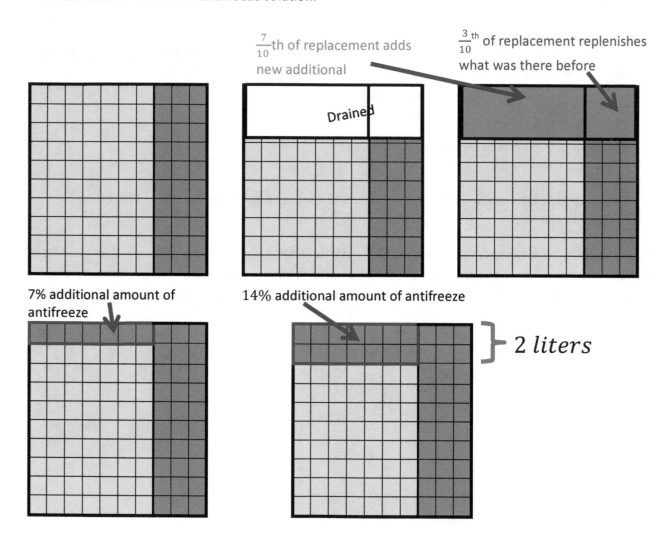

$\frac{7}{10}$th of replacement adds new additional

$\frac{3}{10}$th of replacement replenishes what was there before

Drained

7% additional amount of antifreeze

14% additional amount of antifreeze

} 2 *liters*

Method 2

Let A =Number of liters to be drained and replaced with pure antifreeze

Organizing the given information in a chart might help set up the equation.

	Original	To be Drained	To be Replaced	Resulting Solution
% antifreeze	30%	30%	100%	44%
Number Liters	10	A	A	10
liters of antifreeze	0.30×10	$-0.30A$	$+1.00A$	$0.30 \times 10 - 0.30A + 1A = 0.44 \times 10$

This leads to the equation below

$3 - 0.3A + A = 4.4$

$0.7A = 1.4$

$A = \dfrac{1.4}{0.7} = 2$

Drain and replace 2 liters of the solution.

5. A financial planner needs to allocate $500,000 into two funds so that her client will receive $35,000 of earnings per year. Fund A has a return of 9% per year and Fund B earns 6% per year. How many dollars should be invested in each account to obtain the total of $35,000 earnings in a year?

Let A =Number of Dollars invested in fund A and B the number of dollars invested in fund B.

	Fund A	Fund B	Total
% return	9%	6%	
$ Amount Invested	A	B	$A + B = 500,000$
$ return	$0.09A$	$0.06B$	$0.09A + 0.06B = 35,000$

$\begin{cases} A + B = 500000 \\ 0.09A + 0.06 = 35000 \end{cases}$ We can solve by elimination.

Multiply the top equation by (-0.06) and add to the bottom equation to get:

$-0.06A - 0.06B = -30,000$

$\underline{0.09A + 0.06B = 35,000}$

$\qquad 0.03A = 5,000$

$A = \frac{5,000}{0.03} \approx 166,667$ and $B = 500,000 - 166,667 = 333,333$

Invest $166,667 in the 9% account and $333,333 in the 6% account to earn $35,000 in a year.

6. A building contractor needs to purchase 5000 sheets of plywood or wafer board for a large construction project. He has a budget of $60,000 for this purchase. The wafer board is slightly less durable than the plywood and the contractor would like to get as many of the 5000 sheets to be plywood as possible. If the plywood costs $15 a sheet and the wafer board costs $10 a sheet, how many of each should he purchase if the full $60,000 is to be spent?

We let $P =$ The number of sheets of plywood and
$W =$ The number of sheets of wafer board.

The given information is summarized in the table below.

	Plywood	Wafer board	Combined order
Cost per sheet	$15	$10	
Number of sheets	P	W	$P + W = 5000$
Cost	$15P$	$10W$	$15P + 10W = 60000$

$\begin{cases} P + W = 5000 \\ 15P + 10W = 60000 \end{cases}$ We can solve the system of equations by elimination method.

Multiply the top equation by (-10) and add to the bottom equation to get:

$-10P - 10W = -50,000$
$\underline{15P + 10W = 60,000}$
$5P = 10,000$

$P = \frac{10,000}{5} = 2000$ and $W = 5000 - 2000 = 3000$

Purchase 2000 sheets of plywood and 3000 sheets of wafer board.

7. A dairy plant has a large tank with 1000 gallons of 1% fat milk in it. They need to fill an order for 2% fat milk, so they will add some whole milk that is 3.5 % fat until the mixture is at 2%. How many gallons of whole milk need to be added to the 1000 gallons of 1% milk to make the mixture 2%?

Solving algebraically, we start by assigning x to represent the unknown number of gallons of 3.5% milk that needs to be added. The mixture table below organizes the known and unknowns.

	1% milk	3.5% milk	2% mixture
% fat	1%	3.5%	2%
Gallons of Milk	1000	x	$1000 + x$
Amount of Fat	$0.01 \times 1000 = 10$	$0.035x$	$10 + 0.035x = 0.02(1000 + x)$

We solve this last equation:

$10 + 0.035x = 20 + 0.02x$

$0.015x = 10$

$x = \frac{10}{0.015} \approx 667 \, gal.$

Add 667 gallons of whole milk should be added to make the mixture 1667 gals of 2% fat milk.

In Chemistry, the concentration of chemical solutions is given in molarity which represents the number of moles of a chemical species per liter. A mole is just a certain # of the molecules or atoms, kind of like a dozen eggs is 12 eggs, a mole of sodium is 6.02×10^{23} atoms of sodium. So a Mole is just a very large group of something. If you have a solution that is 4 molar sodium hydroxide, this means that each liter has four moles of sodium hydroxide in it. If you have three liters of this solution, then the total amount of sodium hydroxide is given by $(3\ l) \times \frac{4\ moles}{l} = 12\ moles.$ This follows our definition of multiplication in that we have three groups of 4 moles in each liter.

Thus in chemistry we always have the total number of moles in a given volume of a solution with known molarity is given by # of Moles = Vol × Molarity.

8. A chemist wants to make 5 liters of 2.0 molar sodium acetate solution by mixing appropriate volumes of 0.5 molar and 2.5 molar sodium acetate. How many liters of the 2.0 molar and of the 0.5 molar solutions should be used?

   We start by assigning variables. Let $x =$ The volume of 2.5 molar sodium acetate, and $y =$ The volumes of 0.5 molar sodium acetate solution.
   Putting this into a table to organize it:

Component	0.5 *molar* solution	2.5 *molar* solution	2.0 *molar* mixture
Liters used	y	x	$y + x = 5$
Moles of Sodium Acetate	$0.5y$	$2.5x$	$0.5y + 2.5x = 2.0 \times 5$

   $$\begin{cases} x + y = 5 \\ 2.5x + 0.5y = 10 \end{cases}$$
   Multiply the top eq. by (-0.5) and then add the two new equations.

   $$-0.5x - 0.5y = -2.5$$
   $$\underline{2.5x + 0.5y = 10}$$
   $$2x = 7.5$$
   $x = 3.75\ l\ and\ y = 5 - 3.75 = 1.25\ l$
   The chemist will have to use $3.75\ l\ of\ 2.5\ molar$ and $1.25\ l\ of\ 0.5\ molar$ to make 5 liters of 2.0 molar sodium acetate solution.

Video Log 4.5b

1. A cafeteria has a 20 liter drink dispenser filled with a 25% juice mixture. They want the drink in that dispenser to be 50% juice. The plan is to allow the volume in the dispenser to draw down with student purchases and at some point refill the dispenser completely with an 80% fruit juice mixture so that the full dispenser will be 50% fruit juice. Determine how far down they should allow the dispenser to get before refilling with the 80% juice. You can start with x being the volume remaining in the dispenser at the point when they refill it and y being the number of liters of 80% juice to be added at that point.

2. A butcher has 12 pounds of very lean 5% fat scraps from trimming steaks that she intends to grind up for hamburger. She intends to mix this with some 20% fat hamburger so that the blend can be sold as ground chuck labeled as 15% fat. How many pounds of the 20% hamburger should she add to the 12 pounds of 5% so that the blend is 15% fat?

3. A student paid a total of $3480 for tuition at UWMC and at Rasmussen College. At UWMC the cost is $210 per credit and at Rasmussen the cost is $300 per credit. If the student's total credit load is 14 credits, how many credits did she take at each school?

4. A hiking club has $50 to purchase a gorp mixture for a club outing. They intend to buy chocolate chips and granola and mix the two. They'd like to end up with 20 pounds of the mixture. Also the chips cost $4/lb, and the granola costs $2/lb. How many pounds of chips and granola should they buy?

5. A ferry ship charges $9 for a pedestrian ticket and $45 for a vehicle ticket (covers all the occupants). On a particular day, their total ticket sales amounted to $14,580. If the total number of tickets sold was 652, how many of each type of ticket was sold?

6. A car rental company is planning on purchasing 300 new vehicles. They have a budget of $6,420,000 to spend. They intend to purchase a mix of mid-sized and economy models that cost $26,000 and $14,000 per vehicle respectively. How many of each type of car can they purchase?

7. Larry and Mary work part time. Larry makes $9/hr and Mary $10.50/hr. During a certain week they earned a total of $414 and they worked a total of 42 hours. How many hours did each of them work?

8. A bag of chips and 12pack of soda costs $11. The soda was $3.20 more than the chips. Determine the cost of the chips and of the soda.

9. How many liters each of 12 molar hydrochloric acid, and 4 molar hydrochloric acid should be mixed to make 2.8 liters of 6 molar hydrochloric acid?

4.6 Rate Problems

🖥 Rate Problems (11 min)

http://www.youtube.com/watch?v=prwMJFjTD24

In this section we deal with problems involving rates of doing something. The basic equation that arises is that the quantity (q) of something done is equal to the product of the number of time units (t) times the rate (r). Here r basically states how many or much of something is done in one group or one time unit. The product $t \cdot r$ is then t time units of r units of something per one time unit. This is the multiplication definition for the total number of units of something done in t groups of r. Thus the total amount done in t units of time at rate r is given by $q = t \cdot r$. When the rate is rate of travel, the quantity q is distance traveled and we have $d = t \cdot r$ or $d = rt$. Rate problems come up in a wide variety of disciplines and the examples below give a sampling of such problems.

Distance-Rate-Time formula $d = r \times t$

This formula is quite natural to people who keep track of rates of travel and travel times for driving, running, walking or cycling. If you ask most fifth graders how long it would take them to hike 15 miles when they hike at 3mph, they would correctly answer 5 hours. If the rate is in units of distance per one unit of time, then multiplying $T \times R$ basically says you are going T groups of r distance units or $d = t \times r$ units of distance. From this formula, one can easily derive two other formulas by division, i.e., $r = \frac{d}{t}$ and $t = \frac{d}{r}$. It is probably better to just substitute into the original formula and then solve for whichever quantity is unknown rather than memorizing two more formulas.

There is a lot of humor based on the problem "A train leaves Chicago at 70 mph and a second train leaves Memphis at 65mph ….." Our aim here is not to train students as master train schedulers. However, the ability to assign variables and translate written problem statements into mathematical equations is our objective. We present several perhaps more relevant versions of the train problem.

1. Consider a trip of 231 miles in a car going 55 mph. Determine how many hours the trip will take.

Method 1:

Visual solutions sometimes enable students to see the underlying process.

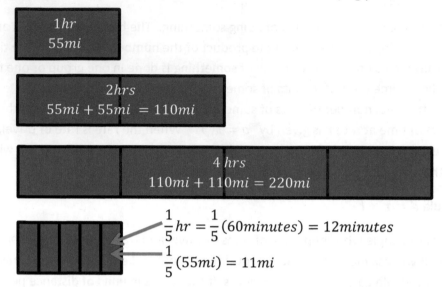

$$\frac{1}{5}hr = \frac{1}{5}(60minutes) = 12minutes$$

$$\frac{1}{5}(55mi) = 11mi$$

Method 2:

Let T = how many hours the trip will take.

	Distance	Rate	Time
Trip	$231mi$	$\dfrac{55mi}{1hr}$	T

$$231mi = \frac{55mi}{1hr} \times T$$

$$231mi \times \frac{1hr}{55mi} = T$$

$4.2hrs = T$, note that $1\ hr = 60min$, or $0.2\ \times 1hr = 0.2 \times 60min$, $0.2hr = 12min$

The trip will be 4 hours and 12 minutes long.

2. A brick that is dropped from the top of a 15 story building is traveling 99 mph just before it hits the ground. Determine the speed of the brick at this time in feet per second. Note that 1 mile = 5280 feet.

    This is a problem of unit conversion. We must change the units from miles to feet and hours to seconds to obtain the desired rate.

Method 1: Change the 99 miles to feet and 1 hour to seconds and compute the rate. This 99 miles is 99 groups of 5280 feet or: $99 \ mi = 99mi \times \frac{5280ft}{1mi} = 522720 \ ft.$

One hour is 60 minutes which are each 60 seconds, thus: $1hr = 60min \times \frac{60sec}{1min} = 3600 \ sec.$

Thus 99 mph is equivalent to $\frac{522720ft}{3600sec} = 145.2\frac{ft}{s}$

Method 2: We can use multiple unit conversion fractions that each represent "one", e.g., $\frac{5280ft}{mi}$ is equivalent to one since the top and bottom represent the same quantity. We also have $\frac{1hr}{3600s}$ is a unit conversion factor representing one.

We convert by multiplying as: $\frac{99mi}{hr} \times \frac{5280ft}{mi} \times \frac{1hr}{3600s} = 145.2 \ ft/s$

(Note that the conversion fractions are "one" with either expression on the top and bottom. We choose the correct order so that the conversion factor units "cancel" with those of the original ratio.)

3. The typical speed of swimming sperm is approximately 2mm/min and the distance a sperm must travel in a human to reach an egg is approximately 20cm. Determine how long it takes a sperm to travel this distance.

Method 1:

We know the distance and the rate here; $D = 20cm, R = \frac{2mm}{min}$. We need the distance units in the rate and the distance to be the same, so we can change the distance to mm by unit conversion $D = 20cm = \frac{20cm}{1} \cdot \frac{10mm}{1cm} = 200mm$. Now, substituting this into the distance-rate-time formula we have $200mm = \frac{2mm}{min} \times T$, solving this equation for T we get $T = 100 \ min.$

It takes the sperm 100 min or 1 hour 40 min to travel this distance.

Method 2:

Pay attention to words like "**how long**" to determine your variable in this problem.

Let $T =$ How long it takes a sperm to travel this distance.

	Distance	Rate	Time
Sperm	$20cm$	$\dfrac{2mm}{1min}$	T

$$20cm = \frac{2mm}{1min} \times T$$

$$20cm \times \frac{1min}{2mm} = T$$

(Note that unless we convert cms to mm we won't be able to simplify the units.)

We know that $1cm = 10mm$. Using this fact and equivalent fraction concept we get

$$\frac{20\cancel{cm} \times 10\cancel{mm}}{1} \frac{1min}{1\cancel{cm}} \times \frac{1min}{2\cancel{mm}} = T$$

$$T = \frac{200min}{2} = 100min$$

It takes the sperm 100 min or 1 hour 40 min to travel this distance.

Visits to Earth from intelligent life on another star-planet system may be possible. Consider Alpha-Centauri, the nearest star to earth, that is 4.3 light-years away. A **light-year** is the distance that light travels in one year. Light travels at $186,000 \frac{mi}{sec}$.

4. How far is the star Alpha-Centauri from Earth in miles?

    Using $d = rt,$ we can compute the distance in miles to Alpha-Centauri as

$$d = \frac{186,000mi}{1\cancel{sec}} \times \left(\frac{4.3 \cancel{yrs}}{1} \times \frac{365\cancel{d}}{1\cancel{yr}} \times \frac{24\cancel{hr}}{1\cancel{d}} \times \frac{3600\cancel{s}}{1\cancel{hr}} \right)$$

$$d \approx 2.52 \times 10^{13} \ mi.$$

The distance from Earth to Alpha-Centauri is about 25 trillion miles!

Even the fastest rockets that man has developed can only go a very small fraction of the speed of light. Consider the fastest manmade spacecraft going out of the solar system headed towards Pluto. This capsule is traveling at approximately 36,000 mph (About once around the earth every 45 minutes).

5. Let's allow for the possibility that a super advanced civilization on Alpha-Centauri has developed space vehicles that travel ten times this speed at 360,000 mph. Determine how long a trip from Alpha-Centauri to Earth would take at this speed.

We use the $d = rt$ formula where the distance is $2.52 \times 10^{13} mi$, and the rate is $360,000 \frac{mi}{hr}$ and we need to compute the time t. Substituting these values in, we get:

$$2.52 \times 10^{13} mi = \frac{360,000 mi}{hr} \times t\ hrs$$

Dividing we obtain $t = 700,000,000$ hours. Converting this to years, we get

$$t = 700,000,000\ hrs \cdot \frac{1 day}{24 hrs} \cdot \frac{1 yr}{365 day} \approx 8000\ years.$$ That is a long time to sit in a space capsule waiting to get to your destination.

6. Adam lives in Hayward WI and his dad lives in Wausau, WI 160 miles away. They decide to each bicycle towards each other and meet to camp for a weekend. Adam rides at 20 mph and his dad is pulling a trailer with the camping gear and his dog and can only manage 12 mph. Adam starts riding at 6:00 AM and his dad leaves at 7:00 AM. Determine what time they will meet and how far from Wausau their meeting place will be.

	Rate	Time	Distance
Adam	$20 mi/hr$	$t\ hrs$	$20t\ mi$
Dad	$12 mi/hr$	$(t-1) hrs$	$12(t-1)\ mi$
Total			$160\ mi$

$$20t + 12(t - 1) = 160$$

$$20t + 12t - 12 = 160$$

$$32t = 172$$

$$t = \frac{172}{32} = 5.375\ hrs$$

Note that

$$0.375 hrs = 0.375 \times 60 min = 22.5 min, \text{ and } 0.5 min = 0.5 \times 60 sec = 30 sec$$

Since Adam started at 6:00am they will meet 5 hours, 22 min and 30 sec later which will make it 11:22:30am.

7. Amy runs at a constant speed of 10 mph for 10 miles. (Pretty darn fast!) How fast must Jacob run if he started 15 minutes after Amy, on the same path, and wants to catch up with her at the end of the 10 miles?

Using $d = rt$ formula we have that for Amy $10 = 10t$ or it will take Amy 1 hour to complete her 10 mile run. Since Jacob started 15 minutes later he would have to run 10mi in 45 minutes or 3/4 hour or $10 = r \cdot \frac{3}{4} hr$ or $10 \cdot \frac{4}{3} = \frac{40}{3} = 13\frac{1}{3} mph = r$. Thus Jacob would need to run $13\frac{1}{3} mph$ to catch Amy by the end of her run. (This is faster than the world record Marathon pace!)

8. A plane travels 1110 miles from Milwaukee, WI, to Boston, MA, in 2 hours with the wind. The plane then returns to Milwaukee against the wind in 2 hours and 25 minutes. Assume that the speed of the wind stays constant. Also assume that the plane speed going to Boston is the speed of the plane in still air plus the wind speed and that the plane speed returning to Milwaukee is the speed of the plane in still air minus the wind speed. Use a system of equations to describe this event, and find the wind speed and the speed of the plane in still air.

Note that the time 2 hours and 25 minutes is the same as
$2hrs + \frac{25}{60} hrs = 2\frac{5}{12} hrs = \frac{29}{12} hrs$
Let w =the speed of the wind in mi/hr, and
p = the speed of the plane without any wind in mi/hr.

	Rate	Time	Distance
With wind	$p + w$	$2hr$	$(p + w)2 = 1110$
Against wind	$p - w$	$\frac{29}{12}hr$	$(p - w)\frac{29}{12} = 1110$

We have the system of equations that represents this event to be:
$$\begin{cases} 1110 = (p + w)2 \\ 1110 = (p - w)\frac{29}{12} \end{cases}$$

We can solve by elimination if we multiply the first equation by $\frac{1}{2}$ and the second by $\frac{12}{29}$ and then add the equations to eliminate w. Thus:

$$\begin{array}{r} 555 = p + w \\ \underline{459.31 = p - w} \\ 1014.31 = 2p \end{array}$$

$p = 507.2 \ mph \ and \ w = 555 - 507.2 = 47.8 \ mph$

The plane can fly 507.2 mph in still air and wind speed was 47.8 mph.

Video Log 4.6a

1. How long does it take to travel from Madison, WI, to Minneapolis, MN which is 245 miles away when travelling at 60 mph?

2. What is the speed of spread of the emerald ash borer in $\frac{mi}{month}$ if it has spread 150 miles over three years?

3. Determine how many years it would take a spaceship going 25000mph to travel to our nearest non-sun star which is $2.5 \times 10^{13}\ mi$ from Earth.

4. Paul and Sarah plan to meet for a week-long camping trip. Paul lives in WI and Sarah lives 1500 miles away in NM. They plan to drive and camp wherever they meet. Paul drives at 60 mph and Sarah is a bit of a lead-foot and drives at 75 mph. Paul is an early riser and leaves WI at 6:00AM. Sarah starts at 9:30AM. Determine at what time they will meet and how far from WI the meeting place is.

5. A bicyclist traveled 45 miles in 3 hours against the wind and 57 miles in the same time with the wind. Find the speed of the bicyclist in still air and the speed of the wind.

6. A kayaker can paddle 5 miles upstream in the Yukon River in 2 hours, and 11 miles downstream in 2 hours. Determine the speed of the current and how fast the kayaker can paddle in still water.

Other Rate Problems $q = r \cdot t$

In rate problems the amount achieved over a time period is given by $Amt = rate \times time$. When two processes work together or against each other the combined rate is either the sum or difference of the two rates. For example, if John can pick $\frac{3}{4} quart$ blueberries per hour and his son Ari is eating $\frac{1}{4}q$ of those berries per hour, then the overall rate of gaining blueberries is $\left(\frac{3}{4}q - \frac{1}{4}q\right) per\ hr = \frac{1}{2}q\ per\ hr$. The rate problems here can usually be solved by assigning just one variable to an unknown time or perhaps two variables for unknown rates.

Examples:

1. John can paint three apartments in a week and Jean can paint 5 apartments in two weeks. How long would it take them working together to paint 25 apartments?

   Let $t =$ the number of weeks the two painters worked together to paint 25 apartments. We can write the number that each does and sum and set this equal to 25 apartments. We can organize the information in a table as well. Note that the combined rate is $(3 + 2.5) \frac{apts}{wk}$.

	Rate	Time	# of Apartments Painted
John	$\dfrac{3}{1}\ \dfrac{appts}{wk}$	$t\ wks$	$3t$
Jean	$\dfrac{5}{2}\ \dfrac{appts}{wks}$	$t\ wks$	$2.5t$
Together	$\left(3 + \dfrac{5}{2}\right)\dfrac{appts}{wk} = \dfrac{5.5\ appts}{wk}$	$t\ wks$	$5.5t$

   Then $25 = 5.5t$ solving for t we get $t = \frac{25}{5.5} \approx 4.5\ weeks$, and $1\ week = 7\ days$ so $0.5 weeks = 0.5 \times 7 days = 3.5 days$, $1 day = 24\ hours$, so $0.5 days = 0.5 \times 24 hrs = 12 hrs$

   It will take the painters 4 weeks, 1 day and 12 hours to paint the 25 apartments.

2. It takes an old copier 15 minutes to print 50 copies of a weekly report, while a new copier can print the 50 copies in 8 minutes. How long will it take the copiers to print 50 copies of the weekly report if they are both used?

Let $t =$ how long it will take both the copiers together to print 50 copies of the weekly report. We have a rate-time problem again $q = rt$. We can consider the weekly printing job as one object or as 50 objects. The units on the rates and on q will be different, but the time will work out the same. In either way, the rates for the machines get added when they are working together.

Using "One weekly Printing Job":

	Rate	Time	Amount of Job Done
Old Machine	$\dfrac{1}{15} \dfrac{job}{min}$	t mins	$\dfrac{1}{15}t$
New Machine	$\dfrac{1}{8} \dfrac{job}{min}$	t mins	$\dfrac{1}{8}t$
Together	$\left(\dfrac{1}{15} + \dfrac{1}{8}\right)\dfrac{job}{min} = \dfrac{23}{120} \dfrac{job}{min}$	t mins	$\dfrac{23}{120}t = 1$

$$1 = \frac{23}{120} \cdot t$$

$$t = \frac{120}{23} \approx 5.22 \ min.$$

Thus it will take just a little over 5 minutes to get the printing done if both printers are used. One may want to know how many copies to put on each machine as well. To do this, for the old machine, we'd have $Q_1 = \frac{50 \ copies}{15 \ min} \cdot 5.22 \ min \approx 17 \ copies$ and $Q_2 = \frac{50 \ copies}{8 \ min} \cdot 5.22 \ min \approx 33 \ copies$.

3. Joey normally does the dishes at the school cafeteria for the noon meal in 3 hours. One day Vanessa helped him and it only took an hour and twenty minutes for them to finish the noon dishes working together. How long would it take Vanessa to do the dishes by herself?

This is a rate problem and we have two known rates Joey's and the combined rate of Joey and Vanessa. From our previous problems we know that Joey's rate plus Vanessa's rate is equal to their together rate.

Let $V =$ Vanessa's Time in hours to do the dishes by herself.

Then her rate would be $\frac{1\ job}{V\ hrs}$.

Joey's rate is $\frac{1\ job}{3\ hrs}$ and their combined rate is $\frac{1\ job}{1\frac{1}{3}\ hrs} = \frac{1\ job}{\frac{4}{3}hrs} = \frac{3\ jobs}{4\ hrs}$.

.	Vanessa	Joe	Together	
Time	$V\ hours$	$3\ hours$	$1\ hour\ 20\ minutes = 1\frac{1}{3}hours$ $= \frac{4}{3}hours$	
Rate	$\frac{1}{V}job/hour$	$\frac{1}{3}job/hour$	$\frac{1job}{\frac{4}{3}hr} = \frac{3\ job}{4\ hr} = \frac{1}{V} + \frac{1}{3}$	

So we have $\frac{1}{V} + \frac{1}{3} = \frac{3}{4}$, or $\frac{1}{V} = \frac{3}{4} - \frac{1}{3} = \frac{9}{12} - \frac{4}{12} = \frac{5}{12}Job/Hour.$

Thus Vanessa can do $\frac{5\ sets\ of\ noon\ dishes}{12hrs} = \frac{1}{V}$. We can take reciprocals of both sides to get $\frac{12}{5}hrs = V$ or divide top and bottom of the ratio by 5, Vanessa's rate as $\frac{1\ set\ of\ noon\ dishes}{2.4\ hrs} = \frac{1}{V} \rightarrow V = 2.4hrs.$

This says Vanessa could do one set of noon dishes in $2\frac{2}{5}$ hrs or 2 hours and 24 minutes.

4. An older machine takes 6 hours to fill one lot of soda cans and it takes only 4 hours to fill one lot of soda cans with a newer machine. How long will it take to fill 5 lots of soda cans with both machines work together?

The rate of the older machine is $\frac{1\ lot}{6\ hr}$ and the rate of the newer machine is $\frac{1\ lot}{4\ hr}$.

	Old Machine	New Machine	Together	
Time	$6\ hours$	$4\ hours$	$T\ hours$	
Rate	$\frac{1}{6}\ job$ $/hour$	$\frac{1}{4}job$ $/hour$	$\left(\frac{1}{6}+\frac{1}{4}\right)\frac{job}{hr} = \frac{5\ job}{12\ hr}$	

The rate when both machines work together is $\left(\frac{1}{6}+\frac{1}{4}\right)\frac{lots}{hr} = \frac{5}{12}\frac{lots}{hr}$. Let $T =$ the number of hours to fill 5 lots with both machines working together. So we have $5 = \frac{5}{12} \cdot T$, solving the equation for T we get $T = 5 \cdot \frac{12}{5} = 12\ hrs$ to fill five lots of cans when both machines are running.

Video Log 4.6b

1. Max and Paul can pick 6 and 8 pints of strawberries per hour, respectively. How long would it take them to pick 30 pints when working together?

2. A newsletter printing job needs to be done each week. Using an older copy machine the job took 2.5 hours to complete. Then a new machine was brought in and using both machines, the job could be completed in 1 hour. Determine how long it would take the new machine to do the job alone.

3. The elephants at a zoo eat a large bale of hay every 5 days. The zebras eat a large bale of hay every three weeks. If these are the only animals at the zoo eating hay, how long will 15 large bales of hay last?

4. It takes 15 hours for a water hose from Jim's house to fill his small backyard pool. One year his neighbor offers to help out with a hose from his house. That year, it took only 10 hours to fill the pool. Determine how long it would take to fill the pool using only the neighbor's hose.

5. An older machine can fill 20,000 soda cans per hour. A new machine can fill 35,000 soda cans per hour. How long will it take to fill 6,000,000 soda cans if we use both machines?

4.7 Using Formulas from a variety of fields

Lecture

🖥 Applications (10 min)

http://www.youtube.com/watch?v=ysORRfBJ7HU

In the next set of applications you are given known formulas from different fields and you have to work with them to find information needed. To be successful in this set of problems you need to follow some basic principles of organizing your information.

➢ Read the problem so you understand what is being asked.

➢ Make a chart with all the variables in the formulas you are asked to use and fill in the chart with given information.

➢ Substitute any known quantities into the formulas.

➢ When working with equations and inequalities, solve for the unknown variable.

➢ Keep track of units throughout your work and be sure your final answer has the appropriate units.

➢ Check your answer and estimate or consider the reasonableness of your answer.

➢ Write your final answer in a sentence that fits the question being asked with the appropriate units.

Chemistry/Physics

Charles's Law

It is a well-established fact that if the pressure remains constant, then the volume of a fixed amount of a gas is a linear function of the temperature of the gas (This is called Charles's Law). This is true for liquids too and is the basis for thermometers. As the temperature increases the volume increases by a small amount and results in the mercury or alcohol level moving higher in the thermometer capillary.

Examples

1. A weather balloon is filled with 10,000 cubic feet of helium when it is 50°F. When the balloon is taken outside where the temperature is 35°F the volume of the cooler helium decreased to 9,706 ft^3.

   a. Find a linear relation between temperature x °F, and volume y ft^3.
   b. Predict the volume if the temperature were to reach 135°F.
   c. Also predict the temperature at which the volume would decrease to zero. This is the coldest possible temperature and is called Absolute Zero.

Solution

   a. From the information in the problem we have

x	y
50	10,000
35	9,706
x	y

   We have two points which can use to find the slope of the linear relation. Then use point-slope or $y = mx + b$ to find the linear equation.

   Using $(50, 10000)$ and $(35, 9706)$ we get $m = \frac{9706-10,000}{35-50}\frac{ft^3}{°F} . = 19.6\frac{ft^3}{°F}$.

   If we use point-slope $y = y_1 + m(x - x_1)$ we get $y = 10,000 + 19.6(x - 50)$.

   <u>Alternatively</u>

   If we use $y = mx + b$, we have $y = 19.6x + b, and\ 10,000 = 19.6(50) + b$, solve the equation for b, and it will give you $b = 9020$. So we have $y = 19.6x + 9020$. Note that if we distribute the point-slope form through, both forms are the same. Also the point slope form uses the 50°F as the reference point, while the slope-intercept form uses 0°F as its reference point.

   b. To determine the volume at 135°F we simply substitute $x = 135$°F to get $y = (10,000 + 19.6(135 - 50))ft^3 = 11,666\ ft^3$.
   c. To determine what temperature will make the volume shrink to zero, substitute $y = 0$ in the equation we found in part a. and solve the equation for x. $0 = 19.6x + 9020$, solving for x we get $x = -\frac{9020}{19.6} \approx -460$°F . This temperature Is Absolute Zero.

Pendulums have been used to keep a certain tempo for many centuries. The metronome commonly used by some musicians to keep a steady tempo is an adjustable pendulum for different types of music. In the early 1600's physicists and mathematicians deduced how the period of a pendulum (i.e., time it takes the pendulum to swing one complete cycle) and the length from the pivot point to the pendulum mass are related. Any child who plays on park swings knows that as the length of the swing chains get longer so does the period of time between each back-and-forth motion of the swing. If the child has siblings, they may also realize that making the weight on the swing heavier or lighter does not seem to change the time to go back and forth. What a child perhaps misses is that doubling the length of the pendulum does not double the swing-time. Physicists have deduced that the length of the period varies directly with the square root of the length of the pendulum. What this means is that there is a relation $y = k\sqrt{L}$ between the period $y = T$ and the square root of the length $\sqrt{L}$. Mathematicians have also deduced that the constant $k = \frac{2\pi}{\sqrt{g}}$ where g is the earth's gravitational acceleration.

2. Jack and Jill have a swing set at the bottom of the hill where they live. One of the swing-pendulums has a 15 foot length and the other is 10 feet. Jack swings on the longer one and notices with his stop watch that it takes him 4.29 seconds for 1 swing cycle ($T = 4.29s$).

    a. Use Jack's Length and Period data to determine the value of k in the relation $T = k\sqrt{L}$.
    b. Predict how long it takes Jill to go back and forth on her 10 foot swing.
    c. Predict how long a pendulum should be so that the period of one cycle is 2 seconds. (This is exactly what is needed in a standard grandfather clock.)
    d. Use your computed value of k to estimate the value of g from the relation $k = \frac{2\pi}{\sqrt{g}}$

    Solutions

    a. We plug in what we know from Jack to obtain $4.29\ seconds = k\sqrt{15ft}$. Omitting units, we have $4.29 = k\sqrt{15}$, or $k = \frac{4.29}{\sqrt{15}} \approx 1.108$. Thus on earth the pendulum period-length relation is $T = 1.108\sqrt{L}$.

    b. We substitute in $L = 10\ ft$ to obtain $T(Jill) = 1.108\sqrt{10} \approx 3.50\ sec.$

    c. We substitute in $T = 2$ to obtain $2 = 1.108\sqrt{L}$ or $\frac{2}{1.108} = \sqrt{L}$ or $L = \left(\frac{2}{1.108}\right)^2 \approx 3.26ft.$

    d. Using the experimental value of $k = 1.108\frac{s}{ft^{\frac{1}{2}}} = \frac{2\pi}{\sqrt{g}}$ we solve this for g. We multiply both sides by $\sqrt{g}$ and divide by $1.108\frac{s}{ft^{\frac{1}{2}}}$ (multiply by the reciprocal) to get $\sqrt{g} = \frac{2\pi}{1.108}\frac{ft^{\frac{1}{2}}}{s}$. Then square each side to get $\approx 32.2\frac{ft}{s^2}$.

Carpentry: Recall the Pythagorean Theorem which states that $a^2 + b^2 = c^2$ with $a, b, and\ c$ the legs and hypotenuse of a right triangle.

3. A carpenter is preparing a rough rectangular opening for a 5' by 6' 8" patio door opening. She needs to have right angles at each corner. How long should the diagonal distance to opposite corners be?

    Solution

We substitute in the leg lengths at $a = 5' = 60"$ and $b = 6'8" = 80"$ into the formula giving us $60^2 + 80^2 = c^2$, or $c^2 = 10000$, solving for c and accounting for the fact that the distance is never negative we get $c = 100" = 8'4"$.

Note: In real life, carpenters measure both the diagonals to see if they are equal.

4. A rectangular garden was enclosed using a 50 foot roll of rabbit proof wire fence. The width of the garden was 10 feet. Determine the area of the garden in square feet.

Solution

We need to know the length of the rectangle to use the area formula. We know that the fence was 50 feet long so the perimeter of the garden must be 50 feet, and the width of the rectangle is 10 ft.

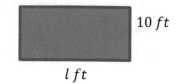

$10\ ft$

$l\ ft$

$50 = 2l + 2(10)$

$50 = 2l + 20$

$30 = 2l$

$15 = l$

Area $= A = lw$

$A = (15)10 = 150$

Area of the garden is $150 ft^2$.

Video Log 4.7a

1. A playground is to be designed so it has swings with periods of three, four, five and six seconds. Determine how long the suspending chains should be for these swings.

2. The amount of lift L that a helium balloon provides is a constant times the cube of the diameter D of the balloon. A toy balloon at a flower shop is two feet in diameter and has just enough lift to float the two ounce weight of the balloon and attached card. $L = K \times D^3$.
   a. Use the toy balloon data to compute the value of K.
   b. Determine the amount of lift balloons of diameter 4 feet, 10 feet and 40 feet would provide (in ounces and pounds, 1 pound = 16 oz.).
   c. Write an equation (formula) that gives the weight W *in pounds* on one side and an expression in the diameter D on the other side where D is in feet.
   d. Determine how many 10 foot weather balloons would be needed to lift 200 pounds of a person in their lawn chair.

3. $\frac{1}{f} = \frac{1}{f_1} + \frac{1}{f_2}$, solve for f_1.

4. $E = mc^2$, solve for c.

5. $F = ma$, solve for m.